D1593848

PSYCHOANALYTIC GROUP THEORY AND THERAPY

Essays in Honor of Saul Scheidlinger

Saul Scheidlinger, Ph.D., D.F.A.G.P.A.

PSYCHOANALYTIC GROUP THEORY AND THERAPY

Essays in Honor of Saul Scheidlinger

edited by

SAUL TUTTMAN, M.D., Ph.D.

Monograph 7

AMERICAN GROUP PSYCHOTHERAPY ASSOCIATION
MONOGRAPH SERIES
Series Consulting Editor:

Bennett E. Roth, Ph.D.

INTERNATIONAL UNIVERSITIES PRESS, INC.

Madison   Connecticut

Copyright © 1991, American Group Psychotherapy Association

Library of Congress Cataloging-in-Publication Data

Psychoanalytic group theory and therapy : essays in honor of Saul Scheidlinger / edited by Saul Tuttman.
    p. cm.—(Monograph series / American Group Psychotherapy Association ; monograph 7)
  Includes bibliographical references and index.
  ISBN 0-8236-4433-2
  1. Group psychotherapy. 2. Small groups—Psychological aspects I. Scheidlinger, Saul, 1918- . II. Tuttman, Saul, 1926- .
III. Series: Monograph series (American Group Psychotherapy Association) ; monograph 7.
  [DNLM: 1. Psychoanalytic Theory—essays. 2. Psychotherapy, Group—essays. W1 MO559PU monograph 7 / WM 430 P97446]
RC488P78 1991
616.89'15—dc20
DNLM/DLC
for Library of Congress
                                    90-5324
                                         CIP

Manufactured in the United States of America

Contents

v

PART V   GROUP TREATMENT OF CHILDREN AND ADOLESCENTS

PART VI   THE EVOLUTION OF PSYCHOANALYTIC GROUP THEORY

PART VII   CULTURAL FACTORS IN PSYCHOANALYTIC GROUPS

Contributors

E. James Anthony, M.D., is Clinical Professor of Psychiatry and Human Behavior, George Washington University Medical School; Training and Supervising Analyst, Washington Psychoanalytic Institute, and Director, Child and Adolescent Psychotherapy, Chestnut Lodge, Rockville, Maryland.

Howard A. Bacal, M.D., F.R.C.P.(C.), is Training and Supervising Analyst and Former Director, Toronto Institute of Psychoanalysis, and Associate Professor, Department of Psychiatry, University of Toronto.

Robert R. Dies, Ph.D., F.A.G.P.A., is Professor of Psychology, University of Maryland and Editor *International Journal of Group Psychotherapy*.

Margaret G. Frank, M.S.S.W., F.A.G.P.A., is in Private Practice, Newton Centre, Massachusetts, and Past President, American Orthopsychiatric Association.

Walter I. Gadlin, Ph.D., is Assistant Clinical Professor of Medical Psychology, College of Physicians and Surgeons, Columbia University and in Private Practice, New York.

Ramon Ganzarain, M.D., F.A.G.P.A., is Associate Professor of Psychiatry at Emory University, School of Medicine, Atlanta; Training Analyst, Columbia University Center for Training and Research assigned to Atlanta.

Emanuel Hallowitz, M.S.W., A.C.S.W., D.F.A.G.P.A, is Professor Emeritus, University of Chicago; Board Certified Clinical Social Worker, Distinguished Social Work Practitioner, National Academies of Practice; Past President, American Group Psychotherapy Association, and in Private Practice.

Ruth Hochberg, Ph.D., F.A.G.P.A., is Assistant Clinical Professor, Department of Psychiatry and Bio-Behavioral Sciences, Neuropsychiatric Institute, U.C.L.A. and Chairman of the Board, Group Psychotherapy Foundation.

Leonard Horwitz, Ph.D., F.A.G.P.A., is Training and Supervising Analyst, Topeka Institute for Psychoanalysis; Former Director of Group Psychotherapy, The Menninger Clinic, and Past President, American Group Psychotherapy Association.

Priscilla S. Kauff, Ph.D., F.A.G.P.A., is Assistant Clinical Professor of Psychiatry (Psychology), Albert Einstein College of Medicine, and Supervisor and Faculty, Postgraduate Center for Mental Health, New York.

James L. Kennedy, M.D., is Post-Doctoral Fellow, Yale University Department of Psychiatry and Human Genetics.

Otto F. Kernberg, M.D., is Professor of Psychiatry, Cornell University Medical College, Associate Chairman and Medical Director, The New York Hospital–Cornell Medical Center, Westchester Division, and Training and Supervising Analyst, Columbia University Center for Psychoanalytic Training and Research.

Paulina F. Kernberg, M.D., is Director, Child and Adolescent Psychiatry, The New York Hospital–Cornell Medical Center, Westchester Division; Associate Professor of Psychiatry, Cornell University Medical College, and Training and Supervising Analyst, Columbia University Center for Psychoanalytic Training and Research.

Howard D. Kibel, M.D., F.A.G.P.A., is Director, Group Psychotherapy The New York Hospital–Cornell Medical Center, Westchester Division; Associate Professor of Psychiatry, Cornell University Medical College, and Past President, American Group Psychotherapy Association.

Jerome W. Kosseff, Ph.D., F.A.G.P.A., is Training Analyst, Group and Adult Departments, Postgraduate Center for Mental Health, New York, and Adjunct Full Professor, Clinical Program, Teachers College, Columbia University.

John E. Mack, M.D., is Professor of Psychiatry, The Cambridge Hospital, Harvard Medical School, and Academic Director of the Center for Psychological Studies in the Nuclear Age.

K. Roy MacKenzie, M.D., F.R.C.P.(C), F.A.G.P.A., is Chief of Psychiatry, St. Joseph's Hospital, Hamilton, Ontario, Canada, and Past Secretary and Publications Committee Chairman, American Group Psychotherapy Association.

Albert E. Riester, Ed.D., F.A.G.P.A., is Professor, Trinity University and Clinical Professor, University of Texas Health Science Center at San Antonio, Department of Psychiatry, and Institute Committee Co-chair, American Group Psychotherapy Association.

Jo Rosenberg, A.C.S.W., is Social Work Coordinator, Child and Adolescent Division, New York Hospital–Cornell Medical Center, Westchester Division, and Lecturer of Social Work in Psychiatry, Cornell University Medical College.

Bennett E. Roth, Ph.D., F.A.G.P.A., is in Private Practice; Past Chairman of the Publications Committee, and Monograph Series Editor, American Group Psychotherapy Association.

Edmundo J. Ruiz, M.D., is in Private Practice, Laredo, Texas.

Gerald S. Schamess, M.S.S., is Professor, Smith College School for Social Work, Clinical Coordinator at the Doctoral Program and Co-Chair, Treatment Methods Sequence, and Private Practice in Group and Individual Treatment.

Alberto C. Serrano, M.D., F.A.G.P.A., is Professor of Psychiatry, University of Pennsylvania School of Medicine, and Medical Director, Philadelphia Child Guidance Clinic, and President-Elect, International Association of Group Psychotherapy.

F. Beaumont Stevenson, M. Div., is Member of the Institute of Group Analysis and of the Group Analytic Society (London), and Psychiatric Sector, Oxfordshire Health Authority.

Walter N. Stone, M.D., F.A.G.P.A., is Professor, Department of Psychiatry, University of Cincinnati College of Medicine; Medical Director for Central Psychiatric Clinic, Cincinnati, and President, American Group Psychotherapy Association.

Max Sugar, M.D., is Clinical Professor of Psychiatry, Department of Psychiatry at Louisiana State University School of Medicine, and Tulane School of Medicine, New Orleans, Louisiana.

Saul Tuttman, M.D., Ph.D., F.A.G.P.A., is Clinical Associate Professor of Psychiatry, New York University School of Medicine–Bellevue Medical Center; Training and Supervising Analyst, Psychoanalytic Institute of New York Medical College, New York Freudian Society, and IPTAR; Chairman, Committee on Programs, American Academy of Psychoanalysis, and Treasurer, American Group Psychotherapy Association.

FOREWORD

Saul Scheidlinger's clear minded conception of group psychotherapy has an inspiring and integrating effect on our field. His contributions to the group psychotherapy movement—as author, journal editor, scholar, president of A.G.P.A., clinician, supervisor, teacher, and film maker—has incalculably affected the practice and theory of group psychotherapy. It is impossible, I believe, to present a paper, or engage in a significant dialogue on analytic group psychotherapy without some reference to Saul Scheidlinger's ideas. One can only admire the remarkable extent of his clinical and theoretical interests for their range and envy his energetic scholarship. Closer inspection of his multiple contributions lead to an inescapable recognition that our clinical or theoretical interests are viewed more clearly from his intellectual shoulders. Since it is not possible to consider all his contributions separately, nor to exhaust their form and quality, I will only address his major influence on group psychotherapy.

In his many papers, there is an obvious analytic model for inquiries into group process where clinical data can only be gathered by an observer in vivo. This model remains constantly reassuring to the inexperienced who finds new and bewildering in themselves the theories of group dynamics. His clear prose style and closely reasoned thinking and observations also clarify complex issues for his colleagues. One result of reading Scheidlinger, even if disagreeing with him, is that what has been blurred becomes clear and the direction of future research and thought becomes apparent.

Those who have worked with Saul Scheidlinger become accustomed to receiving his short notes, accompanied by a photocopy copy of something from a journal or a book. These notes politely asking . . . "Have you seen this?" This is Saul's manner of expressing that we have not exhausted our knowledge of group dynamics and group processes and of our need to continue gathering new insights into the complexity of group process. In addition, he is always available as a first reader for a new paper.

This volume before us reveals a reflected image of Saul Scheidlinger's work. This is not, as certain modern usage suggests, to be mistaken for a "narcissistic" reflection; for Saul requires in others that which we cherish most about him, a capacity for hard work and independent thinking. His enduring reflection, as seen by others, is that of a true group therapist and theoretician—that kind of person who views the human group interaction as engaged in an unending struggle to maintain personal integrity, human kindness, and effectance in the face of pressures exerted on the individual and the group by internal forces, the group dynamic, and the sociopolitical environment.

If today we take for granted these attitudes and other beliefs about group dynamics and psychotherapy, it is probably Saul Scheidlinger who first brought them to our attention or presented the concept in a cogent manner. It is somewhat ironic that his work is referenced in the Freud Library, yet it is in danger of being ignored by the current generation of group therapists and thinkers. This volume may prevent that, for alongside the didactic elements of this monograph, and embedded in it, is the implied historical meaning of group psychotherapy and an image of the sense of the identity of the group therapist.

Group psychotherapy, as a movement and a practice, was not born out of individual effort and insight, nor was it a product of autocratic organizational efforts. If this were true, there would be little to perpetuate the group movement. Group psychology, and its legitimate heir, analytic group psychotherapy, is the natural consequence of the flow of historical and intellectual movements that began in the nineteenth century. These forces were first given direction by Freud's dynamic insights into group psychology, and the emergent critical inquiry of processes by which social groups influence individual and psychological choice. While various academic disciplines have attempted to define the individual in relationship to his natural groups: family, school, work, social class, religion, or country, group psychotherapy importantly remained distinct; that is, involved with the individuals living in the group as the source of kinship and of adaptive problems.

Operationally, by creating or forming a group for therapeutic purposes, the leader places himself against the historical and developmental forces of dehumanizing psychosocial, political, and economic events. He places himself against the postindustrial milieu that has left the individual alienated from his own family, his personal history, and himself. The therapeutic group helps members transcend a mystical religious ethic that sought, by the magic of ritual or rationalism, to explain life's events, man's fate, work, and sexuality. One starts a therapy group believing in the humanistic–psychological value system that advocates interactive understanding and communication by an individual in a group context as antidote. At the same time, the leader or therapist objective is guided by that hard-won hope of liberating those psychic forces that allow people within groups to cooperate and grow and bear with the aggressive and destructive forces that develop from these very same individual and group processes. Group psychotherapy stands in contrast to the idea that the only life worth studying, and the only person worth therapy is the "great life." This form of narcissistic ideal, joined with economic availability, places group treatment as the treatment of the common sufferer, and psychoanalysis proper as the treatment of the privileged.

Those that hedge, I believe, on any of these pillars of analytic group psychotherapy deviate from the goal inherent in its therapeutic action. You will not find, in any of Saul Scheidlinger's work, any loss of conviction for these therapeutic purposes. These pillars are necessary to avoid the generalized tendency to treat the individual in the group as only a product of the therapist's view of dynamics, or existing only in the context of that particular group. This tendency leads to the reduction of people and groups to unidimensional elements, devoid of psychological realness. It fosters the development of a "false self" and "false" group therapy, by preventing any real dialogue within the group and the individuals' other realities. As a result of these tendencies the group becomes mythic, conflict unreal, and defended against by externalizing defences. Then the group norm becomes acting in, acting out, or acting in the sense of performance. In such a false group catharsis is elevated above insight, simplicity above complexity, and the group leader above all others, reversing both the thrust of psychosocial development and Western society's values. Learning as an ego function (requiring synthetic and integrating functions) is impossible under these conditions. Instead, an *Icon* is created composed of innocence, denial, nonadaptive behavior, lack of judgment, personal need and idealization of the leader. Not only does this all too common error deprive the individual of his own developmental history, and the richness and complexity of his own mental life and transferences, it also results in an extrusion of the sociohistorical referents important in his own life and self definition.

Under the rubric of sense of identity falls a range of developmental achievements, in this usage, both personal and professional. Saul Scheidlinger's professional "identity" has been unfaltering in his continuous dedication to professional societies and to the education of interns and residents, and to the writing of scientific papers. It is the personal side of this identity which needs to be addressed, if only briefly. Each of the contributors shares with Saul Scheidlinger a personal identity. Each of us, along with the reader, unique in our own development and sensitivities, has chosen a path to engage therapeutically in the lives of other people. We, reader and contributor, embrace a common though unique set of beliefs and values that govern our actions and thoughts both when working and when living "the rest of our lives." This shared belief system, yet wholly articulated, lies at the core of professional education, practice, and maturity.

Each of us shares a passion for the therapeutic relationship, for the patient's world, for the transference world, and for the group. With these passions (although others may choose a different descriptive term) is the ability to transform our wish for a transference relationship into a specific aim-inhibited kind while being vulnerable to the stimulation of the patient and the group. In this way the first somewhat superficial and transitory identification is achieved, known as empathy. But, this is incomplete. The empathic identification must be held inside, examined sympathetically and critically, and at the proper technical time partially conveyed to the patient(s) in understandable terms. It is this ultimate process of the psychotherapist that permits a psychotherapeutic and psychoanalytic interaction. In the interhuman setting of group therapy this is no easy process, for it means that human behavior in groups must be empathically observed, bearing in mind the existence and complex interactive workings of conscious and unconscious mental functioning, fantasies, defenses, resistances, and affects that work against self awareness for all those present, including the therapist.

This current volume, organized under the able editorial guidance of Saul Tuttman, will reveal a common set of beliefs and values. It is, as much as possible, composed of possible personalities and models of thinking that are not uniform. One result of this mixture is that this monograph is not a bland clone of Scheidlinger's ideas; rather, it is a good group. It is arranged around some of Saul Scheidlinger's main areas of interest; his concern for refining psychoanalytic principles and applying them to group dynamics; his firm belief that current practice is dependent upon a discriminating study of our theoretical roots, and his interest in applying the core concepts of group interaction to areas of group leadership, education, research, and social problems of adults and children.

There are some who may see the motivation for this monograph as founded on a particular crisis in analytic psychotherapy. The strains of this external crisis have been with us from the beginning: the pressure for rapid cure, the popularizing and frequent misuse of various group cultures, and the effort to force upon psychotherapies "scientific" criteria for proof. There are those who will understand the motivation for this monograph as the result of an internal crisis within our field: particularly a crisis of education, membership, or maybe a personal crisis for analytic group therapists. This is not so. But it is increasingly clear that if analytic group psychotherapy is to persevere, we ourselves must move continuously, by those therapeutic processes we know and observe in groups, to remove the analytic false self. We must be continually alert to impart the educational and personal experiences that influence the development of those unique experiences that engender independent and therapeutic thinking. We must encourage and supply those personal experiences that lead to a hard-won optimism for the therapeutic. One other needed ingredient is the ability to become the kind of individual able to respond both as a therapist and as a person.

If we have embarked in that direction, it is because Saul Scheidlinger has steered a true course that has gained us the respect and acceptance of our professional colleagues while keeping us mindful of the ultimate, though unreachable human goal of living with ourselves while living with others. To enlarge his legacy of dialogue between practitioners it remains increasingly important to avoid confusion in conceptual terms, and be operationally explicit about our clinical phenomena. No amount of confusion in terms can disguise operational dissimilarity and then dialogue is impossible.

Looking over the material in this monograph I found a particular question coming to mind. What is it that makes analytic group psychotherapy diatrophic? The answer is not as simple as the question. At best I may offer a partial answer. Certainly group leadership; regression (safely); identification, and interpretation have significance in the ultimate outcome of any psychotherapy. However, the uniqueness of the group setting offers a special opportunity to gather answers from these papers.

In conclusion, in this volume we openly emulate, acknowledge, and demonstrate our indebtedness and gratitude to Saul Scheidlinger; in the multiple roles he has assumed in the furthering of group psychotherapy, and its organizational arm, the American Group Psychotherapy Association. Hopefully, I am expressing the response of future generations of group therapists who would arrive upon this work, and be moved to read Saul Scheidlinger's original contributions, and find in both fertile ideas, direction and guidance.

Bennett E. Roth, Ph.D.

Part I

Introduction

Mentor and "Mensch":
An Introduction to Psychoanalytic Group
Theory and Therapy

SAUL TUTTMAN, M.D., Ph.D.

Saul Scheidlinger has been an inspiring model and outstanding catalyst in furthering the application of psychoanalysis to group dynamic theory and treatment. He has encouraged and supported most of the prominent theorists and practitioners in the field of psychoanalytic group therapy today.

Many were eager to participate in this project honoring their mentor and friend. Scheidlinger has had a major impact as group therapist, supervisor, teacher, and author for over forty years. Furthermore, he has contributed significantly to so many crucial areas that others have been inspired to follow in his footsteps. Among Scheidlinger's many papers which contain psychoanalytic formulations regarding groups are those on regression (1968), identification (1955, 1964), the mother group (1974) and leadership (1982a). These are essential reading for anyone practicing group therapy. We have all been enriched by his ideas about scapegoating (1982b), empathy (1966a), and interpretation (1987), as well as his work with children (1952, 1959, 1965, 1966b, 1984); adolescents (1972, 1985); and the socially disadvantaged (1970).

Scheidlinger has had a life-long personal interest in social, cultural, and economic factors that influence individuals in groups. Throughout his career, he has devoted himself to "exploiting" the group modality as a means of understanding and communicating with people in diverse cultures and circumstances. His important educational films and videotapes have helped inner city youngsters learn about the practical aspects of sexuality. His concern with excellence in research on group psychotherapy and with the development of a high level of scholarship in the group therapy literature was directly manifested in his role as editor of the *International Journal of Group Psychotherapy* over a ten-year period. He has introduced many important concepts, which not only have intrinsic value, but which often provide a framework or a catalytic "link" to other contributions to theory and practice. An important part of his ongoing quest has been to seek a "next step" toward a meaningful integration of group dynamics and individual psychodynamics.

At a graduate class in psychology many years ago, I saw a film about Slavson's technique of group therapy. The impressive young therapist conducting the session was Saul Scheidlinger. From time to time thereafter, I would hear about his work regarding his efforts to relate psychoanalytic theory to group concepts. More recently, the editor of a psychoanalytic journal requested that I review Scheidlinger's then new book: *Focus on Group Psychotherapy* (1982c). I was impressed and wrote an enthusiastic essay. Shortly thereafter, I received a gracious letter from the author. At the next annual meeting of the American Group Psychotherapy Association in New York, Saul (as president) addressed the meeting. At the conclusion, I introduced myself and we quickly became fast friends. The deep admiration and affection for Saul that I feel is similar to the reactions of many others who also value the profound impact he has had on so many of us who are interested in group psychotherapy and various social issues. His availability is unusual in both its depth and in his willingness to be helpful. Whenever someone he knows makes progress in the field, Saul's joy and gratification is extraordinary. Everyone recognizes his commitment to excellence and his uncompromising, high standards. Although I have seen him take a "hard line" when he needs to be critical or practical, his attitude is always tempered by compassion and empathy. He is a stark realist who values the stabilizing effect of some traditional positions, while maintaining a strong humanistic flexibility.

Saul is devoted to human welfare, to social action and to increasing political awareness. He values the strivings of human beings in their efforts to find constructive identities, to overcome prejudice and scapegoating, to free themselves from deprivation and poverty. His life history is the story of a struggle to survive and excel and this can help us understand the origins of his concerns and interests. His early life in Europe was facilitated and structured by his involvement in group activities where he functioned as an active participant from the first, and in a leadership role as he matured. He arrived in a strange country at a young age without funds and without knowledge of English, but with a determination to obtain an education and to make meaningful contributions. I have come across two rather moving papers about the details of his life and work. One is an interview by Gerd Fenchel (1983) which appeared in the journal *Group* and the other is called *Recollection: A Personal Memoir of Saul Scheidlinger* written by Mary C. O'Connell (unpublished, 1982) and privately circulated.

The touching though brief chapter written by Saul's close friends, Ruth Hochberg and Manny Hallowitz, along with this introduction and Margaret Frank's reminiscences, make up the introductory section of this volume. Saul Scheidlinger's personal background is interesting in that from the very first, intense group involvements were vital to his survival and growth. How fitting that he should help clarify and develop group theory and practice which has helped others in need. In this we can see the passing on of a legacy.

Personal recollections and sentiments are usually of value primarily to those who know the person being honored in a *Festschrift*. In this instance, that is far from the full story. Scheidlinger's role has been so unique and pioneering in the development of psychoanalytic group theory and practice, that a focus on his work offers an opportunity for students and practitioners of group therapy to expand their perspectives. Thus, the purpose of this volume is twofold: first, to "celebrate" Saul Scheidlinger and express an appreciation of his personality and his work; second (perhaps more important), to further explore, true to his traditions, the study of psychoanalytic group dynamics, from both a theoretical and treatment framework. It is hoped that those unfamiliar with his writings will follow up and benefit from further exposure to Scheidlinger's books and papers.

Scheidlinger's personal history gives testimony to the positive power of the group for healing and growth. There are also indications that the group can be an ominous negative force generating pathology and destruction. Scheidlinger's respect for the group's awesome potential is apparent in his work on scapegoating. His life reflects his passionate concern for overcoming the destructive and encouraging positive potential via a constructive social activation by group and by other means.

These concerns are reflected in Part II of this volume which deals with group processes as they relate to the world in which we live. Saul Scheidlinger's concerns about *The Group and Society* are reflected in the chapters on scapegoating and lessons from the Nazi doctors for the nuclear age.

Part III concerns leadership and the group, a matter of primary interest to thinkers and practitioners involved with group process. Both papers relate to Scheidlinger's contributions and interests, although each author explores different aspects of leadership. The first deals with qualities of a group therapy leader while the second concerns organizational leadership and problems of morality.

Part IV is devoted to preoedipal pathology and the group matrix. Scheidlinger's seminal paper on the mother-group (1974) sensitized many group theorists and therapists to the therapeutic value of the group as a matrix, of particular significance for those difficult-to-treat individuals suffering preoedipal problems. Important applications of this concept are to be found in the chapters of Part IV.

Scheidlinger's early work as well as his most recent contributions deal with young people. Part V contains papers concerned with children and adolescents in group treatment. The papers of part VI are all related to the evolution of group treatment from both a historical and theoretical view. A chapter dealing with cultural factors in psychoanalytic groups appears in part VII.

Issues concerning different research approaches to group therapy are examined in the final three chapters. A focus on research relates to Scheidlinger's passion and determination to enrich our comprehension of group theory and its relationships and applications. Along with greater awareness of the connections between group dynamics and psychoanalytic concepts comes the hope of developing still more effective utilization of the powerful group instrument as a means of enhancing therapeutic processes. Another major goal of Saul Scheidlinger and of this book has been to seek connections and bridges of understanding between "islands" of theory on group and individual dynamics.

In conclusion, this volume has as its objectives: to honor Saul Scheidlinger by acknowledging his work and impact; to strive toward further advances built upon Scheidlinger's contributions and those of others; to make available to those who are entering the field an opportunity to learn about Scheidlinger's work and its applications, with the hope that this will provide a perspective which may lead to further advances in psychoanalytic group theory and therapy.

REFERENCES

Fenchel, G. (1983), Interview of Saul Scheidlinger. *Group*, 7:47–56.
O'Connell, M. C. (unpublished), *Recollection: A Personal Memoir of Saul Scheidlinger.* March 14, 1982.

Scheidlinger, S. (1952), Group factors in promoting school children's mental health, *Amer. J. Orthopsychiat.*, 22:394–404.

—— (1955), The concept of identification in group psychotherapy. *Amer. J. Psychother.*, 9:661–672.

—— (1964), Identification, the sense of belonging and of identity in small groups. *Internat. J. Group Psychother.*, 14:291–306.

—— (1965), Three group approaches with socially deprived latency-age children. *Internat. J. Group Psychother.*, 15:434–445.

—— (1966a), The concept of empathy in group psychotherapy. *Internat. J. Group Psychother.*, 16:413–424.

—— (1966b), The concept of latency: Implications for group treatment. *Soc. Casework*, 22:363–367.

—— (1968a), The concept of regression in group psychotherapy. *Internat. J. Group Psychother.*, 18:3–20.

—— (1974), On the concept of the "Mother-group." *Internat. J. Group Psychother.*, 24:417–428.

—— (1982a), The psychology of leadership revisited: An overview. *Group*, 4:5–17.

—— (1982b), On scapegoating in group psychotherapy. *Internat. J. Group Psychother.*, 32:131–143.

—— (1982c), *Focus on Group Psychotherapy, Clinical Essays.* New York: International Universities Press.

—— (1984), Short-term group psychotherapy for children: An overview. *Inter. J. Group Psychother.*, 34:573–585.

—— (1985), Group treatment of adolescents—An overview. *Amer. J. Orthopsychiat.*, 55:102–111.

—— (1987), Interpretation in group psychotherapy. *Internat. J. Group Psychother.*, 37:339–352.

—— Douville, M., Harrahill, C., & Minor, J. D. (1959), Activity group therapy with children in a family agency. *Soc. Casework*, 40:193–201.

—— Rauch, E. (1972), Psychoanalytic group psychotherapy with children and adolescents. In: *Handbook of Child Psychoanalysis*, ed. B. B. Wolman. New York: Van Nostrand Reinhold, pp.364–398.

—— Struening, E. C., & Rabkin, J. G. (1970), Evaluation of a mental health consultation service in a ghetto area. *Amer. J. Psychother.*, 24:485–493.

Chapter 1

Saul Scheidlinger: Scholar, Educator, Colleague, and Friend

RUTH HOCHBERG, Ph.D., and EMANUEL HALLOWITZ, M.S.W.

The distinguished contributors to this book honor Saul Scheidlinger as a leading theoretician in the field of group psychotherapy. As writer, teacher, editor, and film producer, Saul has added significantly to group psychotherapy's knowledge base; he has developed quality training programs and has expanded the use of group psychotherapy as a clinical modality. He has published three books, written over seventy articles, and produced three prize-winning films and two videotapes. He has lectured nationally and internationally. Saul is an innovator, always on the cutting edge of the profession.

Saul is also gracious, charming, and compassionate. He has a wonderful sense of humor, and a mind like finely tempered steel. What is not known to many is that Saul immigrated to this country in 1938 at the age of twenty. He intended to go to college but arrived in the United States without funds and with no knowledge of the English language. He immediately went to work in a factory and four months after arriving in New York City, he had learned enough English to enroll in night classes at City College. Shortly afterward, he received a scholarship that enabled him to attend day college and work at night. *The New York Times*, in June 1942, headed an article "One Man Wins 4 Honors." Saul Scheidlinger had won four distinguished academic awards as well as becoming a member of Phi Beta Kappa and graduating Magna Cum Laude. After graduation, without the resources to attend medical school, but deeply interested in the field of

9

mental health, Saul attended the Columbia University School of Social Work for his Master of Science degree. Saul's close relationship with group psychotherapy started in 1944 at the Jewish Board of Guardians under the direction and guidance of Sam Slavson. It wasn't long before colleagues, supervisors, and administrators became impressed with Saul's conceptual ability and his clinical acumen. During the four years he was at the Jewish Board of Guardians, he moved up the hierarchy from individual and group therapist to Supervisor and Assistant Director of Group Therapy. During his last year at the Agency he worked with Slavson and Mort Schiffer on producing the film *Activity Group Therapy* (Slavson, 1950).

In 1948, Saul started doctoral studies at New York University. In 1952, his dissertation formed the basis of a first book, *Psychoanalysis and Group Behavior*. That same year he became the group therapy consultant to the Community Service Society, where he did most of his experimental clinical work.

Saul progressed from working with children with mild reactive disorders using a nonverbal, nondirective approach to working with severely deprived children and adults who needed different models of group treatment. He pioneered the use of structured groups with verbal interventions for these ego-disturbed borderline children and adults. It was through his work in groups with populations heretofore considered inappropriate for group therapy, and through his other clinical work that Saul developed the concept of the "Mother-Group," and clarified and elaborated the dynamics of such phenomena as scapegoating, regression, empathy, leadership, and, most recently, interpretation, in group therapy. His formulations have become an integral part of the theoretical foundation of group psychotherapy.

In addition to concept development, Saul was mindful of the proliferation of different kinds of groups and group leaders—professional and paraprofessional. Saul sought to bring clarity to the definition of group psychotherapy as distinct from therapeutic groups, encounter groups, educational groups, support groups, and so on. Although he trained many different kinds of group leaders, professional as well as paraprofessional, Saul has always asserted that group psychotherapy must remain the province of the well-trained and skilled professional.

In 1962 Saul joined a group of dedicated clinicians at Einstein Medical College who were instrumental in creating a very innovative comprehensive community mental health program in the South Bronx, a socially and economically deprived area. Saul, as part of this program, organized a consortium of churches, temples, and community centers. He assisted them in identifying community needs and enabled them to work in concert to share resources and to develop meaningful programs for children, adolescents, and adults. During this same period Saul obtained foundation grants to develop films for adolescents and human service workers. Responding to the need for sex education for adolescents and training for group workers, his films were part of the effort to combat the large number of unwanted pregnancies and the venereal disease rampant in the South Bronx. These films are still used today as a teaching tool in clinics, social agencies, and in graduate schools of social work, psychology, and medicine.

After seven or eight years the Community Mental Health Center was taken over by another operating group and Saul and his colleagues moved to Einstein proper, where as part of his functioning as a professor in the Department of Psychiatry, he teaches and trains residents in group psychotherapy.

During ten years as editor of the *International Journal of Group Psychotherapy*, Saul's commitment to excellence developed this publication to its present status as the premiere journal in the field. With great foresight as to the emerging need to document outcomes of group psychotherapy, he selected and published papers on research and theory, encouraging contributions from a broad spectrum of theoreticians and practitioners. Although his primary orientation is psychoanalytic, as editor Saul respected and encouraged others of different persuasions to write and submit papers to the journal. In this way, it has been truly representative of the best of the many different group psychotherapy models.

The Saul we know, love, and respect is a man who readily applauds and acknowledges the contributions of his colleagues. He is a good friend and teacher, who provides a wealth of enthusiasm and unflagging encouragement to his friends, young professionals, and students. His genius lies in his ability to grasp the importance of an idea or a clinical experience that will add to the knowledge base of the profession. His help and guidance insures that valuable contributions are published or presented at public forums. His illustrious career continues to be a hallmark of excellence. We are proud to be among his friends and colleagues.

REFERENCES

Scheidlinger, S. (1952), *Psychoanalysis and Group Behavior*. New York: W. W. Norton.
Slavson, S. R. (1950), *Activity Group Therapy*. Produced by S. R. Slavson, Jewish Board of Guardians. New York: Campus Film Productions.

Chapter 2

Expanding Knowledge/Expanding Practice in Group Psychotherapy with Children

MARGARET G. FRANK, M.S.S.W.

Over thirty years ago Saul commuted from New York City to Boston, Massachusetts. He arrived each week to teach a gathering of educators, psychiatrists, psychologists, and social workers. The subject was the theory and practice of group psychotherapy for latency aged children. It is not easy to capture the content, the method, and the process that went into those years of education. One can only ask the reader to summon up a vision of an oriental carpet in which each thread is no longer distinguishable but the weave is obviously priceless. The foundation of theory was psychoanalytic, including a rich appreciation of the development of children. He taught the principles of forming a group for therapy. Thus, one had to learn a process of diagnosis which went beyond labels and entered the realm of anticipating the chemical mixture of six or seven children who were being considered for a group. He taught method always informed by theory. He understood the anxieties of his students as they started their first groups, and he provided a support that reached over the miles between the two cities. Humor and warmth were always present. Among the many treasures was his continuous encouragement of the process of inquiry. The title of this essay is designed to capture the balance Saul created which involved learning theory for practice and learning from practice to refine and enlarge theory. Such a process is never ending, and in the process both practice and theory are enriched.

Activity group therapy as first devised and articulated by S. R. Slavson, M. Schiffer, and later, Saul Scheidlinger capitalized on the observation that children of the latency ages are most comfortable in groups. They apppear open to therapeutic influence both from their peers and an adult leader. The latter maintains a facilitating stance, benign, essentially noninterpretative, ever watchful, and ever protective of both the group process and the individual. Winnicott's concept of a "holding environment" is an apt description of the ambience of the traditional activity groups. The therapeutic role of the leader was ensured by the leader's ability to understand what was happening both with each individual in the group as well as the larger dynamics which lay in the interaction. The therapeutic potential offered through the members came from careful selection of the children. There was no question that the children chosen for these groups had their unique psychological difficulties, but they had much to offer one another. In fact the very "pathology" of one child might well work to the benefit of another.

Composing a group was an arduous task which, as mentioned above, involved the therapist's best ability to infer future "chemical" interactions. Those involved will remember how many children were reviewed but could not be accepted for a given group. In addition, many were seen who were not good candidates for the traditional activity group therapy.

As the group of the "unaccepted" children increased, many practitioners were forced to look more carefully at traditional practices. This investigation involved an attempt to see why the approach worked on the children selected. Our purpose was to create modifications which would enable treatment of the unaccepted children.

A discussion of evolving theory and practice is made richer by placing it in time. The work and concerns discussed here took place in the late 1950s and the early 1960s. Ego psychologists had been at work for many years. It is, however, well known that there is a considerable lag between the evolution of theory and the time it finds its place on the frontiers of practice. The contributions of ego psychology seemed to provide answers for the many questions which were posed by group psychotherapists.

The effectivenesss of the traditional activity groups, it appeared, rested to a great degree on the ego capacities of the children chosen for those groups. In the terms of later theory, the children chosen for the traditional groups had achieved a degree of psychic separateness. They had a sense of self, albeit not an optimally good enough self. They wished to belong. They had the ability to perceive the behaviors of others, both that of peers and of the leader.

One need only imagine a rather typical scene in the traditional activity group when the children have their first argument in which both words and bodies are involved. The therapist, keeping an eye on both individuals and the group momentum, chooses to get up from his spot. As the affect mounts he atypically starts to sweep the floor near the argument. There is no discussion, no interpretation, and certainly no confrontation. In this way, the therapist provides a caretaking nonintrusive presence which offers symbolically and concretely an orderly new object very much present in the service of reasonable everyday controls. Such therapist behavior can introduce useful identificatory figures to children who need such influences which have been absent in their lives. Children belonging to these groups are aware that the adult has "intervened." In addition, they are aware that they have been spared the anticipated reminder about good behavior or kindness to others they have come to expect from adults. They are able to take advantage of what we would now call a "new object experience." Understanding a therapeutic approach as it was illuminated by evolving ego psychology opened the way to establishing modifications for children with lesser ego capacities.

This author and others have written about modified activity group therapy for what we then called ego impaired children. Informed by new understanding, groups were formed for borderline children. These are children with little sense of themselves, who have little tolerance for differences. The principles of group formation shifted. While there was still room for differing ego capacities these groups had members who were more alike in functional terms. Just as the principles of the group composition had to shift to accommodate the psychological needs of these children, so did the setting, the materials, and most importantly, the stance and role of the therapist.

In the beginning stages there was less reliance on the group members providing a therapeutic milieu for each other; that was the most prominent responsibility of the therapists. The setting, while containing some materials for activity, was less encouraging of action. The child patients of these groups were action prone. It is important to distinguish between action and acting out. The latter implies resistance to unconscious material which is acted out. These children did not have the containing structure for acting out, they were action prone. Unlike the children accepted for the traditional activity groups, they lacked language as an organizing capacity of the ego. This observation led to a marked difference in the role of the therapist.

The therapist of the modified groups would appear to the outside observer far more active than the therapist of the traditional groups. The activity had similar purposes, however. Still a facilitator of development in a benign way, the therapist is called upon to maintain emotional safety for the members and the group. The reader may recall that a group argument was discussed above, in which the leader swept the floor near the children who were fighting. Discussion of this technique pointed to capacities lacking in the children with less structure. In these groups the leader would use both words and actions. For example, one might see the leader rise and walk over to the arguers putting a hand on a couple of shoulders. The words that followed could range from "I wonder how this can be settled so that you kids can enjoy yourselves?" Or, "It seems very hard to find a way to share. Can anyone think of a method?" Many children will assert that they are in fact enjoying fighting. The leader then needs to follow up with a comment like "I think none of you know about good times when you are not hurt."

The reader who is watching the influence of theory on technique will begin to observe the use of object relations theory as it informs the therapist's role. In the late 1960s, ego psychology was beginning to evolve into an object relations theory. The studies of Margaret Mahler (Mahler, Pine, and Bergman, 1975), which articulated development as a process of separation–individuation (a movement from relative oneness to separateness) made it possible to understand the population of children treated in these modified groups in a more refined way. The therapist who studied psychoanalytic developmental theory was now privy to a view of impaired ego functioning within an object relations context. The children being treated lacked certain basic functions and were essentially emotionally ignorant of the more advanced levels of object relations.

CASE TO THEORY

It seems useful, at this juncture, to look more closely at the children who for many years were not accepted in and could not use traditional activity group therapy. In current diagnostic nomenclature they would be labeled "borderline." However, this label tells us only that they have not developed enough psychic structure to warrant being considered neurotic, despite the fact that many demonstrate neurotic-like concerns, symptoms, and issues. A closer look shows them to be children who have not acquired a sufficient sense of themselves as separate psychic beings. A period of observation shows a good deal of magical thinking operates in their view of themselves and others. They are action prone, dispelling anxiety through action because they have not developed sufficient means for psychic containment. While there is no question that they suffer from psychic conflict it cannot be approached as yet in therapy. The reason is clearly related to the fact that they have not developed sufficient ego equipment to deal with the anxiety which would be aroused as a result of therapeutic attention to their conflicts. Many live with an inability to differentiate affects. Thus their affect experiences are similar to those of a baby who feels either pleasure or discomfort from head to toe. While these children have the use of words, mostly in the four-letter category, language has not yet developed as a tool of the ego. They lack many of the functions seen in higher structured patients. They have little capacity to tolerate frustration or to plan for themselves with positive anticipation. They often lack the capacity to keep themselves safe. Their expectations of self and other are rarely trusting or positive.

The danger inherent in an attempt such as this to draw a profile of the children under consideration is the temptation of the reader to conclude that there is a borderline syndrome. The author is presenting an array of deficits in development that may be found in this patient population. If we had seven children under discussion there would be considerable variation among them. What these children have in common is a range of incomplete aspects of development. They can be understood better when their behaviors are framed by a psychology of object relations. By virtue of endowment in some combination with the caretaking environment, these patients have little sense that there is a positive value to the object (other) or to the self. They live internally in a representational world which has a paucity of positive experiences. They cannot perceive an adult as benign with any ease because they have not had sufficient experience with benign caretakers to form such a positive representation.

THEORY TO CASE

An understanding of this patient group, framed by ego psychology and object relations theory, clarifies the therapeutic task. Simply stated, the goal of therapy is to promote ego capacities which have not been sufficiently developed. The task can be stated simply, but we are all aware that the translation into practice is not so simple. All development takes place within the context of object relations. The deficiencies observed in these children are the result of the nature of their original self–object experiences. The promotion of change must also take place within an object relations context, one which facilitates growth. This discussion leads to an increased ability to define the role of the therapist. The therapist must intend to provide a corrective experience. All actions and words contain that purpose. At the same time there must be an awareness that each child has a scenario, a program which will make him or her predominantly unreceptive to the experience promoted by the therapist. The therapist needs to be able to discern the patients' original self–object scenario. He needs to be able to discuss their object expectations. These interventions will not be welcome. This can be viewed as a resistance to change in the realm of object relations. An understanding of this resistance is important in the management of potential countertransference. If the therapist appreciates the patient's need to cling to their original definition of self and other he will find greater resources in himself to maintain his stance. The innate movement in the direction of separation and growth in each patient ultimately sides with the therapist's endeavors. A few case vignettes will clarify the preceding discussion:

AFFECT DIFFERENTIATION

The following vignette is offered to demonstrate beginning work on affect differentiation and management.

A girls' group had been meeting for several months. The therapist had purchased some supplies and was unaware that she had less than she needed for the number in the group. (It was too early to promote a frustrating situation.) The girls began to fight over the materials, destroying many of them. There was a mounting feeling of rage in the room with insulting words being flung from child to child. The therapist stepped in and asked them to sit down. They did not, but the affect and noise level subsided. The therapist told them that she had upset them, that they were disappointed. One of the girls cried out, "No, we are pissed!" The therapist asked what that meant. The chorus replied, "Angry." The therapist agreed that they were angry but they were also disappointed. She added that they were used to being disappointed but didn't know what to do with such feelings, so they swore at each other and ripped the materials. One of the girls remarked that they could swear at her and rip her up. The therapist replied that they could not but they could tell her what they felt and plan how to handle the shortage. In a mocking tone a girl said, "Oh, Miss Lange we are so disappointed!" The other girls laughed. The therapist suggested that they were not used to sorting out how they felt and that they were not used to anyone being interested in hearing them express their feelings. No single anecdote can capture what occurs through a process. This vignette was a beginning. The therapist's interventions were, at first, met with mockery and skepticism. But the interaction was repeated in different forms over and over, and eventually the girls were moved by their wish to be heard and by the relief of managing feelings.

NEW OBJECT EXPERIENCE

All interventions have within them the potential for a new object experience. This vignette shows the therapist's actions and further attempts to challenge the group to relate in new ways.

A group of boys had been in group therapy for almost a year. They were planning an outing, which was an unusual event (until the planned excursion they had met only in the therapy room). Their plans were surrounded with a combination of excitement and pessimism. Many voiced their certainty that something would go wrong and prevent the trip. A week before the trip they got into a fight which involved damage to items in the group room. The therapist stopped their action and sat them down to talk. The children were certain that the trip would be taken away as a punishment. Watching the therapist's affect they pondered why he didn't seem angry. One child called out "You're not for real!" The therapist replied that they just did not know what to do with him. He told the children that they were more comfortable with angry and punishing adults; maybe even wanted him to be that way. In fact he knew that they had gotten into trouble that day because they were so excited about the plans for next week. He also had a hunch that they were so certain that something good was going to be taken away from them, that they were trying to bring the disappointment about. He assured them that while they would have to figure out a way to fix the room, that he had no intention of canceling their plans. Again he was told that he was not "for real" and that he really could not be trusted. But the words were stated with humor and affection.

Obviously, no single interaction brings about a shift in object relations. However, the consistency of response coupled with the verbal challenge to that which is familiar to the patient begins to shift expectations of object and self.

In the following months this group had many discussions on the topic of trust. They wondered how the therapist could like them when they were so "bad." This gave the therapist the opportunity to differentiate between behavior and a core self. They were helped to verbalize feelings and doubts. While activity remained the medium for the group's meeting they seemed increasingly hungry for the discussions. They tested the therapist to the hilt. There were times when he became discouraged or annoyed with them. He would use his feelings to interpret their attempts to make him resemble emotionally the adult figures they had known. After a while he invited them to consider him, not to be "good" but to allow him to be free to work well with them. "If I am always having to break up fights, how can I have those good discussions with you that we have had? I deserve better from you."

PROTECTION NOT CONTROL

The children who are selected for these groups often, by the nature of their ego deficiencies, arouse in the therapist the need to control behavior. This can be viewed as a countertransference, but, in the view of this author, it is a limited perception. When the therapist understands that the children lack capacities he can keep an eye on the ways the egos of the children are functioning. This on-going diagnostic work enables the therapist to intervene out of the needs of his patient rather than his own anxiety. Further, such knowledge prompts the appropriate verbal interventions.

A boys' group had decided to prepare a spaghetti dinner. The planning and execution of the meal involved an assumption of autonomy that was beyond their collective egos. Their regression took the form of tossing spaghetti around the room. Few adults could maintain a sense of calm in such a scene. As the action escalated the therapist tested their capacity for control. He asked them if they could calm down before they ruined their own nicely planned meal. His words were not heard by egos which were becoming overwhelmed. He then stood up and began to collect the dishes of food. He put them aside, saving each one. The children said that he was punishing them. He responded that he was not. He was helping them to restore some order. He added that maybe next time they would be able to do it themselves. Within a moment the meal was served again with an atmosphere of calm and pleasure.

RESISTANCE OR STRIVINGS FOR AUTONOMY?

It is now within the capacity of the therapist to ask the diagnostic question about group behavior as to whether an action is resistance or an attempt at autonomy. It is an important question to pose. The answer will prompt different therapeutic stances. A girl's group which had met for several years had been settling into discussions for part of every session. As they got closer to revealing their feeling for the therapist they began to get up and move around the room, darting into the hall, reverting to physical behaviors of shoving and pushing each other as they had in the early phases of the group. The therapist saw their behaviors as resistance to exposure of feelings and the concomitant closeness involved. She remarked that she was curious about all the sudden action that was going on. The girls giggled. The therapist continued raising the question as to whether they were feeling uncomfortable about so much talk of feelings. These girls, who were ostensibly tough, cracked jokes about feelings and sissies. The therapist remarked that it took great strength to know and talk about what a person felt. The discussions were resumed.

At a later phase of the same group, some of the girls would leave the meeting room for periods of time. This behavior was repeated many times. In addition, they began to come late to group meetings. The therapist viewed these behaviors as attempts to try out their separateness and autonomy. She shared her thoughts with the girls, saying that she thought they were telling her that they were more ready to be in charge. She suggested that perhaps they could be more in charge in the group and not have to be late or always leaving the room. The behavior shifted and the girls did take more responsibility for activities and discussion.

The vignettes offered demonstrate the evolution of a therapeutic approach informed by expanding theory. The theory of ego development and object relations does not replace conflict theory, it expands it. Therapists use theory to inform their practice. The population served in these groups is impaired in realms of fundamental psychic equipment. The approach that has evolved aims to promote that development. One can envisage when patients speak of being "bad," that if treatment continues it will eventually focus upon id wishes. Such work can then be successful because the ego can manage the exposure of the unconscious. For those who have practiced traditional activity group therapy there is a clear recognition that the vignettes above demonstrate a process which is quite different. It is a process which evolved out of a recognition of differing psychic needs informed by expanding theory.

For this author, the process of learning fundamental theory and practice, of watching the needs of the patients, of working therapeutically always informed by theory, began some thirty years ago with the model and encouragement of Saul Scheidlinger.

REFERENCES

Frank, M. G. (1968), Current trends in group therapy with children. *Internat. J. Group Psychother.*, 18:447–460.

———— (1976), Modifications of activity group therapy: Responses of ego-impoverished children. *Clin. Soc. Work*, 4:102–103.

Mahler, M. S., Pine, F. & Bergman, A. (1975), *The Psychological Birth of the Human Infant.* New York: Basic Books.

Slavson, S. R. (1945), Group therapy with children. In: *Modern Trends in Child Psychiatry,* eds. M. D. C. Lewis & B. L. Pacella. New York: International Universities Press.

Scheidlinger, S. (1960), Experiential group treatment of severely deprived latency-aged children. *Amer. J. Orthopsychiat.*, 30:356–368.

Schiffer, M. (1984), *Childrens Group Therapy.* New York: Free Press.

Part II

The Group and Society

INTRODUCTION

The papers of part II deal with important issues concerning the group and society. Scheidlinger's interest in the effects of group identifications (1955) and their impact on the quality of life led him to study certain intrapsychic factors and group dynamics. These would include the therapeutic effects of the group matrix or "mother group" (Scheidlinger, 1974) and cohesiveness. Among the potentially destructive mechanisms are *scapegoating* (1982), and related to it are other dehumanizing forces, including the Holocaust. Such issues, as well as the present danger of nuclear threat, must be better understood if human society is to survive.

Scheidlinger's work on scapegoating can help us comprehend the unconscious mechanism operant in all kinds of groups including political, institutional, family, and psychotherapy. Walter Gadlin (in chapter 3) acknowledges Scheidlinger's influence, and devotes his paper to elucidating examples of the psychodynamics of scapegoating in biblical and classical literature, world affairs, and group therapy.

John Mack's "Ideology and Technology: Lessons from the Nazi Doctors for the Nuclear Age" (chapter 4) also relates to group dynamics and social issues. Mack explores how technology and ideology can infest group functioning. Among the vital variables in such group functions is the inclination of ordinary people to obey authority and bend to group pressure even when they know this causes harm to others. It is important to note how the technological use of power can gratify, strike with awe, and sometimes arouse detachment in those who "push the buttons." It is possible to develop, out of the killing operation, a complex social system which offers a fixed structure of belief, rationale, and justification. Here ideology and technology blend into destructiveness. Since the issues are awesome, Mack concludes by expressing concern about the sense of powerlessness which threatens to overwhelm us when contemplating such problems and seeking solutions.

These are important issues concerning the nature of life in society as it is influenced by intrapsychic mechanisms and those of group dynamics. It is important that we learn more about intrapsychic defense mechanisms and group dynamics if we are to avoid destructive acting out in leaders and by groups. Unless these dangerous trends are better understood and dealt with, we may not be able to preserve human society and individual dignity. It is crucial in conducting group therapy that such unconscious mechanisms be identified and harnessed.

Both the potential for helping disturbed individuals and groups and the vital importance of resisting and overcoming societal trends toward alienation necessitate that further efforts be dedicated to the subjects under consideration in this section on the group and society. Clearly the group is a powerful instrument for good or for evil.

REFERENCES

Scheidlinger, S. (1955), The concept of identification in group psychotherapy. *Amer. J. Psychother.*, 9:661–672.

———— (1974), On the concept of the "mother group." *Internat. J. Group Psychother.*, 24:417–428.

———— (1982), On scapegoating in group psychotherapy. *Internat. J. Group Psychother.*, 32:131–143.

Chapter 3

On Scapegoating: Biblical–Classical Sources, Group Psychotherapy, and World Affairs

WALTER I. GADLIN, Ph.D.

"On Scapegoating in Group Psychotherapy" (1982) is an enduring testimony to both Dr. Saul Scheidlinger's breadth of mind and to his influence on our field. In this short paper, Dr. Scheidlinger demonstrates a commanding presence in the diverse fields of Biblical, classical, psychoanalytic, and group process literature and offers a clear and dynamic definition of an important though ambiguous concept, clarifying the human characteristics that underlie the abstraction. He edifies us not only with crisp and lucid logic but with a human sensibility that has informed his writing, teaching, and patient care over more than four decades. This paper is offered as a tribute to these qualities of Dr. Scheidlinger and as an attempt to further define scapegoating from a psychoanalytic viewpoint as it operates in families, groups, and societies.

Scapegoating is a process that is used by a community (which might be as small as a group, family, or even a couple) at moments of perceived great danger, to transfer responsibility for the commission of a necessary evil from the whole community to one of its members. This transfer is supposed to trick a specific audience, the authority figure (real or imagined: parent, teacher, therapist, or God), into thinking that the designated scapegoat acted alone in performing his evil actions; the community as a whole can then be held blameless and therefore may escape punishment and benefit from the desirable consequences of the evil act. The scapegoat is punished and/or banished in order to clearly (1) dissociate the community from the scapegoat, and (2) separate the good consequences from the evil actions that brought them about.

Unlike many authors, I am excluding the innocent victim from the category of scapegoat by narrowing the definition and insisting that the scapegoat, in fact or in myth, performs a vital "good" for the community. The tendency for individuals and groups to escape responsibility and cast blame on others is ubiquitous, and infinitely varied in its mechanisms. Scapegoating is one of the more developed and sophisticated of these magical mechanisms because it affirms the primacy of the community over the individual and of superego restraints over id impulses. Nevertheless, scapegoating is a defensive maneuver and as such requires the interpretation of its unconscious underpinnings in settings where it is possible to do so, for example, in consultation with organizations, groups, and families. What is perforce unconscious is the communal desire for the "good" produced by the evil act. The exploration and interpretation of this unconscious desire and the anxiety and depressive affects associated with it allow community avowal of desires, affirmation or denial of their legitimacy, and a review of methods for attaining unconscious goals. Thus, the defense is made unnecessary and the hate and aggression directed at the scapegoat is reduced.

We will begin where Dr. Scheidlinger (1982) does, with a Biblical ritual for the Day of Atonement, because the myths and stories contained within the Bible and within the classical mythologies are powerful confirmations of the enduring human qualities that we also find in our work with patients. In this ritual, two goats are selected by the high priest and subjected to a lottery, "one marked for the Lord and the other marked for Azazel" (Leviticus 16:8). The goat "marked for the Lord" is slaughtered in a ritual congruent with the laws of sacrifice found throughout the Book of Leviticus. However, the high priest is then given unusual instructions: "While the goat designated by lot for Azazel shall be left standing alive before the Lord, to make expiation with it and to send it off to the wilderness for Azazel" (Leviticus 16:10).

> Aaron shall lay both his hands upon the head of the live goat and confess over it all the iniquities and transgressions of the Israelites, whatever their sins, putting them on the head of the goat; and it shall be sent off to the wilderness through a designated man. Thus the goat shall carry on it all these iniquities to an inaccessible region; and the goat shall be set free in the wilderness [Leviticus 16:21–27].

This strange ritual leaves the reader with many questions: Who or what is Azazel? Why the duplication of one goat sacrificed and the other scapegoated for the seemingly identical function of cleansing the people of their sins? How are we to differentiate these two goats and the two processes they undergo? Both are innocent victims, randomly picked to eradicate the sins of others, and both meet unwelcome fates. Are they not two varieties of the same animal meeting a similar sacrificial fate (as the traditional Biblical commentators would insist) or is there an essential difference between what is being done to them? Is it, as Dr. Scheidlinger speculates (pp. 108, 113), a Biblical example of the primitive psychological defense of splitting with one, all bad, for the demon Azazel and one, all good, for the Lord? (see also Wright, Hoffman, and Gore [1988]). And finally, how essential is the scapegoat's innocence? Is it, as Dr. Scheidlinger states, that "the term scapegoat has nowadays come to stand for any person or group who innocently bears the blame for others" (p. 108), or, as he (and others) also state, "a scapegoat in a small group is likely to range from a wholly innocent person to a more or less willing and involved recipient . . ." (p. 112)? Or, as still others maintain, "there is always unconscious collusion between scapegoater and scapegoat"? (Jaques, 1955, p. 486, see also Kraupl-Taylor and Rey, 1953; Foulkes and Anthony, 1957, 1964).

My attempt to address these questions relies on an original thesis proposed by the psychoanalytically informed classicist Hyam Maccoby in his book, *The Sacred Executioner: Human Sacrifice and the Legacy of Guilt* (1982). Before we consider Maccoby's solution, we must discard the simple hypothesis of splitting to explain the use of two goats as there is no evidence from the text or the context that either goat is perceived as having an inherent attribute of goodness or badness. Evidence of a *perception* of this sort would be necessary to diagnose the mechanism of splitting.

A second and possibly more sophisticated hypothesis that could be advanced by a psychoanalyst is that the two goats reflect two different stages in human superego development. In this schema, the first goat signifies the more advanced stage when guilt has been internalized and a sacrifice is required for atonement. The thought is, "We have sinned—taken something of value from you, God—and we offer this gift of value as reparation and as a sign of our contrition." The second goat is an archaic ritual from the time the people had included in their pantheon the worship and propitiation of the demon Azazel, and it reflects a more primitive stage of superego development where instead of internalization there is denial and projection of blame, and instead of communal contrition there is a propitiation of the angry God through magical substitution. The accompanying thought at this stage of moral development would be, "We didn't do it—he did."

This explanation is both congruent with our knowledge of cognitive and emotional development and faithful to the text and the moral purpose of the Bible as a "fascinating repository of information about a crucial [element] in man's development—his slow progress from modes of shifting blame and responsibility through institutions of sacrifice to the acceptance of full personal responsibility for his actions both as an individual and as a member of society" (Maccoby, 1982, p. 10). Nevertheless, a fatal flaw remains with this answer and it lies primarily in the continuation of the archaic ritual (goat two) along with its more sophisticated supplanter ritual (goat one). Much as with individual development, we are not surprised when primitive thinking dominates the rituals, myths, and mundane practices of primitive societies or when in more developed societies it breaks through to the surface of consciousness in moments of extreme communal stress, but we do not expect it to dominate either well-developed individuals or societies in normal times. The redaction of the Bible was not the product of primitive individuals nor of a primitive society. In passage after passage, and with few exceptions, we observe the transformation of primitive methods of denial and disavowal of moral responsibility into more sophisticated ways of accepting and atoning for guilt.

Why then do both goats continue as coequal rituals ordained for each and every Day of Atonement? The rabbis attempted to bypass this problem by insisting that the goats were just different forms of sacrifices. In second-temple times the ritual was therefore changed from loosing the scapegoat in the wilderness with an uncertain outcome to throwing it off a cliff near Jerusalem to an improper but nevertheless predictably sacrificial death.[1]

Maccoby ventures a bold solution to this problem which meets the demands of the text and of psychological understanding. He argues that the ritual of the two goats is originally that of human sacrifice at a time of great *societal* need, with the scapegoat standing for the sacred executioner (now symbolized by the second goat) who per-

[1]For primitive people magical thinking was preserved as the preferred means of dealing with shame, guilt, and anxiety. Perhaps it is the most efficient form of defense for those who can fool themselves with it, in that it totally obliterates the problem. A remnant of this mechanism resides in a Yom Kippur ritual that has persisted in some segments of Orthodox Jewry until today. Despite generations of rabbinic rulings against the practice, some penitents will twirl a live chicken around their heads on the eve before Yom Kippur while reciting an incantation transferring their sins to the hapless bird. This ritual is a direct successor to what they understood the scapegoat to be, even though it contradicts more sophisticated rabbinic authorities who have been helpless in their attempts to weed out this practice and replace it with an act of charity. The folk tradition is retained because of its primitive power to assure people that they have forced God to accept the substitution of another being in their place.

formed the actual sacrifice of a human being (now symbolized by the first goat). Afterward, as part of the community's need to disclaim responsibility for the necessary murder–sacrifice, the sacred executioner is banished to the desert, no longer a member of the community of God, to become a devotee of the demon Azazel. According to Maccoby, this ritual dates from the period of the ascendancy of patriarchal society over a matriarchal one, when human sacrifice was no longer the essential component of annual fertility rites but was reserved for the rare moments of great communal stress, when the very existence of the tribe or city was endangered. By this point in human tribal development, the guilt over the murder of a member of the tribe was considerable and could no longer be whitewashed through the defensive operations of a matriarchal society which had featured the avoidance of memory and responsibility through the use of the drunken orgy as the setting for the murder–sacrifice.[2]

The endangered developing patriarchal community faced a desperate choice: to do away with sacrifice was to chance enraging the god at exactly the moment of the greatest danger to the tribe. He might take offense at their hubris, cause them to lose the battle, continue the plague or famine, and wipe them out. A similar end would result if the god were just weakened by their lack of devotion. Proof of their absolute submission was therefore necessary both to propitiate and to strengthen him in his competition with the neighboring deities and the still looming tribal goddesses. To perform the sacrifice, however, was to commit murder and therefore to bear personal and communal guilt, and even to implicate the god in this wanton destruction of human life.

Ancient societies resolved this dilemma by using human sacrifice at moments of great peril (such as famine, plague, war, and, paradoxically, the founding of a new city or tribe). But these societies also attempted to disguise one or more aspects of the murder with a variety of crude communal defensive operations in order to sever the guilt associated with the murder from the necessity of the sacrifice. These defensive operations all relied on a split in the consciousness of the

---

[2]In the typical matriarchal myth of Dionysus (Bacchus) there is a drunken orgy of sexual activity followed by dismemberment and resurrection. The god is associated with the realm and power of women, both in the story of his upbringing exclusively among women and in the emphasis given his youthful, effeminate attributes. In the full matriarchal society the goddess decrees the death of the young king each year to make room for a new consort for the queen. His body and especially his genitals are scattered in the field and waters to ensure fertility by revivifying the goddess (e.g., the myths of Attis, Adonis, Osiris (see Frazer, *The Golden Bough* [1907]; Graves, 1983, p. 126).

community so that its members could simultaneously sacrifice a human being and deny that they had committed murder. This "split" could not indefinitely continue to protect the community from guilt because of the slow but inexorable maturation of cognitive and moral capacity in many ancient societies. This psychological sophistication developed over millenia as an effect and in turn a cause of the advancement in primitive technologies, the establishment of larger and more complex communities, and the widening of human consciousness into areas of artistic, philosophical, and existential concern. The maturation of cognitive and moral functioning made it increasingly impossible to maintain the "split in the ego" (Freud, 1940, p. 202) that allows the coexistence of the two contradictory attitudes, one accompanying the sacrifice to the god and the second accompanying the murder of a fellow human being. As the existence of this contradiction forced itself into their consciousness, societies attempted increasingly sophisticated defensive operations in order to reestablish the efficacy of this split in consciousness so that they could continue their ritual without experiencing overbearing guilt. We will look at a series of these communal defenses embodied in the myths of many societies and we will discern major differences in their sophistication, but as ego and superego functions continue to mature, all of these defenses ultimately fail in their purpose of protecting the community from the anxiety and guilt that results from murder.

The simplest communal defensive operation we will consider is found in one version of the story of Leos, who sacrificed his three daughters to stop a famine afflicting Athens. In this myth, the defense was the daughters' great love for Athens which led them to volunteer for the honor of saving their city; there was, therefore, no murder because the sacrifice was willingly made. This, however, is a weak defense only sufficient against the guilt of daughter sacrifice, since to the ancient mind this was neither as shocking nor as serious as male sacrifice. A somewhat stronger defense is the ritualized combat where the ruling priest of the city's holy grove or temple is challenged to mortal combat by a rival to the priesthood. The loser becomes the sacrifice to the god without the community having to bear the guilt of slaughtering a passive victim (Frazer, 1907). A still stronger defense is contained in the story of the founding of Rome by Romulus and Remus. It obscures the fact of the sacrifice by turning it into an accidental death resulting from a quarrel over the plans while working on the foundation. When Remus, with derision, jumps over a trench that Romulus had dug, the latter kills his twin in justifiably hot-blooded anger and therefore is not held responsible. The sacrifice itself was necessary, in reality or at least in myth, at the inauguration of the newly founded city, "to placate the gods at a moment of *hubris* and avert their jealousy by inflicting a loss upon oneself; and also possibly to send an ambassador to the upper world who would act as tutelary spirit of the new city and intercede for it with the gods at closer quarters than any mortal being could command" (Maccoby, p. 11). The fact that this is a story of a sacrifice is disguised by the quarrel, and is betrayed by the fact that only good flows from the killing: Romulus is not punished, indeed is rewarded by the gods with the sight of a flight of vultures promising that the city–nation being founded would be as strong and pitiless as the vulture.

The myth of the death of Balder contains perhaps the greatest number of defenses used by a community to disown its mythical and ritual participation in the needed sacrifice. In this story from the Norse *Edda*, the beautiful and good Balder dreamed that he was to die. The goddess Frigg undertook to protect him by taking an oath from all beings and substances on earth that they would not harm Balder. On the strength of these oaths all the gods now regarded Balder as invulnerable and amused themselves and honored him by encircling him and shooting arrows of many substances at him. Seeing his opportunity to harm Balder, the evil god Loki disguised himself and tricked Frigg into telling him that she had not required an oath from the mistletoe on account of its insignificance. Loki then approached the blind god Hother, who was sitting outside the circle, invited him to join in doing honor to Balder, put a bow and mistletoe arrow into his hand, and directed him where to shoot. Hother shoots, Balder dies, and the gods grieve as they immolate him in a huge funeral pyre.

If we apply the explanation Freud advanced in *The Interpretation of Dreams* (1900, p. 514) to this myth, we would understand the many details as the secondary revision produced by the (dream) censorship. The details are unconsciously calculated to disguise the meaning of a simple, powerful scene: a ring of people surround a man, kill him by flinging missiles at him, and then burn his body. The secondary elaboration within the myth defends the community's innocence nine different ways exactly because it requires and profits from the death of Balder. It is as if the community as a whole is saying: (1) None of our missiles harmed the man; (2) the missile that killed him came from one man only; who was (3) standing outside our circle; (4) even he was not responsible as he was blind; and (5) did not know what he did. (6) The death happened through the evil plotting of a villain; (7) who was not one of our community at all; and so you see (8) there was never a sacrifice at all; (9) this is just a story about our gods. As each community matures its members come to believe that the effectiveness of their sacrifice is limited by their simultaneous denial of its being a sacrifice. They realize that they can't have it both ways: to the extent that the guilt of murder is explained away by the claim that the sacrifice is an accident, or self-defense (ritualized combat), or justifiable revenge (Romulus and Remus), or a murder committed by an outsider (Balder), to that same extent the death fails in its primary mission as a free-will offering to the gods.

Another set of myths defends against the guilt of murder with the idea that the victim is responsible for his own death because of his own crimes. In effect the same victim is the sacrifice and the scapegoat. The clearest example of this comes from the Athenian Bouphonia ritual which we know only in a late form where the original human sacrifice had already been supplanted by the sacrifice of a bull. In this ritual the bull is enticed to eat corn placed on the altar and thereby performs an act of desecration, which justifies his slaughter. The community bears no guilt because there has been no murder: the victim deserved his fate (Yerkes, 1953, pp. 68–74). Similarly, we have the story of the death of Neoptolemus, the son of Achilles who often repeated insults to Apollo at his shrine at Delphi. One day when he went too far and tried to appropriate Apollo's animal sacrifices for himself, his death was pronounced by the Priestess and carried out with a *sacrificial* knife. The Priestess then ordered Neoptolemus buried beneath the threshold of the new sanctuary to guard the new shrine as a ghostly presence and to watch over the sacrifices made in honor of heroes. The problem with the defensive mechanism embodied within this myth can be put simply: if Neoptolemus was such a bore and sinner that his death is deserved, how can he be a suitable gift to the gods and guardian of the city? Conversely, if he is good enough to be worthy of sacrifice, how can he be guilty enough so that his murderer is held blameless? With the increase in sophistication of man's cognitive style, it also becomes impossible to maintain the primitive splitting of consciousness that allows these contradictory elements to coexist without resolution.

Nevertheless, human sacrifice was too powerful a method of propitiating the gods to be abandoned, so more sophisticated methods of defending the community against the guilt of murder were attempted. The lottery, where the gods are held responsible for choosing the victim so that the community can feel innocent of murder, is one of the more sophisticated defenses. In chapter 7 of the Biblical book of Joshua, the children of Israel are surprisingly defeated in their attempt to conquer the small city of Ai. The entire enterprise of the conquest of Canaan is therefore threatened and a sacrifice is required to prevent the destruction of the people. "When the Canaanites and all the inhabitants of the land hear of this they will turn upon us and wipe out our very name from the earth. And what will you do about your great name?" (sentence 9). Through a series of lots, Joshua narrows the choice of victim to the tribe of Judah, the family of Zachites, the household of Zabdi, and the man Achan, who was then stoned. To the seventh century B.C. redactors of the Bible and even to earlier writers and codifiers, the story of sacrifice was horrible, blasphemous, and therefore impossible. It had to be disguised, indeed obliterated, through the introduction of Achan's admission that he sinned by taking booty from Jericho against God's and Joshua's commands. This not only removes the guilt from the nation for having sacrificed an innocent man, it also clears the name of the god who has required such a murder. Herein lies the difficulty with the use of the lottery as a disguise: it attenuates the guilt of the community at the cost of accusing its god of blood-thirstiness to his own community; hardly a deity in whom the community could place its trust, or build a covenantal relationship.

By the time of the redaction of the Bible the cognitive and moral development of the Israelites had proceeded to the point where it was impossible to continue the murderous practice of human sacrifice, no matter the danger to the nation. The lottery had therefore lost its defensive function and the story was transformed into another example of God's punishment for sin and there is no need to retain, indeed there is the absolute need to deny, any idea of this being the story of a sacrifice. Indeed, by the time of the compilation of the Bible all reservations that human sacrifice would ever be used again by its people were absolutely put aside. Even the myth of the founding of the tribe, the story of the sacrifice of Isaac,[3] was recast by these redactors as powerful propaganda against human sacrifice. If a sacrificial victim was not necessary at the most dangerous moment in its history (Abraham's founding of the tribe–nation), how could it ever again be needed or even considered?[4]

The scapegoat belongs in this line of communal defensive opera-

---

[3] The Hebrew term is *the Binding of Isaac*. The English term *Sacrifice of Isaac* derives from Christian theology in that it is seen as a "type" for the sacrifice of Jesus.

[4] With the slaughter of whole Jewish communities at the time of the Crusades, it is noteworthy that the original story of the *sacrifice* of Isaac again became temporarily ascendant. The Paytanim, devout medieval religious poets, rediscovered early (pre-Christian) midrashic commentaries testifying to the death and resurrection of Isaac (Spiegel, 1964). That this theme which so flatly contradicts the revered received Scripture is elaborated in their poetry is witness to the resurgence of primitive magical thinking at a time of great societal despair and stress. They prayed for the salvation owed to them *due* to the *sacrifice* of Isaac thereby reviving the idea that Judaism too had a foundation sacrifice where father Abraham had offered up his son Issac to God in order to protect the nation from danger in succeeding generations.

tions as an even more sophisticated device used to deny the community's complicity in murder while sacrificing a human being to its god. The scapegoat must be cosmically important and heroic enough to have been an appropriate vehicle for the good he has brought the community and at the same time he must be bad enough to have committed the evil for which he is being blamed. This dichotomy is neither as logically contradictory nor as psychologically irreconcilable as the two aspects of the character of the sacrifice (Neoptolemus) who must be simultaneously holy enough to achieve the sanctity required of a gift and messenger to the god, and evil enough to be responsible for having deserved his death. Therefore, to maintain the efficacy of the scapegoat as a defense requires a less primitive split in consciousness. The scapegoat did it all by himself and is therefore the only one who should be held responsible, *and* the community is to share in all of the benefits that accrued from the evil action.

In world mythical and religious literature there are many examples of human sacrifice with the executioner then treated as a scapegoat. Indeed the story of the crucifixion can be seen as a primary example of the scapegoat motif. Jesus is killed in order for him to fulfill his mission of bringing salvation to the faithful community; no less of a sacrifice is sufficiently powerful to have provided the necessary "good." But who is to perform, and to be forever blamed, for the required horrible deed of murdering God? The clearest choice is the Roman Empire in the person of its Viceroy Pontius Pilate, who actually pronounces the death sentence on Jesus and supervises his execution. According to both Maccoby and Jay Haley (1986) it was Paul's genius to realize that for political reasons it was impossible to blame the Romans without making it much more difficult to convert and dominate the Hellenistic as well as Roman populace. Paul therefore shifted the blame for Jesus' death from the Romans to the Jews, and Pontius Pilate was assigned the hapless but innocent role corresponding to that of Hother in the myth of Balder. In the Jews, Paul found the perfect compromise, an adversary important enough to be worthy of the guilt, but not strong enough to be an important obstacle to the growth of the Church.[5] The Jews remained the perfect scapegoat, always present to shoulder the blame for the ills of this world while

[5]At the time of Jesus, the adherents of Judaism comprised 9 percent of the population of the Roman Empire, and Jews were the only people exempted from the worship of the gods of Rome. The Jewish worldview was acknowleged as one of the few prevailing religiophilosophical systems to be potentially capable of achieving a dominant position in the empire (as Christianity eventually did). There were large Jewish communities throughout the empire and anti-Semitism had already begun within Hellenistic and Gnostic circles (Grant, 1973).

their continual wandering and degradation served as proof of their guilt, and of the innocence of those who disavowed their own complicity in the world's evil (see Toynbee [1934] for his argument as to how the existence of the Jews provides "fossil" evidence of the divine truth of the Christian religion).

The following are the essential features of the scapegoat's role in myths that feature it as a community's primary defense against the experience of guilt: (1) The scapegoat is or was a member of the community who acts alone and with premeditation. Therefore, no one else is responsible for the evil committed. (2) All in the community agree that what he did was terrible. (3) He and no one else should be punished. (4) It turns out, accidentally as it were, that what he did was necessary for the community, which innocently enjoys the beneficial consequences.

That the scapegoat must be seen as having sinned in order to produce good for the community is what differentiates the scapegoat from the victim and from the sacrifice. The actions of a victim are irrelevant and his suffering produces nothing for the community. The actions of the sacrifice are also irrelevant but his suffering produces a tangible good for the community. The scapegoat performs an evil act, produces good, and the community can defend itself against the feeling of guilt by denying that the good it enjoys is related to its own needs, wishes, or, most important, actions.

In this formulation the scapegoat serves the indispensable function of allowing the community to psychologically separate the aggressive acts that are necessary for its continued existence or salvation from the love felt toward and hoped for from the Needed Object (man or god). The community maintains its posture of supplication and assigns the need for murder, the act itself, and the accompanying guilt, to the scapegoat. This process of assignment is best understood within the rubric of projective identification. Although there are many contradictory definitions of the term, we can describe it phenomenologically as occurring when an individual or group maintains the split between different aspects of its internal world and incompletely projects the undesirable attributes onto another person or group. The subject thus remains in contact with what he has incompletely projected, and attempts to manipulate the object into an affective state that is congruent with what he, the subject, has assigned to that object. In the terms of this study we have the following proposition: the community defends itself from experiencing guilt by utilizing projective identification. It thereby seeks to manipulate the scapegoat into accepting sole guilt for committing the sacrifice in the hope that it would then be fully free to enjoy the resulting benefits without any unpleasant affects marring the occasion. Often the scapegoat accepts this attribution as its only hope of maintaining the libidinal tie to the community. For the scapegoat to fully reject the accusation would mean to accept total dissociation from its community.

Can this formulation account for and differentiate between various forms of victimization? Again I will begin by using an example of Dr. Scheidlinger's, this time from the international scene. He reminds us that after the overthrow of Gomulka in 1970, the new leaders of Poland utilized the 25,000-member remnant of the Jewish community (that only thirty years before had numbered more than 3 million) as a scapegoat on which to blame the economic and political troubles in their country. This tactic proved successful and these new leaders managed to retain their political control despite continued economic disintegration until the Solidarity rebellion of 1980. If our argument is to be considered, we must show that the Jews were being accused of a great crime that was simultaneously regarded as necessary for the "good" of the community. I suggest that the crime was none other than the bringing of Soviet domination over Poland at the end of World War II.[6]

[6]According to the 1970 leaders of the Party, this was not just a corollary to the establishment of the Communist order that freed the people from their oppression by the aristocrats and capitalists of Nationalist Poland. It was a necessary prerequisite to their maintenance of power over the country because without the Soviet hegemony and the threat of invasion, these Polish Communist leaders would have been immediately overthrown. Nevertheless, the intention of bringing Soviet domination had to be repudiated because of its unpopularity, and assigned to the purportedly pro-Soviet "internationalist" Jews. As with human sacrifice, the community (here the Polish Communist leaders) holds onto the "good" (Soviet protection of their power) while repudiating the intention of inviting Soviet hegemony and projecting that onto the scapegoat (the 25,000 remaining Jews). In this schema, the Polish people at large are the authority figure that serves as the audience to be fooled by the scapegoat. This analysis is necessarily incomplete in that it omits considerations of three issues more important to the understanding of the event itself than to the process of scapegoating. (1) The contributing factor of Polish anti-Semitism that allows the populace to readily accept the scapegoat. (2) Consideration of the degree of guilt of the Jewish community for the "crime" that is charged: although some did participate in the establishment of Communism and Soviet hegemony over Poland, it is the mark of the projective identificatory aspects of scapegoating that there is no differentiation between those who were "guilty" and those who were not. Similarly, it is unimportant for the phenomenon that the Soviet Union would have established its hegemony by the presence of the Red Army with or without the help of the Jewish Communist leaders in postwar Poland. (3) Given the realities of political expression in Eastern Europe after the Soviet invasion of Czechoslovakia, the accusation needed to be disguised by utilizing the easily accepted compound derogatory code words *Jewish-Trotskyite-Zionist.* How is it that only the valence and intensity, never the legitimacy or correctness of the invective seem to matter in scapegoating?

A similar meaning of the term was utilized in a very different situation by the lawyers of Admiral Poindexter and Colonel North in the Irangate investigation. According to Phillip Shenon, in the *New York Times Magazine* article of October 25, 1987, entitled "Walsh Makes His Move," their attorneys argued that North and Poindexter were scapegoats in an essentially political dispute between the President and Congress. The government, they claimed, wished to profit from what they did without taking responsibility for having been a party to the doing. Shenon argued that it was irrelevant to this very strong defense that Poindexter and North actually performed the crime as long as Special Prosecutor Walsh is unable to show that the scapegoats personally benefited from their action. In other words it was possible that the defense could prevail with, "I did the deed but I am innocent because I am a scapegoat. The country, not I personally, benefited." *The Wall Street Journal* took exactly this position in an editorial on November 30, 1987: "North and Poindexter did not benefit from their actions—the United States did—therefore they should be pardoned because they are scapegoats." Clearly Poindexter, North, and their supporters would agree with my definition in their argument that they were being scapegoated for doing a "good" for the nation that the nation simultaneously needed and denied, wished done and disavowed.

Dr. Scheidlinger also uses the term *scapegoating* to account for the hostility against Iranians residing in the United States during the time of the hostage crisis. Here I disagree with Dr. Scheidlinger because I can find no purported communal "good" attributed to these victims. Indeed, I believe this is an example of simple victimization where the only requirement of the target is that he is weak enough for the bully to safely attack him. Some U.S. citizens, unable to accept the country's passivity and their own feelings of weakness during the crisis, utilized the more primitive defensive operation of turning passive into active by attacking those associated through ethnic origin to the Iranian insulters. In this and similar examples it is necessary for the authorities to prohibit the bullying and victimization and redirect the energy in less hateful, if not more productive, ways (e.g., recall the popularity of "Tie a Yellow Ribbon" during the hostage crisis), as there is no hope of successfully affirming or denying any communal good since none is involved.

Does this formulation add anything to our present understanding of group psychotherapy? As Dr. Scheidlinger pointed out, one of the few empirically based definitions in the group therapy literature is provided by Beck (Beck, 1981; Eng and Beck, 1982) and her collaborators. Although they certainly did not express it this way, their observations are in accordance with our definition of the scapegoat as performing distasteful acts for the "good" of the group. In Beck's schema of group development (Beck and Peters, 1981), leadership is divided into four components, each taken by a different group member or therapist. One of these is the scapegoat leader, who is often criticized or "put down" in some way enabling the rest of the members to feel "on top" and "together" in their viewpoint (Eng and Beck, 1982). Were this the primary function of the scapegoat leader we could hardly adduce this as evidence for our hypothesis since the group could utilize an innocent or even unknown bystander for the same purpose. But Eng and Beck (1982) go on to explain how the actions (or the fantasy of actions) of the scapegoat leader is important for the group. In what they describe as the second stage of group development, the group, having been fully constituted, now seeks to establish its norms, define its goals, and form an initial group identity. To do so, it must find a way to manage negative emotions and resolve competitive needs while achieving agreement and cohesion. When the group attempts to achieve a positive ambience, it is willing to sacrifice clarity about goals and negative emotions. The scapegoat seeks active leadership by "misunderstanding" group compromises, by being insensitive to nonverbal cues, and by not acknowledging the tacit agreement being forged by the group to maintain resistance and defenses. He attacks leader and group for their inconsistencies and unclarities, thereby forcing (in groups that survive) greater honesty and therapeutic work. The entire group, therefore, profits from the clarity and resolution that follows this attack; but true to our formulation, the other members disavow its necessity, their compliance in it, and the group's need and gain from it. "He—the scapegoat—has some good points but it would be easier for us to discuss and resolve them without all that anger." Often this paraphrase of what other members say is true but many other times the difficult inconsistencies would not have been resolved were it not for the insistence of the scapegoat's attack. Eng and Beck report that many groups are unable to get beyond phase II and achieve a cooperative work process (their phase III). For this too, the scapegoat leader is also blamed, but the "good" achieved is more apparent than real. The group and/or therapist claims that the reason the group is stuck is because the scapegoat is too obstreperous for them to handle, thus absolving themselves of responsibility. The group is killed off, or worse, ineffectively continued, and no one has to confront their neuroses (this is the unfortunate communal "good"); but it is not their responsibility, it is the scapegoat's fault.

An important advantage of the formulation that I am advancing lies in the way it forces the group therapist to consider the "good" being done by the scapegoat for the group. Without the therapist's active focus on the way other group members profit from the scapegoat's actions the group avoids confronting its own need for that "good." When the therapist is able to highlight this need it is then possible to explore the shame, guilt, or anxiety that accompanies the group's or family's desire for that "good."

Similarly, many writers (Ruiz, 1972; Gibbard, Hartman, and Mann, 1974) have described how T-groups often wish to scapegoat and expel the "strong bad" leader in the hope of creating a "good maternal" group. These episodes of scapegoating usually occur just after the "bad" leaders have set limits and otherwise used their controlled aggression to calm, structure, and save the group from its own non-discriminatory, overinclusive trustingness. These examples of the leader's power disrupt the beginning group's attempt to achieve a loving atmosphere because they reintroduce within the group the aggressive impulses that it has been attempting to split off and project outward. The group correctly fears that it cannot achieve the warm maternal (and regressed) state it desires if it allows any member to vitiate this split in their self–object state and remind it of the within-group aggression. It is usually suggested, but it is not sufficient to intervene in such a group, by interpreting the wish for a warm and accepting mother who allows all behavior. However, too frequently the group simply agrees with this interpretation and insists on the leader's capitulation to their "reasonable" demands and too often that group leader capitulates to the powerful group pressure. Instead, the leader must also interpret the group's wish to *benefit* from his forcefulness without having their loving atmosphere interrupted by the traces of anger. This forces the group to consider what it would be like without the leader's needed/feared anger.

In his paper, Dr. Scheidlinger presents two examples of scapegoating in children's groups. In both we observe that a sadomasochistic relationship developed in place of the usual and healthy libidinal group ties; however, each scapegoat performed a "good" for its group by acting out within the treatment situation the issues of deprivation and fear which allowed the other group members to partially disown their similar shameful anxieties and displace them onto the scapegoat. In neither case were the therapists successful in their efforts to confront the behavior patterns of the scapegoat and of the group. The group with less pathological scapegoating was nevertheless able to work on its disowned and displaced shameful, childish impulses. In the group with the more pathological scapegoating, no work could be done until the therapist began to suggest that the scapegoat's provocation served a purpose for the group: that he "was being made to reenact their own unwelcome fears and wishes, such as being a baby again, or feeling like murdering a pesky sibling" (p. 118). Only then were the group members able to acknowledge their childish needs, reown their projections, and reduce the scapegoating behavior. In turn, and secondary to the change in the group's behavior, the scapegoat was able to become more age-appropriate and reduce his provocations. It was the making conscious of the disavowed needs in the other members of the group, heretofore represented by them as existing only in the scapegoat, that allowed the diminution and even the elimination of the scapegoating.

We have not addressed the question of the scapegoat's guilt or innocence. In our clinical situations the scapegoat indeed has had some role in introjecting the projective identifications used by the scapegoating community, but that is clearly a biased sample. In our examples from the political scene the participation and the guilt of the scapegoat are less clear. North and Poindexter clearly were willing scapegoats; up to a point, perhaps, so were some of the Polish Jews, but most were clearly not. A scapegoat's introjection of the role makes the process easier but is not entirely necessary especially with a strong community that insists on getting its way.

We have seen that scapegoating is one of a series of possible communal defenses against the guilt of having performed an "evil" act in order to produce a necessary "good." Through a "split in the ego" the community maintains two contradictory attitudes, simultaneously denying its need for and complicity in the "evil" act, while enjoying the benefits of that action. Through the mechanism of projective identification responsibility and motive are displaced from the community and localized in an individual or group that is then punished and/or banished. The banishment cannot be absolute nor the punishment final as the community requires the continuing witness of the scapegoat, to God, parent, or therapist, of his sole guilt and therefore of their innocence. If the scapegoat were to disappear then the community would have to find another scapegoat, accept responsibility for its continued "evil" actions, or do without the "good" produced by the scapegoat.[7] With maturation and interpretation it becomes

[7]An example of the communal consequences of losing a favorite scapegoat is embedded in the events of the Solidarity rebellion of 1981. When confronted with this uprising the Polish establishment tried to distract the populace with the familiar tactic of blaming the usual Jewish scapegoats for the country's economic woes, despite having banished all but a few hundred old Jews in 1970. Finally, the bounds of incredulity had been reached and the scapegoating attempt was rejected as patently absurd, first by Lech

impossible for the community to continue its "split in the ego" and its projective identification. It then must evaluate its needs, and choose either to legitimize them and find acceptable methods to achieve satisfaction, or to relinquish those needs in favor of others less morally objectionable.

In view of the horrific events of the twentieth century, at the pinnacle of which stands the Holocaust, the phenomenon of scapegoating looms large as a major instrument of public policy. In an age of increased technological sophistication, rising nationalism and religious xenophobia, and diminished faith in the divine *forgiveness* of a personal God, the need exists to forge a group identity with a concomitant sense of moral as well as physical security. What better way to derive the benefits of civilization without paying the price than to ascribe all the evils of our time to those among us—the soldier, the nuclear physicist, perhaps even the psychoanalyst—who can be held solely responsible for war, radioactive fallout, or teenage sexual promiscuity?

Perhaps W. B. Yeats best understood the particular problem of our time in the confusion of will and ideals: "Mere anarchy is loosed upon the world, / . . . The best lack all conviction, while the worst /Are full of passionate intensity." In light of this paper one wonders, "And what rough beast, its hour come round at last, /Slouches toward Bethlehem to be born?" Is he the Redeemer, the Antichrist, or just another scapegoat?

Walesa and then by the country. With scapegoating unavailable as a defense, there was little choice for the government but to enforce a harsh military crackdown. These measures were not successful in destroying the Solidarity movement or in preventing recurrent uprisings. Contrast this to 1970 when the availability of the Jews as scapegoats, in combination with a military crackdown, served to completely eliminate that protest movement. In this case the loss of the scapegoat has resulted in the failure of the community to resolve its internal tensions and achieve a peaceful coexistence between its diverse elements. The Solidarity movement continues on guard against the government's attempts to reintroduce anti-Semitic scapegoats as a shortcut method of eliminating protest and regaining control of the populace. In July of 1989, the official Polish government press published a report of Jewish hooligans who had attacked the Carmelite convent at Auschwitz. The Solidarity newspaper carefully corrected this distortion with an accurate report of the beating of six peaceful Jewish protestors.

A much more critical question is raised by the Holocaust. If Christianity requires the eternal presence of the Jewish scapegoat how could the Nazis have sought to absolutely annihilate them? It is Maccoby's conclusion that the Nazis no longer required the Jews as scapegoats because they believed that a new mythical age had dawned: God was dead, and the thousand-year Reich was the successor to Christianity. Therefore, the Christian myth and its scapegoat were no longer required and could be destroyed in a final paroxysm of hate and vengeance.

REFERENCES

Ackerman, N. W. (1964), Prejudicial scapegoating and neutralizing forces in the family group. *Internat. J. Soc. Psychiat.*, 2:90–96.

Beck, A. P., & Peters, L. (1981), The research evidence for distributed leadership in therapy groups. *Internat. J. Group Psychother.*, 31:43–71.

Eng, A. M., & Beck, A. P. (1982), Speech behavior measures of group psychotherapy process. *Group*, 6:37–48.

Foulkes, S. H., & Anthony, E. J. (1957), *Group Psychotherapy: The Psychoanalytic Approach*, 1st ed. Harmondsworth, UK: Penguin.

———— ———— (1964), *Group Psychotherapy: The Psychoanalytic Approach*, 2nd ed. Harmondsworth, UK: Penguin.

Frazer, J. G. (1907), Adonis Attis Osiris. In: *The Golden Bough*, Part IV, 3rd ed. London: St. Martin.

Freud, S. (1900), The Interpretation of Dreams. *Standard Edition*, 5. London: Hogarth Press, 1958.

———— (1940), An Outline of Psychoanalysis. *Standard Edition*, 23. London: Hogarth Press, 1964.

Gibbard, G. S., Hartman, J. J., & Mann, R. D., eds. (1974), *Analysis of Groups*. San Francisco: Jossey-Bass.

Grant, M. (1973), *The Jews in the Roman World*. New York: Dorset.

Graves, R. (1983), *The White Goddess*. London: Peter Smith.

Haley, J. (1986), *The Power Tactics of Jesus Christ and Other Essays*, 2nd ed. New York: W. W. Norton.

Jaques, E. (1955), Social systems as a defense against persecutory and depressive anxiety. In: *New Directions in Psychoanalysis*, ed. M. Klein, P. Heimann, & R. Money-Kyrle. New York: Basic Books, pp. 478–498.

Kraupl-Taylor, F., & Rey, T. H. (1953), The scapegoat motif in society and its manifestations in a therapeutic group. *Internat. J. Psycho-Anal.*, 34:253–264.

Leviticus. In: *Tanakh*. Philadelphia: Jewish Publication Societies, 1985.

Maccoby, H. (1982), *The Sacred Executioner: Human Sacrifice and the Legacy of Guilt*. New York: Thames & Hudson.

Ruiz, P. (1972), On the perception of the "mother-group" in T-groups. *Internat. J. Group Psychother.*, 22:488–491.

Scheidlinger, S. (1982), On scapegoating in group psychotherapy. *Internat. J. Group Psychother.*, 32:131–143.

Shenon, P. (1987), Walsh makes his move. *New York Times Magazine*, October 25.

Spiegel, S. (1964), *The Last Trial*. New York: Behrman House.

Toynbee, A. (1934), *A Study of History*. London: Oxford University Press.

Wall Street Journal (1987), Editorial. November 30.

Wright, F., Hoffman, X. H., & Gore, E. M. (1988), Perspectives on scapegoating in primary groups. *Group*, 12:33–44.

Yerkes, R. K. (1953), *Sacrifice in Greek and Roman Religions and Early Judaism*. London: Ayer.

Chapter 4

Ideology and Technology: Lessons from the Nazi Doctors for the Nuclear Age

JOHN E. MACK, M.D.

Some of those who lost loved ones in the European Holocaust are understandably troubled by efforts to relate the evils of Nazism to the current threats which face our planet. Yet if there are lessons to be learned from the Holocaust which might help us to gain a deeper understanding of man's propensity to commit murder on a large scale, we would be foolish indeed to overlook such an opportunity.

There is an understandable desire to place the phenomenon of the Nazi Holocaust outside the realm of the humanly possible, or at least to exclude it from ordinary human experience. Yet there have been a sufficient number of instances of genocide and other grotesque forms of killing and torture committed by ethnonational groups in recent decades for us to begin to look more dispassionately at what there is about human beings that makes us behave this way under certain conditions of group life.

Insistence that the European Holocaust was unique in some quasi-mysterious way might seem to guard us from facing the possibility that it will recur on a larger scale should we make no special effort to prevent it. On the contrary, it seems to me that a hard-headed acknowledgment that the Nazi-led genocide was expressive of recognizable elements in human individual and collective psychology, of which we all may be capable to some degree, may be the most likely way to prevent a final holocaust that will employ the far more deadly instruments which are now at our disposal. Further, lest the argument that the nuclear threat has been devised to prevent or deter the threat

45

of annihilation appear attractive as a distinction, it is well to keep in mind that mass killing is often justified on the grounds of some lofty prophylactic purpose, such as the prevention of the takeover by a Godless ideology or the protection of a revolution from contaminating forces.

Lessons of the Nazi Holocaust, in which his mother and sisters perished, seems an appropriate subject for a volume honoring Saul Scheidlinger. For the Holocaust might be thought of as an extreme example of group psychopathology, of which Saul is one of our foremost students. As a teenager in prewar Poland, Saul became a leader of a Zionist youth group, one of several political organizations, each with its own ideology, that flourished in Europe during that period. "I grew up in groups, in that youth movement," he said in his memoirs (O'Connell, unpublished, 1982, p. 4). In conflict with bourgeois adult society, the group which Saul led stressed physical activity and communion with nature. It also adopted the philosophy, uniforms, structure, and ideology of scouting. According to Saul, all of these groups were "an offspring of what was called in Central Europe the *Wandervogel*, which, in English, means the wandering bird. It was the name of the independent youth movements. They were completely independent of the adult world, antibourgeois, led usually by college students, younger people who had studied Freud, Pestalozzi, and other very liberal thinkers. "Each of us, in turn, led our own youth group" (O'Connell, unpublished, 1982, p. 4). By the time he left for America in 1938 Saul was the leader of over one hundred young people. It was not long afterwards that Hitler, in creating the Nazi Youth Movement, was able to turn to the purposes of German nationalism, the idealism, symbolism, mystical power, and longing for identity and belonging which characterized the various European youth movements of the time (Scheidlinger, 1948).

A nation is a particular kind of group. Like other groups, nations have the power to heal and to build and may devote themselves to overcoming suffering, at least within their own borders. They are also the only kind of group capable of harnessing sufficient destructive energy to end life as we know it on this planet. This essay, in which I consider the lessons to be gained from the cooptation of physicians and other professionals by the Nazis for understanding the present global threat, might be considered a study of group psychology and psychopathology. It has been inspired by Saul Scheidlinger's work.

Raul Hilberg has documented the extent to which all of the professions in Germany contributed to the success of the Nazi enterprise (Hilberg, 1985). Robert Lifton has shown how German physicians in particular, including a large part of the psychiatric community, played an essential role in carrying out the Nazi "biomedical vision" of racial and national healing through killing (Lifton, 1986). The doctors' motivations were complex, ranging over the familiar incentives of dedicated professionals: personal ambition and career advancement; loyalty and obedience to authority; desire for power and control (especially over life and death); pleasure in exercising technical expertise; scientific curiosity; fear and the desire for personal security; and satisfaction of camaraderie and close male bonding. Above all they were patriots, committed to the higher purposes of the German nation, and immersed themselves in varying degrees in the Nazi political and racial ideology. Each claimed to be personally without power, merely a cog in a larger machine not of his own making. A sanitized, technoscientific language helped further to protect the doctors as individuals from a sense of personal responsibility. Most were able to maintain a split between their private, family selves and their institutional or corporate roles, a process which Lifton calls doubling. Through these mechanisms the Nazi leadership was able to keep the responsibility for Germany's suffering and limitations focused always on outside enemies, especially on the Jews and other allegedly inferior peoples. Although there were some physicians who gained sadistic pleasure from direct killing, these were a minority. Most simply played their chosen or assigned parts in the complex professional bureaucracy of mass murder.

What to me is most instructive in the Nazi example is not the corruption of the medical profession as such, although this is one of the more appalling perversions of the Nazi period. It is, rather, the degree to which many of the psychosocial mechanisms which enabled individuals within the Nazi machinery, and therefore the machinery itself, to function, are familiar to us in the everyday life of virtually all professional or corporate organizations and institutions—health, religious, scientific, educational, industrial, military, or political. What characterizes our present time, even more than the Nazi period, is the degree to which technical expertise or specialization and technological advances in communication, information processing, transportation, biomedical science, manufacturing, weaponry, and space exploration have made it more difficult for individuals to experience personal effectiveness, responsibility, and power in relation to their work and lives as a whole.

Nuclear weaponry provides perhaps the most dangerous example of the distance afforded through advanced technology between manufacturing and decision-making and the personal experience of consequences for human beings should the product of such labors actually be put to use. But each of us feels in varying degrees a sense of loss of control, separation, and powerlessness in the face of a cultural and political environment that is increasingly automated, technically unfathomable, and seemingly remote from human direction. In such a climate it is particularly difficult to exercise social and political responsibility. Primary religious emotions, a striving for connection with a transcendent power, seem to be essential dimensions of human life. In the United States, a blind faith and a sense of wonder before the achievements of science and technology seem to have replaced to a degree the worship of more traditional religious objects. Psychoanalyst Joel Kovel has characterized our new faith.

> Modern man (again the masculine term applies to what has happened to the species) worships technology. This is understandable, since he is swaddled in it from the day of birth. It becomes his *alter* mother, a cocoon that carries him passively through the world, as visitors to Florida's Disney World are encased in a plexiglas vessel and wafted before the universe's wonders.... The machine expands the body, and replaces the body [Kovel, 1983, p. 95].

Ronald Reagan's Star Wars program, Strategic Defense Initiative (SDI), has evolved out of the fear and vulnerability of the nuclear age and plays upon an insecure public's wish to believe in the omnipotence of technology. The program offers what theologian Edward Linenthal calls "the cheap grace promised by missile defence" (Linenthal, 1987, p. 1061).

Although it seems inconceivable that American physicians would become complicit in a genocidal enterprise, each of us can tell his story of terror and dehumanization at the hands of the American biomedical technocracy. A colleague of mine told of an experience which accompanied cardiac catheterization. He had been informed beforehand by the physician of the 1 percent mortality associated with the procedure. While the needle was in one of his coronary arteries, the doctor answered a telephone call from his wife and stayed on the phone talking about a routine matter for several minutes. While my colleague lay on the table, becoming increasingly terrified, he wondered what the mortality rate might be under these disturbing circumstances. It seemed as if the doctor, at ease and familiar with his technology, seemed not to appreciate the frightening distance it enabled him to create between himself and his patient. My own profession of psychiatry, though relying less (so far, although there are ominous trends) upon mechanisitic technologies, has its own way of creating distance between the practitioner and the person for whom he is responsible, most notably in the use of technical language or jargon. A sterile argot often covers an ignorance we refuse to admit, partitions our patients' psyches into structures which become reified through repetitive labeling, and leads us to look upon their troubled emotional and spiritual states as conditions or disorders little or no different from medical illnesses.

The nation state is the group which is usually the administrative agent of mass killing. At least until the rise of well-armed, politically disenfranchised rebels—usually called terrorists or freedom fighters, depending on the political sympathies of the observer—only the nation state had the economic resources to mobilize enough killing power in the form of poisons, guns, and other "conventional" arms, and now nuclear devices, to make genocide feasible. The modern nation state as a group or institution has other particular characteristics which make it an agency capable of committing mass murder. Its leadership is able to control a large bureaucratic organization, economic resources, the army, transportation and communications, and the rest of the apparatus necessary to put together the killing enterprise.

But beyond these obvious economic and political features, the modern nation state has certain psychological qualities, and fulfills important human functions, equally necessary for a genocidal operation, but that have received less emphasis. Its dominant ethnic group has generally forged its union in blood, at the expense of some other human group, or indigenous population, which had to be exterminated, driven out, or forced into minority status. As a cause or effect of this history peoples invent mythologies of divine origin which justify their national boundaries and existence, linking their destinies to higher spiritual powers, a single God or a pantheon, depending upon the dominant local or state religion. Reflecting perhaps some universal ethical sense that is at least latent or nascent in the human individual and group psyche, there seems to be a need to downplay the morally repugnant aspects of a people's early history and to glorify the deeds of its historical founders.

Motives of revenge for past grievances, common, for example, in the wars which lead to the establishing of national borders, are rarely emphasized in the versions of national history which children read in their textbooks. The emphasis rather is on the visions and possibilities of national greatness, permitting individual citizens to experience a positive sense of identity, belonging and self-esteem (Mack, 1983), and to experience themselves as part of something larger than themselves or spiritually transcendent (Kelman, 1987). Furthermore, the nation state, having created itself at the expense of other peoples, faces always the possibility that an enemy, either in reality, or as a fear of the return of its suppressed history through the vengeance of its murdered victims, may turn upon it, retake its lands, and kill its people. Nation states thus provide their citizens with structures of psychological externalization through which not only political fears and insecurities are lived out but private hurts, fears, and grievances may be projected onto whomever may be the designated enemy in a particular historical moment (Volkan, 1985). Some of the most successful national leaders, though not necessarily the most historically admired ones in the long term, seem to be individuals who can match their private hurts and angers to the political contingencies and strategies of the day, and then play upon the readiness of a people to use the international political situation as an arena for the displacement of personal and social hurts and discontents.

A political ideology furnishes the ideational system which permits a national group to carry out its policies, especially in relation to other national groups. Each analyst of political processes tends to provide his own definition of ideology and I am no exception. I will use a definition which places greater emphasis than is usual in the social sciences upon the psychological nature and purposes of ideology while at the same time staying close, or close enough, to the generally accepted connotation.

I define ideology as a system of belief, implicit or explicit, through which a society justifies its collective actions, especially in relation to other nations. Sometimes ideologies, at least ideologies as total structures, are hard to locate. They seem to hover, float over, or surround a nation, or permeate its psyche—if there is such a thing as a national psyche. The commitment to an ideology is far greater than to the historical facts from which it seeks to derive legitimacy and meaning. So ideology tends to contain obvious distortions and oversimplifications of reality when made explicit, like Nazi theories of Jewish malevolence and inferiority. National ideologies are associated especially with warfare and mass killing for obvious reasons since they provide the powerful justifications needed to overcome ordinary ethical scruples against murder. Even the nation state, which is the only human institution permitted to kill other human beings on a large scale, has to give its people a good reason for doing so. This is why all countries seem to offer the justification of defense, even when they assert their power in faraway lands where no threat is evident.

Stereotyping, blaming, demonization, and dehumanization of other peoples and nations are collective mechanisms that operate as substructures within an overall ideological matrix. The self-esteem-maintaining purpose of ideology would not be served, at least until a new way of achieving national self-worth was discovered, should a people be forced to take responsibility for its own murderous history and policies. Therefore the focus on outside enemies becomes an essential aspect of ideological thinking.

Nationalistic ideologies are associated closely with particular economic systems and philosophies, which determine how material resources are distributed and that are believed to furnish the best opportunity for a nation's people, at least certain of its classes or subgroups, to achieve material, and ultimately spiritual, well-being. Prevailing national ideologies may not always be made explicit, as in political tracts like *Mein Kampf* or *Das Kapital*. But they are readily discoverable in popular literature, especially children's textbooks, which show simple idealizations of the nation's history, often at the expense of other nations and ethnic groups which are depicted as threatening or of lesser human value. A nation's ideologies can be distinguished from its visions, which are less simply or rigidly defined but may offer new possibilities for growth and political originality. Finally, ideologies are generally easier to detect in other political cultures than one's own. For, like the unconscious attitudes of patients in psychotherapy, they contain unsavory elements that are painful to individual and collective self-regard when confronted too directly. It is easier, for example, for an American to see anti-Semitism in the Soviet Union than the racism that has dominated our own political history (Zinn, 1980; Hunt, 1987). Ideological self-blindness is one of the primary causes of war, for it prevents a nation from taking responsibility for its own contribution to a given state of belligerency. Such blindness is, of course, particularly dangerous in the age of nuclear weapons.

The negative connotation of political ideology grows out of the discrepancy between the promise of higher sociopolitical purposes and national accomplishment on the one hand and the unwelcome facts, inconsistencies, and human consequences which these rigidified thought structures must overlook. Indeed human lives, especially those of other ethnic groups and races, come to be regarded as cheap when compared to the exalted promise offered by a compelling political ideology.

Ideology brings us close to the essential nature of evil itself which has eluded philosophers and theologians throughout history. For the idea of evil carries with it something more even than hatred, cruelty, murder, and suffering, however essential to its definition these may be. Evil also has the connotation of a disjunction between alleged purpose, as embodied in an idea, and the actual human behaviors that are carried out in the name of that idea. Thus action takes place and creatures with feeling are tortured or die, but responsibility is not taken for the hurtful outcome, but only for an idea quite removed from these results. This lack of responsibility for the hurtful outcome or even for an awareness of destructive motives, makes appeal or redress remote.

Nadezhda Mandelstam, whose poet husband Osip was among the millions of Russians murdered by Stalin and his regime in the purges of the 1930s, is an important witness of the evils of that time (Mandelstam, 1983). Yet it is not Stalin she blames for her husband's death but a theory of society, an ideology, in whose name the killings took place. It is the "end to all doubt and the possibility of absolute faith in the new, scientifically obtained truth" (p. 164), or the "craving for an all-embracing idea which would explain everything in the world and bring about universal harmony at one go" (p. 162), which she held responsible. "For the sake of what idea," she asked, "was it necessary to send those countless trainloads of prisoners, including the man who was so dear to me, to forced labor in eastern Siberia?" (p. 363).

At a manifest level the development of nuclear weapons in the United States appears as a logical response to a real threat—the emergence of Soviet power in Europe and Asia after World War II. In response, the United States was unwilling as a nation to commit sufficient conventional weaponry to maintain the peace and create national security and relied instead on nuclear weapons, which were cheaper and more powerful. Further, we cannot dismiss out of hand the argument that American nuclear weapons have deterred Soviet aggression or prevented war. Herbert York, former Director of Livermore Laboratory, reflects a widely held view when he says, "I find that the strategy of peace through nuclear deterrence is working and seems to be very stable" (York, 1988, p. 30). But George Kennan, one of the most thoughtful contemporary figures who have questioned the basic assumptions upon which nuclear deterrence rests, provides a searching challenge. Kennan said recently that the concept of nuclear deterrence

> has lain at the heart of our entire national discussion of the nuclear weapons race for years and decades in the past. It has infused tens of thousands of statements and calculations. In its name, and in no other, have many tens of billions of dollars been expended, and vast, unnecessary arsenals of highly dangerous explosives created. And on all these millions of occasions when the term has been used, it has carried with it the implication that there were fearful things the Russians wanted to do—attacks on Western Europe, first nuclear strikes, or what you will—and would assuredly have gone ahead and done, had they not been "deterred" by the threat of our nuclear retaliation.
>
> Well, and good. But suppose there had never been any reality to this

assumption in the first place. Suppose the Soviet leaders never had either the desire or the intention or the incentive to do any of these things [Kennan, 1988, p. 33].

In response to Kennan's argument I would suggest that a deeper look at the psychological and political forces involved will reveal a historical continuity, that deterrence policy represents an extension in the postwar period of the interplay of technology and ideology that was manifest in Hitler's Germany and have characterized first world geopolitical policy in our time.

To begin with, from the standpoint of sheer destructive power nuclear weapons have been created in quantities which far exceed *any* rational purpose. Furthermore, many of our weapons systems, such as the MX and Pershing II missiles, seem designed more to threaten and coerce, being vulnerable on the ground and therefore "useful" only if fired first ("first strike" weapons). During much of the five decades since World War II a faith in nuclear technology to create safety and security, of which the recent Star Wars program is but a kind of terminal apotheosis, has taken precedence over a restructuring of the political and psychological relationships with our principal adversary. Some of the scientists who have worked on nuclear weapons have acknowledged the excitement of the sheer power of nuclear technology. Theodore Taylor, for example, said, "I spent some sixteen years knowing directly the intense exhilaration and sense of personal power that comes from deep involvement in the conception, testing and deployment of new types of nuclear weapons" (Sheff, 1987), and Freeman Dysen acknowledged "the glitter of nuclear weapons."

> It is irresistible if you come to them as a scientist. To feel it's there in your hands—to release this energy that fuels the stars, to let it do your bidding. To perform these miracles—to lift a million tons of rock into the sky. It is something that gives people an illusion of illimitable power and it is, in some ways, responsible for all our troubles, I would say—this, what you might call technical arrogance that overcomes people when they see what they can do with their minds [Quoted in Else, 1981, p. 30].

At the same time that nuclear weapons have grown in number and danger, a "technostrategic" language has been developed by civilian political defense analysts to discuss nuclear weapons and their use in a manner so sanitized that the discourse separates completely the devices themselves from what they actually do, while at the same excluding those outside the technocratic elite from influencing nuclear weapons policies (Cohn, 1987).

A closer examination will also reveal that our attitude toward the Soviet Union has been far more ideological and less pragmatic than we have maintained. To the real threat which Soviet expansion after World World II created for the Western democracies we have added an additional dimension which is ideological and psychological. A simple image of a monstrous evil giant, incapable of change and demonically determined to impose its will upon the world has embellished the reality of the complex, alien Soviet system. Although the extreme expressions of this "ideology of enmity" (Mack, 1986) are the creation of the political far right, ideological distortion of Soviet experience and intentions has dominated the mainstream of American political life to such an extent that even the most nondoctrinaire or pragmatic political candidates of both major parties seem not to hazard a declaration that the Soviet menace is other than that which the prevailing ideology has declared it to be.

The leading German psychoanalyst, Carl Nedelmann, has suggested that contemporary West German anti-Sovietism derives in large part from the suppressed criminal and quasi-genocidal policy of Nazi Germany against Russian soldiers, civilians, and prisoners during World War II. "Collectively, we behave as if it had not been ourselves who invaded the U.S.S.R., brought her close to defeat, and caused unspeakable suffering. We have not taken the guilt upon ourselves, but repressed, split off, displaced and projected." By acknowledging these facts, and recognizing these psychological mechanisms, Nedelmann suggests, "it should be possible to gain the insight that a part of the Russian danger is largely imaginary" (Nedelmann, 1986, p. 300).

But Nedelmann writes of West Germany. The sources of American anti-Sovietism are more difficult to fathom. They include the threat to private property and to established domestic social and economic class arrangements and the challenge to American political and economic dominance and interests overseas which the Soviet system represents, as well as a deep Christian Manichaeism, untempered by much experience with defeat and impotence in foreign affairs, that leads us to perceive the world in simple dichotomies of black and white, good and evil.

What is difficult to dispute is that U.S. anti-Communism, or more precisely anti-Sovietism, since we are less hostile to Communist regimes which do not challenge American global hegemony, is the ideological structure, or enabling force, that allows the perpetuation of an enormous, nuclear weapons dominated, military establishment that exceeds in size, cost, and destructive power any the world has ever seen (Sivard, 1985). The group psychological processes or mechanisms which operate within the nuclear weapons community need to be examined within the context of this enabling ideology.

Although the majority of Americans do not appear actively to question the dominant anti-Communist world view, most of us are not ideologues. As Yankelovich and Doble reported in a 1984 poll, "large majorities now support a relatively non-ideological, pragmatic live-and-let-live attitude that can potentially provide the political support for a new approach to normalizing relations between the superpowers" (Yankelovich and Doble, 1984, p. 35). It is probably this political grass roots attitude, together with the fear of nuclear war, which has made it possible for the Reagan administration to move toward an accommodation with Gorbachev's Russia.

In an unpublished interview study of nuclear weapons decision makers, which included prominent figures in the weapons labs, executive branch, military service, Congress, and corporate sector, I found, with rare exception, little anti-Communist ideological fervor, or personal inclination to demonize the Soviet Union. But, there was just enough acceptance of the image of the Soviet Union as an intractable, dangerous enemy to permit the war machinery to grind on undisturbed. Perhaps when "their system" moves "in our direction," change will take place, several people suggested. An arms control specialist at one of the weapons labs admitted, "ideology," at times, "is driving the system as opposed to technical facts." A concern that the Soviets will "take advantage" of any perceived letdown in our efforts to pursue technological advances was frequently expressed, but how this had or could take place was not forthcoming, nor have I heard the idea voiced that we might take advantage of Soviet weakness. A high-level weapons designer echoed the assumption, often heard throughout our society, that the Soviet menace is heightened by their leadership's "more task like or business-like attitude" toward human life, due to the many millions lost through war, purges, and famine.

None of my interviewees would acknowledge an equal, or even a major share of responsibility on the U.S. side of the nuclear weapons competition, although Herbert York, former Director of Livermore Laboratory, has done so publicly. In his book, *Race to Oblivion,* York holds the United States responsible "for the majority of the actions that have set the rate and scale of the arms race." He asks, "why have we led the entire world in this mad rush toward the ultimate absurdity?" He then replies to his own question:

The reason is not that our leaders have been less sensitive to the dangers of the arms race, it is not that our leaders are less wise, it is not that we are more aggressive or less concerned about the dangers to the rest of mankind. Rather the reasons are that we are richer and more powerful, that our science and technology are more dynamic, that we generate more ideas of all kinds [York, 1970, pp. 238–239].

Several of my interviewees went so far as to admit a weapons-loving or dark side of human nature, but the darkness on the U.S. side was not stressed.

Within the broad, as yet largely unchallenged, framework of U.S. anti-Soviet ideology several group psychological processes can be identified which contribute to the perpetuation of the huge warmaking apparatus. Overriding other mechanisms, I would place the division between the private self, where personal values, social responsibility, and empathic human identifications are unchallenged by public roles and responsibilities, and the organizational, national, or institutional self, which enables us to be bystanders in the face of atrocities at home and abroad or to comply, or acquiesce in, national policies with which we may privately disagree (Staub, 1989). For business executives the anonymity and limited liability which characterizes their place in the corporate structure facilitates this split between the private and the institutional self (Mack, 1988a). One CEO of a large information technology corporation said that in the case of government defense contracts, it is the government's, not the corporate executive's, responsibility to question the uses to which the products a company manufactures are to be put.

Related to the split between the private and the institutional or corporate self is the fragmentation of responsibility that characterizes our relationship to nuclear weapons policies and to warmaking in general. The sense of powerlessness that ordinary citizens feel, and which is the most usual reason given for political inaction, is shared by defense analysts, policy makers, and others ordinarily perceived as possessing political power (Chasin and Herzig, 1988). In my interviews of nuclear weapons decision makers, who included a former president and secretary of defense, each person expressed his limited sense of power and responsibility in relation to the overall problem of the nuclear arms race. The highly specialized, arcane nature of nuclear weapons technology adds greatly to the fragmentation of responsibility as each decision maker must rely on experts and advisors while at the same time dealing with the pressures from political and institutional constituents. It takes great courage to contradict the political and technical constituencies which build up around nuclear weapons systems and to acknowledge publicly the emperor's and the state's nakedness and vulnerability before the destructiveness of nuclear weapons.

The influence of career opportunity upon individual decision making inside and outside of the warmaking system is powerful and often subtle. In my own discipline of medicine, for example, which values "hard science" and the absence of political controversy, a strong personal or academic interest in the medical and psychological dimension of the nuclear weapons competition is hardly a rapid road to career advancement. Within the defense and arms control communities a too-ready willingness to question the mission of the lab, corporation, or government agency will lead before long to the necessity of finding other employment. As a prominent electrical engineer who helped to develop antiballistic missile technology put it, "Suddenly people walk into this crazy world with very simple rules of how you think about these things . . . my impression is that first they think it's crazy but they are not willing to say it because they'd lose acceptance and position. And then, after a while, they begin to think the same way." The availability of money and other resources within Defense Department weapons facilities can appear irresistible to young physicists and other scientists who cannot find such research opportunities elsewhere. The excitement associated with difficult technical challenges like the X-ray laser can prevent doubts about whether solving the given question is a good idea from ever reaching psychological prominence. A senior defense systems analyst at one of the weapons labs described to me a debate between the Los Alamos and Livermore labs about the best way among several exciting new technologies to find Soviet submarines under the polar ice caps. There seemed to be few voices raising the question of whether it was wise in the first place to deprive Soviet submarines of their hiding places.

Since the experiments of Stanley Milgram in the 1960s, there has been considerable interest among psychologists about the inclination of ordinary people to obey authority even when they know they are causing harm to others by so doing (Milgram, 1963, 1965). The complex assembly of motives and identifications which underlie the human willingness to obey loyally, at practically all costs, an authority perceived as legitimate lies beyond the scope of this discussion (Ellsberg, 1988). My impression from interviews of nuclear weapons decision makers is that such obedience has a powerful place among the mechanisms which keep the war system going. One sensible nuclear weapons physicist, responsible to his agency for advocating in a high-level policy discussion a particular weapons system he thought would be stabilizing, found himself losing the argument to other presidential advisors who advocated a more traditional approach. I asked him at what point he would decide he was "not going to play" and would get out. "I haven't crossed that yet," he said, "but sometimes you're in a situation where you're being a 'lawyer' for the wrong position. [The Secretary of Defense] says 'we're going to do this,' and you think it's not the best thing then you can either resign or do your duty in order to try to influence things later on." I pressed him to say at which point he might feel he could no longer do his duty and might want publicly to contradict authority. He replied, "That has not come up, not with me, but with others. You have to try to look at each thing individually as things go on. Sometimes you're carrying the ball for the President and elected representatives when you decide to go to Washington and participate in the policy process. If you're not willing to do that you don't go in."

Finally, I have been struck by the strength of male bonding which connects members of the nuclear weapons elite. United by a common "technostrategic" language, nuclear weapons decision makers and scientists are insulated by the high level of security which surrounds their labors, the limited exposure to the views of others, and their own paradoxical (considering their influential and privileged position) self view as beleaguered, unappreciated, without power, and constantly under criticism. There is a camaraderie, sometimes almost a locker-room-like atmosphere, with self-affirming notions that are perpetuated by a consensus of belief and the bonds created by shared mission, work, and language, and sometimes by shared values. According to the engineer mentioned above, a newcomer who enters this world tends to adapt to it or has to leave or lose influence. "They'd just say, look, while [I'm] here I've got to go along with this and unless I think like they do—it's like any anthropologist in a different culture. You can't just constantly be critical of everything you do, or you'll never have any impact on the culture or be accepted."

In returning to the lessons to be learned from the Nazi doctors I wish to stress once again the nonuniqueness of their experience and behavior as viewed from the perspective of the second half of the twentieth century and the examples of realized or threatened mass violence which have characterized our era. From the work of Hilberg, Dawidowicz, Lifton, Gilbert, Staub, Charny, Montville, and others we have come to appreciate that genocide is the product of a whole society. It requires not only the motivation and planning of political leaders and others who are direct perpetrators, but the more or less active participation of the rest of the population (Staub, 1989). Personally cruel or sadistic behaviors may be important elements in the implementation of such destructiveness, but the killing operation is the expression of the intention of an entire social system. A fixed structure of thought or belief, a political ideology that guides a nation, provides the impetus, rationale, and justification for the killing. Advanced technologies of an explosive, biomedical, or chemical nature, together with modern systems of communication, information processing, and transportation, make mass murder feasible. Ideology and technology are the twin agents of genocide and omnicide in the nuclear age.

It has been especially difficult for us to change our collective habits or to develop the kind of self-awareness which could lead to the reduction of the likelihood of our bringing about a "final solution" to planetary life as we know it. We do not learn, or learn much, about our nationalistic behaviors (Etheredge, 1985). Whether we believe that the dark side of the human collective psyche is the outgrowth of identifiable elements such as historical and personal humiliation and hurt (Davies, unpublished, 1988), and drives for wealth, power, and revenge, or is, instead, a more inexplicable, mystical demonic force, it is surely conceivable that the large-scale evils committed by human groups can be better understood and the impulse better managed.

I cannot see that the transformations needed in our collective life necessary for long-term survival (Walsh, 1984) can occur without some sort of political maturation, a form of responsibility at the level of large-group life that is analogous to what a clinician tries to achieve with individuals, families, and other small groups (Mack, 1988b). At the very least this responsibility will mean an owning up by the leaders and citizens of nations themselves to the contributions which they are making to global tensions and problems. It will surely mean a willingness to forego the ready externalization and blaming of other peoples for our ills which we have come to expect of national leaders and is so fundamental to the psychology (really psychopathology, if we think in terms of evolution and adaptation) of nationalism. Philosopher Michael Zimmerman has traced the American habit of externalizing our dark, unacceptable human impulses back to the time of the early Christian settlers:

> [T]he settlers, unable to integrate their own shadowy side, projected this onto the Indians as well. By killing Indians, the settlers convinced themselves that they were killing evil, death, sensuality, and bestiality. Such splitting-off and projecting have continued for many people throughout American history. Today, it would appear that we are projecting our dark side onto the Soviet people, the new Indians: bloodthirsty, insidious, cruel, and rapacious [Grof, 1988, p. 182].

Although the American flirtation with Armageddon may have particularly ominous consequences, the denial or walling off of the dark
or shadow side of the human psyche appears to be a universal tendency of all human groups. Psychologist and theologian James Garrison
writes of the necessity "to integrate the antinomial polarity within our
experience of the Godhead we worship" (Garrison, 1988, p. 175).
Only then, he writes, "will we survive and continue our slow painful
advance toward wholeness (p. 173).

In approaching the challenge of political self-responsibility and
transformation, I return to the problem of ideology. For ideology as
a political thought structure seems to function for ethnic or national
groups much as personal defenses or resistances operate for individuals. They keep out of mind, ward off, or blind us to what we do not
wish to see in our own nation's or empire's collective psyche. It is
useful to return to the distinction between ideologies and values.
Ideologies are rigid, exclusive, singular, and deny contradicting facts.
They admit of no compromise. In a conflict of opposing ideologies,
therefore, the holders of these belief systems are unlikely to yield,
which must inevitably lead to violence and mass killing. Political values
are less exclusive, rigid, and theocratic. In their pluralism they can
tolerate other values simultaneously. British historian Isaiah Berlin
believes it is possible for members of one culture "by the force of
imaginative insight" to understand:

> [T]he values, the ideals, the forms of life of another culture or society,
> even those remote in time or space. They may find these values un-
> acceptable, but if they open their minds sufficiently they can grasp how
> one might be a full human being, with whom one could communicate,
> and at the same time live in the light of values widely different from
> one's own, but which nevertheless one can see to be values, ends of life,
> by the realization of which men could be fulfilled [Berlin, 1988, p. 14].

Berlin goes even further:

> [T]he world in which what we see as incompatible values are not in
> conflict is a world altogether beyond our ken; that principles which are
> harmonized in this other world are not the principles with which, in
> our daily lives, we are acquainted; if they are transformed, it is into
> conceptions not known to us on earth. But it is on earth that we live,
> and it is here that we must believe and act [p. 15].

Sir Isaiah is clear that his prescription of pluralism and political
toleration is necessary for survival and to avoid suffering. He is less
specific about how to achieve it. Nor do I have a single set of rec-

ommendations. Education about ideology itself would be a useful place to begin. Michael Hunt's recent book, *Ideology and U.S. Foreign Policy*, traces three ideological strains which have remained virtually constant in U.S. foreign relations from the eighteenth century: belief in a mission of national greatness; a racist or hierarchical view of the world's people; and a conservative intolerance of political revolutions which threaten or would change the socioeconomic order (Hunt, 1987). Similarly, works like Howard Zinn's *A People's History of the United States*, which tells the story of our nation from the standpoint of peoples who have been the victims of the dominant U.S. ideologies, are valuable texts for the process of political maturation. They provide bad-tasting intellectual medicine, perhaps, but this is far less painful than the suffering, including to our own psychic health, caused by ideological rigidity, and the accompanying ignorance, suppression of truth, and the resort to mass violence which has so often been the result of acting out of unexamined ideological assumptions. Psychologists, psychiatrists, psychoanalysts, group therapists, economists, historians, political scientists, theologians, indeed all psychologically minded analysts of political processes, can play a role in the massive public education effort that will be needed to overcome the temptation of national leaders, their loyal followers, and a willing public to succumb to ideologically motivated blaming of other peoples and countries for political conflicts whose complexities we do not wish to take the trouble to understand.

Perhaps the general public, if not our leaders, is at last learning to be skeptical about the ideological justifications used to employ military power against poorer, weaker countries and is beginning to question our support for the murderers of civilians because they are said, at least for the time, to be on the correct side of the ideological divide. My hope is that a more politically sophisticated public, made familiar with stereotyping, scapegoating, externalization and blaming, dehumanization, blind loyalty and patriotism, surrender of individual responsibility, the extremes of careerism, obscurantist (largely male) discourse, and all of the other large-group psychological mechanisms which support the ideologies of enmity, and which the Nazis used so effectively, will, eventually, become more resistant to the easy seductions of these group mechanisms. This is not a Utopian dream but a practical necessity if human life is to endure. As George Kennan said when he was honored by Physicians for Social Responsibility for his commitment to the prevention of nuclear war, "our problem is deeper than we have commonly supposed, for it is one that will have to be tackled not in the statistics of nuclear competition but in the states of mind that underlie much of our participation in that competition" (Kennan, 1988, p. 34).

Before concluding I wish to say a word about powerlessness, or the "sense of" powerlessness, a lament heard so frequently as the reason why people remain politically inactive. I do not question that the feeling is real enough, but it does not reflect the actual state of affairs. For we have seen, even, or especially, during the Reagan years, countless instances in which public outcry, concern, and political action brought needed change, including the signing of the first U.S.–Soviet arms control treaty to actually require the removal of deployed nuclear weapons. Rather, I see this sense of helplessness as part of the ideological system, one defensive structure among many. It is interesting that at a recent group psychological exercise at the John F. Kennedy School of Government, representatives among the defense analysts present, thought to "have" power by the psychologists or members of the "peace" group, felt as much of a sense of powerlessness as did their counterparts in the second group (Chasin and Herzig, 1988). Powerlessness as a form of compliance serves the ideological system. It is reinforced by the belief—false in my view—that great expertise is needed to take an effective part in debates about national or global security and nuclear weapons. In my experience the sense of powerlessness can be overcome by relatively little focused activity in the service of nuclear war prevention *if* adequate group support is available.

The recognition of unacknowledged dominant ideological assumptions becomes the first step in a process of national change and political maturity. As Hunt has written, ideology has "proven disabling by cutting Americans off from an understanding of, not to mention sympathy for, cultures distant from our own." When we feel "frustrated and resentful," observes Hunt, we "indulge [in] dehumanizing stereotypes that make possible the resort to forms of coercion or violence otherwise unthinkable" (Hunt, 1987, p. 176). We live now in a developing world in which each of us has become dependent on the other, where resources are increasingly scarce, and in which the United States can no longer impose its will, militarily and economically, upon the rest of humankind. To fail to recognize this reality, and to continue to live in ethnocentric isolation, with little concern for the welfare of most of humanity, will surely result in a vast tragedy for the United States and the rest of the world.

The general public must play a central role in the transformational processes which are essential for planetary survival. National leaders can, of course, implement major political change, but their paths to office are too likely to have included a professed faith, if not a genuine belief, in the dominant political ideology. They too often experience themselves as its appointed carrier. At the same time such leaders are likely to be surrounded by career-minded political and military advisors who are even less questioning of dominant ideological strains, and may be selected for their knowledge of specific technologies rather than for habits of independent thinking. The public, on the other hand, though susceptible to ideological manipulation, especially when people feel insecure, frustrated, and vulnerable, is, as numerous polls have shown, more flexible and pragmatic, less ideologically rigid, in its positions on foreign policy questions.

No one method of public education can by itself bring about the change toward greater political modesty, tolerance, and social responsibility that seem called for by emerging planetary realities. Teachings at every school level about other societies and political philosophies, which include genuine exposure to their struggles, values, and cultural differences, is a place to start. The methods learned in the peace movement of the 1980s of citizen-to-citizen support and nonviolent resistance to antidemocratic secrecy and control within our own society need to be applied on a larger scale. In an essay on the role of the peace movement in bringing about social reform in contemporary America, professor of anthropology Lisa Peattie notes that "to put an end to the nuclear arms race requires very deep changes in society" (Peattie, unpublished, p. 18).

Political psychologists can play an important role not only in familiarizing the public with the group mechanisms which support the dominant ideology, but also in enabling the citizenry to endure the pain and frustration of trading the easy gratifications of mythic national glory and domination for a less exploitative, more limited view of the United States' role in the world. Ideology can be replaced by a less rigid, more adaptive vision of cultural diversity that is embraced rather than feared and an acceptance of ecological fragility and planetary interdependence that is inspiring rather than threatening.

Education "beyond ideology" for young people needs to include examples of moral courage. Saul Scheidlinger has been a pioneer in demonstrating the importance of such identifications for individual and group change. This will mean learning not only the biographies of leaders who created or perpetuated the dominant nationalistic ideology, but also about people like Daniel Ellsberg, John Stockwell, John Ryan, and Brian Willson who refused to carry out ideologically driven orders, or risked their lives in fighting the war system. We also have a lot to learn from people like Louis Raymond, who left his job as a supervisor at General Dynamics where he was working on nuclear weapons-laden Trident submarines because "it just didn't jive to be making this kind of instrument that . . . could be all destructive. . . . I just thought it was the wrong place for me" (Bettino, 1987).

The critical point is that each of us can participate in the process of transformation, the movement "beyond ideology." In a democracy this is far less difficult than in a totalitarian state if we do not become intimidated by the physical power of technology and the obfuscations of technocratic elite jargon. As Nadezhda Mandelstam said of Stalin's Russia, "either by silence of consent we ourselves helped the system to gain in strength and protect itself from its detractors . . . our submissiveness only spurred on those who actively served the system" (Mandelstam, 1983, pp. 96, 369).

We often ask ourselves, does what I do matter? And others ask us, will it make a difference? The best answer I have heard to this question was given by Louis Raymond's thirteen-year-old son when he was asked if he thought his father's action would make a difference. "I think my father moved the world an inch in another direction," he replied (Bettino, personal communication, 1987).

REFERENCES

Berlin, I. (1988), On the pursuit of the ideal. *NY Rev. Books*, 25 (March 17):11–18.

Bettino, L. (1987), Choices of the heart. *All Things Considered*, National Public Radio, October 20.

Chasin, R., & Herzig, M. (1988), *Breaking the Peace Activist Defense Analyst Impasse*. Report of the Center for Psychological Studies in the Nuclear Age, April 13. Cambridge, MA: Center for Psychological Studies in the Nuclear Age.

Cohn, C. (1987), Sex and death in the rational world of defense intellectuals. *Signs: J. Women in Culture & Soc.*, 12:687–718.

Davies, J. C. (unpublished), The dark side of human nature and levels of analysis, 1988.

Ellsberg, D. (1988), Commitment to catastrophe: A new interpretation of Milgram's experiments "Obedience to authority." Annual Spring Lecture, Center for Psychological Studies in the Nuclear Age, Cambridge, MA, May 24.

Etheredge, L. S. (1985), *Can Government Learn? American Foreign Policy and Central American Revolutions*. New York: Pergamon Press.

Garrison, J. (1988), The darkness of God: Theology after Hiroshima. In: *Human Survival and Consciousness Evolution*, ed. S. Grof. Albany: State University of New York.

Grof, S. ed. (1988), *Human Survival and Consciousness Evolution*. Albany: State University of New York.

Hilberg, R. (1985), *The Destruction of the European Jews*, 3 vols. New York: Holmes & Meier.

Hunt, M. H. (1987), *Ideology and U.S. Foreign Policy*. New Haven, CT: Yale University Press.

Kelman, H. (1987), On the sources of attachment to the nation. Paper presented at the Annual Meeting, International Society of Political Psychology, San Francisco, June 6.

Kennan, G. F. (1988), Network organization news and comment: Kennan on deterrence and mass neurosis. *Nuclear Times*, May–June:33–34.

Kovel, J. (1983), *Against the State of Nuclear Terror*. Boston: South End Press.

Lifton, R. J. (1986), *The Nazi Doctors: Medical Killing and the Psychology of Genocide*. New York: Basic Books.

Linenthal, E. T. (1987), Moral rhetoric, moral confusion in the star wars debate. *Christian Century*, November 25, 1987: 1058–1061.

Mack, J. E. (1983), Nationalism and the self. *Psychohist. Rev.*, 11:47–69.

———— (1986), National security reconsidered: New perspectives generated by the prospects of the nuclear winter. In: *The Long Darkness: Psychological and Moral Perspectives on Nuclear Winter*, ed. L. Grinspoon. New Haven, CT: Yale University Press, pp. 103–140.

———— (1988a), Conversations for wholeness: The challenge for corporate self-responsibility. Concept and discussion paper, Center for Psychological Studies in the Nuclear Age, Cambridge, MA, March 18.

———— (1988b), The challenge of political self-responsibility in the nuclear age. *J. Hum. Psychol.*, 28:75–87.

Mandelstam, N. (1983), *Hope Against Hope: A Memoir*. New York: Atheneum.

Milgram, S. (1963), Behavioral study of obedience. *J. Abnorm. & Soc. Psychol.*, 67:371–378.

———— (1965), Some conditions of obedience and disobedience to authority. *Hum. Rel.*, 18:57–76.

Nedelmann, C. (1986), A psychoanalytic view of the nuclear threat—from the angle of the German sense of political inferiority. *Psychoanal. Inq.*, 66:287–302.

O'Connell, M. C. (unpublished), Recollection: A personal memoir of Saul Scheidlinger, March 14, 1982.

Oppenheimer, J. R. (1980), The day after trinity: J. Robert Oppenheimer and the atomic bomb. Producer and director, John Else, Public Broadcasting Service, April 29, 1981, PTV Publications, Canton, Ohio.

Peattie, L. (unpublished), The peace movement, 1986.

Scheidlinger, S. (1948), A comparative study of the Boy Scout movement in different national and social groups. *Amer. Psychol. Rev.*, 13:739–750.

Sheff, D. (1987), A physicist who turned his back on the bomb tells why. *Rolling Stone*, September 24:59.

Sivard, R. L. (1985), World, military and social expenditures. *Washington World Priorities*.

Staub, E. (1989), The evolution of bystanders, German psychoanalysts and lessons for today. *Pol. Psychol.*, Tenth Anniversary Edition, 10:39–52.

Volkan, V. D. (1985), The need to have enemies and allies: A developmental approach. *Pol. Psychol.*, 6:219–247.

Walsh, R. (1984), *Staying Alive: The Psychology of Human Survival*. Boulder, CO: New Science Library.

Yankelovich, D., & Doble, J. (1984), The public mood: Nuclear weapons and the USSR. *Foreign Affairs*, 63:33–46.

York, H. F. (1970), *Race to Oblivion*. New York: Simon & Schuster.

———— (1988), Making weapons, talking peace. *Bull. Atom. Scient.*, 44:27–30.
Zinn, H. (1980), *A People's History of the United States.* New York: Harper & Row/Perennial
    Library.

Part III

Leadership and the Group

INTRODUCTION

Scheidlinger's (1982) paper on leadership focused interest on this important subject, so vital for society in general as well as for group psychotherapists. He stated that there appears to be no "encompassing concept of leadership within social psychology, psychoanalytic theory and group psychotherapy, even though the phenomenon of leadership lies at the very core of human existence and touches our daily lives" (1982, p. 105). He concluded that, at best, we have numerous partial conceptualizations, portrayals, and research findings all aimed at ascertaining the dimension of leadership. He wondered if Lao-tzu (Henricks, 1989) may not have expressed the leadership function of the ideal group psychotherapist:

A leader is best
When people barely know that he exists
Not so good when people obey and acclaim him,
Worst when they despise him.
Fail to honor people,
They fail to honor you;
But a good leader, who talks little,
When his work is done, his aim fulfilled,
They will all say, "We did this ourselves.
                                    —Lao-tzu, *The Way of Life*

In the first chapter of this section, E. James Anthony (chapter 5) describes the dilemma of a leader who does not lead. As the junior cotherapist working with Foulkes, Anthony remembers how the subtlety of Foulkes's style made it difficult to observe his functioning as leader* or determine his philosophy of leadership (Foulkes, 1965).

---

*Whereas Americans use the term *leader*, the British prefer the term *conductor*.

Anthony's ideas as expressed in this paper are essentially in agreement with Scheidlinger, Foulkes, and Lao-tzu.

Anthony goes on to describe the skills necessary to successfully conduct a therapeutic group, and, in so doing, communicates his deep understanding of the leadership function.

Otto Kernberg's contribution (chapter 6) also is concerned with leadership, but he uses a different framework. He addresses the moral dimensions of leaders in organizations. This is a focus of contemporary significance since group functioning and team approaches in government, school, hospital, and industry and problems in these areas are increasingly important. Kernberg observes that psychoanalytic theories about group leadership have tended to ignore the personality of the leader! This is ironic since psychoanalysts recognize transference–countertransference issues and the impact of the therapist's personality on treatment. It is thus particularly significant that analysts (who have historically tended to ignore group therapy as a treatment method) have also neglected the personalities of leaders when considering the psychology of leadership. Kernberg is one of the few analysts to have examined such issues. He notes that there are key personality factors of leaders which in interaction with group and intrapsychic mechanisms, greatly influence the quality of organizational functioning. Among them are level of narcissistic integration, degree of paranoid tendencies, intelligence, and moral integrity.

Such issues are vitally important, not only from the vantage point of group dynamics and our professional organizations, but for all of society.

REFERENCES

Foulkes, S. H. (1965), *Therapeutic Group Analysis.* New York: International Universities Press.
Henricks, R. G. (1989), *Lao-tzu Te Tao Ching.* New York: Ballantine Books.
Lao-tzu, (1955), *The Way of Life.* New York: New American Library.
Scheidlinger, S. (1982), Psychology of leadership revisited. In: *Focus on Group Psychotherapy: Clinical Essays.* New York: International Universities Press.

Chapter 5

The Dilemma of Therapeutic Leadership: The Leader Who Does Not Lead

E. JAMES ANTHONY, M.D.

In 1988, the American Group Psychotherapy Association invited me to deliver an address in honor of Saul Scheidlinger, and I chose the topic of leadership. There were several reasons for this. First, Scheidlinger himself (1982) had tackled this nebulous area and had brought in some degree of clarity. He had left his essay open-ended as an encouragement to others. A second reason for my selection stemmed from a piece of history and sentiment. Forty years ago, my close colleague, friend, and mentor S. H. Foulkes was also invited to address the American Group Psychotherapy Association on leadership, and had felt himself somewhat misunderstood by his audience in New York. What becomes clear now in reading his presentation is his sensitivity to the dilemma which he perceived as much more than a semantic issue. If I now bring Bion into the picture as a third reason, it is because, like Foulkes, Ezriel, and others in Britain, Bion did group work concomitantly with psychoanalysis. This meant that he came to the group from an analytic situation in which he mainly listened and allowed things to happen rather than causing them to happen. He followed in the wake of the patient's associations, shadowing the process until the moment for insight arrived. It was not, therefore, unexpected that his handling of the group situation had the same degree of indirectness. However, since the group situation is an arena that is more in touch with immediate reality and realistic requirements, the question of more control, more active leadership arises. Thus, the possibility of a dilemma is set up.

Toward the end of his essay, Scheidlinger (1982) quotes an old saying by Lao-tzu that a leader is best when people barely know that he exists. It is not clear from the rest of the article why the author selects this particular quotation since it is not quite in keeping with his general views on therapeutic leadership. There is nothing to suggest that this degree of self-effacement is appropriate or desirable in a therapeutic leader. There are other graceful qualities attributable to the therapist that shine through Scheidlinger's writings, and they all glow with a positive light stemming from a positive philosophy that values involvement as expressed in caring, helping, sharing, enabling, and supporting. Basic to his work, the group therapist should provide a group climate of support. The biographical sketch by Fenchel (1983) draws a portrait of Scheidlinger's courage, reflecting his caring, calm, easefulness, helpfulness, vitality, and energy, all of which have been cited in various profiles of leadership. He is clearly a "natural" leader who carries his inherent and acquired leadership qualities into therapeutic groups and organizations in both of which they served the same vital purpose. In the same biographical sketch (Fenchel, 1983), Scheidlinger outlines five capacities that the "natural" leader tends to show. These are a capacity to perceive shared themes, to know when to deal with the individual or the group, to be able to attract the group's attention, to set the group at ease, and to exude a controllable amount of "magical charm." In short, the leader must be able to connect, discern, attract, facilitate, and fascinate, none of which suggests self-effacement. In his listing of the therapist's functions (Scheidlinger, 1982), the more managerial and benignly manipulative qualities emerge dealing with structuring, encouraging, fostering, controlling, and intervening. The caring and acceptance are, of course, also there.

As can be seen, the dilemma is not there and one would not expect it to be an issue. The question that arises at this point is whether it is possible to be a good therapeutic leader, to function with negative characteristics, and not be overwhelmed by ambiguity.

THE LEADER AS CONDUCTOR

The title that one gives the group therapist may or may not affect his mode of therapy, but it will undoubtedly influence his frame of theory. The question that I am asking of the theory-generating therapist is whether he is sensitive to the built-in dilemma confronting all therapists in a therapeutic group. In turning to Foulkes (1964), I feel that he is, even though he is full of hedging qualifications. For instance, he feels that the term *leader* is unsuitable because the therapist does not act as a leader of a group "in the usual sense." The ordinary meaning of the term suggests someone who wishes to lead a group to a certain goal, which is, "in some respects" the opposite of what a good group therapist does who sets out to wean the group from its wishes to be led. The group analyst does not "often" function as a leader "in the ordinary sense" and in thus "refraining from leading, he shows up by default, as it were, what the group wants and expects from a leader" (p. 54). Foulkes also appears to have underlying political objections to the term *leader* which is understandable in the light of his own experiences in Germany. His objection to "director" is that it is misleading "in a technical sense" in that the therapist is "nondirective." Similarly, I am sure that he would have objected to other "misleading" titles such as "benign manipulator," controller, and structurer. The term that he feels at home with and that I inherited in my work is *conductor,* and the question immediately arises as to whether this particular epithet is any less active: not according to the dictionary where the conductor is defined as someone who guides, someone who collects fares or fees, and someone who leads a musical ensemble. It is difficult not to think of the conductor of an orchestra as "active," although unsophisticated people have questioned whether the conductor is anything but a figurehead who waves his baton in order to keep the orchestral group in time. Freud made use of archaeological metaphors to describe the work of psychoanalysis, and Foulkes has used a musical metaphor to illustrate the dynamics of groups. First of all, he points out that the conductor is primarily a listener who tunes in on different wavelengths to pick up the specific emissions of different parts of the ensemble. The two basic wavelengths to which he is attuned are, when translated into psychoanalytic language, manifest and latent. In most situations, listening is relatively passive, but in the musical or group therapeutic setting, the conductor is a very active listener. The therapeutic leader listens actively with his "third ear" (Reik, 1948) for the latent aspects of what is being said in the group.

One must admit that the therapeutic group is by no means an ordinary type of group, and, in understanding the role of leadership, is very much governed by its own context. Foulkes insists that the group therapist does not assume active leadership and is not concerned with leading the group anywhere. He "defaults" on the group's expectations of his leadership. He listens, he observes, he participates, and he helps to make easier the translation from latent to manifest. This bifocal view of the group helps to explain some of the dilemmas we have been discussing. The therapeutic leadership of the group is, at any one time, an amalgam of manifest and latent leadership tendencies. We have here, therefore, two wavelengths of listening, two levels of understanding, and two basic problems of leadership that gradually become comprehensible during the course of the group.

The interaction between the manifest and latent life of the group resolves the crucial dilemma to which the group is exposed from its beginning. At the latent level, the group shows a craving for a father who is all-powerful and all-knowing, as the child does in the family. The group demands that the leader be absolute. On the manifest level, the therapist receives this latent projection, but, as Foulkes puts it, his therapeutic aim is "to spoil it." He spoils it therapeutically, tactfully and gradually, allowing for the fact that there is an immense, immature need for his authority from the individual members. He accepts the position as leader "in order to be able to liquidate it later on." It is clear that any form of authoritarian utterance or behavior would fixate the group on the level of its unconscious demands. A therapist never "actively" assumes the position of leadership, never acts upon it, but on the other hand, never denies it "by word or deed." As Foulkes says, "he behaves in this respect very much in the same way as the psychoanalyst does in the transference situation" (p. 61). In weaning the group from its leadership wishes, two profound movements take place: a decrescendo whereby the group dethrones the therapist from his "authoritarian pedestal" and brings him "down to earth" and a crescendo which enables the group to replace the leader's authority by its own. In this way, the infantile leader-centeredness gives place to group-centeredness. The therapist "behaves passively and lets it happen."

As the therapist accepts the idealizing transference in psychoanalysis, so the group therapist is prepared to work with the projections of power and prestige that come his way from the group. The manifest level needs the support of the latent level if the problems of the group are to be addressed.

> Without having this basic authority at the back of him, the conductor might simply lose all prestige by behaving as he does. The group might be bewildered and anxious, succumb to a hopeless feeling of frustration, and interpret the conductor's reluctance simply as weakness and incompetence. In its despair, it would look for another leader; not necessarily for another therapist, but worse still, would elevate somebody sufficiently vociferous out of its own ranks into the position of leader. He, particularly if neurotic, could be expected to abuse this position and certainly not to use it . . . for the benefit of the group [Foulkes, 1964, p. 62].

Thus, without the sanction of the leader, the group at its start would lack the courage to inaugurate the analytic process, to break new ground, to test values and accepted codes of behavior.

In Lewinian terms, the Foulkes group is essentially democratic so that, in his view, the therapeutic group provides not only a better way of life for the individual in the group but also for the individual in the world. For the group to be prepared to accept the therapist deeply as a leader, there must be some qualities that facilitate such transference reactions. The therapeutic leader needs to be democratically oriented in his everyday life, reasonably secure and reality-prone, and especially immune from any temptation to play God. For the psychoanalytic group therapist, there should be a resolution of the oedipal conflict which enables him not to abuse power. The analytic group therapist's aim is to create peers, and it is not surprising to learn how many ex-patients have become active in the field of group analytic psychotherapy. Foulkes was well aware that the manifest qualities of leadership by no means told the whole story, and that the profiles omitted the extraordinary underlying components related to charisma that seemed to be inherent or acquired very early in the life of the future therapist. This brought its own enchantments, and so it might very well be that the group, even the most group-centered group, never quite surrenders its adoration of the therapist, and this was evident in the case of Foulkes.

In brief, this point of view regards the need for leadership as a symptom of the group that is curable only by a therapist who does not lead.

OBSERVING CONDUCTION

Foulkes, with myself as cotherapist, ran an intensive closed group for about seven years, and there was never any doubt, even when Foulkes was on vacation, who was the senior therapist, since all questions from the group were directed to him. I was interested to learn how he was able to command such regard and attention from the members over such a long period of time. As a therapeutic leader, he was a master builder whose structural elaborations were carried out so delicately and unobtrusively that the group was there acting coherently as a therapeutic group without my being aware of how he had brought this about. His most salient capacity was in being able to wait, almost interminably it seemed at times, and yet, you felt that he was always in close touch with what was going on. He sat almost immobile. He came to life and spoke, always questioningly and hesitantly, whenever the group pulled him into some ongoing conflict or dissention. At such times, with characteristic indirection, he would attempt laboriously to find out what was being asked of him. He appeared less comfortable than I imagined that he would be, but I came to understand that this was in the nature of a creative tension that allowed him to work along with the group inside his own head. As far as I can remember, he never interpreted sharply, precisely, and concisely, and this was also true of him in the psychotherapeutic situation. Together with the group, he would seem to fumble toward an understanding, somewhat in the manner of a "negative capability" defined by the poet John Keats (1947) as "a capacity to endure ambiguity, doubt, and mystery without an irritable reaching out for fact and reason" (p. 72). He almost seemed to relish the ambiguity as a stimulus to further exploration.

When I was feeling negative toward him, I would wonder why he could not be more positive, more active, more clarifying, and more authoritative, in fact someone who could articulate the dynamics elegantly like a Kernberg. He had very little organizational and structuring capacity and would fall over backwards to avoid any exercise of control. At his most nebulous, I would wonder whether he had some trouble with the foreign language until I noted, over and over again, that his role of a perplexed and somewhat confused person had the effect of clarifying the thoughts of others and giving them the confidence to speak out. The group would try to make something of him, irritated that he appeared to be making nothing of them. It was up to them to carry him along as Aeneas carried his father, but for all the members, there seemed to be an implicit belief that there would be no group worth speaking of without him. At times, it seemed as if they squeezed the inside out of him against his extraordinary reluctance to show and tell. He never gave answers, only raised further questions.

I came to see him as a master builder whose special skill was in the construction of group-centered groups. Once this was accomplished and the group was a growing concern, I could detect his gratification at this unique piece of creativity.

Where, then, lay leader "enchantment?" As time went on, I saw him in his different roles as therapeutic leader, organizational leader (in founding a society and institute), and ideational leader whose theories began to come together in some form of system. As the group's analytic system evolved, he became surer in his approach and more of a guru with a demonstrable mode of treatment. Even before beginning the first group session, his patients were aware that they were in the presence of the international authority, and the weaning from therapeutic leadership was therefore much more difficult.

On a more personal note, he displayed at times a curious needfulness that made the members of the group, especially the women, want to fuss over him. It was quite a shift from his meeting their needs. There was something parallel in the helper being helped to the leader who is led. Helper and helped and leader and follower are somehow bound together in the group matrix.

Of charisma, often declared to be the prerequisite of all leaders, he seemed to have very little. I saw him once in Zurich in the company of Moreno, and by contrast he seemed almost startlingly uncharismatic. Certainly, he had nothing of the aura that Yablonsky (1976) attributed to Moreno. "All attention focused on Dr. Moreno, who appeared suddenly from the wings like a magician. He stood quietly in the center of the stage for several minutes, simply surveying the group. He had a happy-omnipotent look on his beaming face . . . although he stood silent on the stage for two to three minutes, his presence seemed to produce emotional waves" (p. 8).

Although one could credit him with some charm, Foulkes was the very antithesis of this. Had he exuded more grandiosity and self-importance, he might have infused more drama into his therapy and produced followers with more extraordinary and unconventional approaches. I am sure that there is a match between leaders and followers which can be discerned at national and international meetings.

Perhaps there are positive and negative sides to charisma as reflected outwardly in personality manifestations and inwardly in thought and ideation. I would believe, along with Shils (1965), that there is a type of charisma that is embodied in some "very central feature of man's existence" (p. 201). There is also some truth in the statement by Winer, Jobe, and Ferrono (1984) that this central feature is derived from the two-layered nature of the charismatic leader's appeal. "He is an identificatory model for activity where there is passivity in the present, and more importantly, he is a model for activity where there is passivity in the unconscious fantasy." According to them, this is the reason why the leader requires followers. "As each follower becomes like him, the leader repeats the reversal of passivity into activity" (p. 171). There is no doubt that the therapeutic leader gets his momentum sometime in the past out of the resolution of personal suffering and conflict. Through his active reversal of his own helpless situation in the past, he not only repairs himself but gains the capacity to transform others (Winer et al., 1984). It is further argued that there must be a very significant unconscious element in his self representation where he is passive, powerless, and "acted upon" by the object. The unconscious fantasy of traumatization from the leader's past can be matched by patients drawn toward him with similar unconscious passivity and powerlessness: these are crucial reversals from passive into active, from helped into helpers, and from having done to into doer. The shift from passive to active is probably then the essential element in the therapeutic group process. Much of this argument is based on the "supernatural charm" but it does seem to me to apply to almost any use of leadership. In all instances, leaders and followers can find themselves in the same psychological situation, sharing the same unconscious fantasy and reenacting it in the group situation.

LEADERSHIP AND THE OBLITERATION OF THE INDIVIDUAL

Bion is an even better example than Foulkes of a "gray eminence" in group psychotherapy. Both of them discussed leadership on two levels, and both were inclined to assume that other group theorists and therapists tended to work mainly on the upper level so that their discussions of leadership were somewhat descriptively and optimistically tinged. It was true that Redl (1942) had already referred to "basic assumptions" long before Bion and "deep-seated powers" but, for the most part, he was concerned with his "central person" behaving patriarchally, tyrannically, lovingly, hatefully, agonizingly, seductively, heroically, and influentially in good or bad ways. He appeared to be still fascinated by the "primal horde" and his thinking is not much of an advance on Freud's group psychology. I know that the ten types have made very little impact on me whereas I am still constantly struggling with the notions of Bion and Foulkes. When I find myself resonating sympathetically to their approaches, I have to remind myself that I was brought up in the same group climate. The similarity is that one is dealing with the same two levels, the interactions between them, and the primitive mechanisms at work in the depths. In general, Bion was more provocative and eccentric than Foulkes. Having experimented with leaderlessness, in the services, Bion seemed ready to try out some degree of leaderlessness in a therapeutic group. Like Foulkes, he saw that the crucial struggle was between the group's need for a leader and the therapist's reluctance to lead. He, too, is concerned with the two levels of leadership, the one formulated by the leader at the level of full consciousness and the other arising from the conscious, primitive wishes of the group members functioning at the level of "basic assumptions."

Bion's group is regarded by him as representing an interplay between individual needs, group mentality, and the simple culture of leader and followers. Under certain conditions of imbalance, such as a crisis, the neglected therapist is propelled into leadership. One of the members manifested symptoms of madness, and instantaneously, "I found I had been readmitted to the group. I was the good leader, mastered the situation, fully capable of dealing with a crisis of this nature—in short, so outstandingly the right man for the job that it would have been a presumption for any other member of the group to attempt to take any helpful initiative" (Bion, 1957, p. 56). The therapist became "the center of a cult in its full power . . . a miniature theocracy." Bion points out that a group structure in which one member is a god cannot work as a group. Under such conditions, the group becomes analogous to children in a playground with problems typical of the latency child. While in the Foulkes group, the group's image of him as the absolute leader only very gradually abates, in the Bion group, he sets out to wreck any such projection from the very start with predictable reactions—indignation, discontent, resentment, and a marked increased in tension. And what is more, the group is supposed to deal with its own tensions without help from the therapist.

There is another interesting difference between Foulkes and Bion in the way in which they articulate their own feelings and thoughts vis-à-vis the group's operations. Although both these therapeutic leaders worked ambiguously and groped their ways toward understanding themselves and the group, Bion is much more explicit in his intellectual and emotional meanderings. For example, "I am aware of feeling uneasily that I am expected to do something . . . it may be argued that I provoke this situation, and it has to be admitted that this is quite possible, although I do not think so. But even supposing my observations are correct, it may be wondered what useful purpose is served in making them. Here I can only say I do not know if any useful purpose is served in making them" (Bion, 1959, p. 31). And again,

> I begin to feel as the conversation becomes more desultory, that I am again the focus of discontent. Without quite knowing why, I suggest that what the group really wants to know is my motives for being present, and, since these have not been discovered, we are not satisfied with any substitutes . . . in the tense atmosphere prevailing, my own thoughts are not wholly reassuring. For one thing, I have recent members of a group in which my exclusion had been openly advocated; for another, it is quite common for me to experience a situation in which the group,

while saying nothing, simply ignores my presence, and excludes me
from the discussion quite effectively as if I were not there . . . [p. 34].

This time the group really is annoyed, and it is necessary to explain
that they have every right to be. It is perfectly clear that nobody ever
explained to them what it meant to be in a group in which I was present
[p. 36].

Once again, one is confronted with the two levels of leadership: the
manifest or work group leader and the latent or basic assumption
leader. However, there is a difference: whereas the Foulkes latent
leader is godlike and therefore beyond comprehension, the Bion
leader, at this deeper level, is tinged with psychosis and apt to be
irrational. As the leadership image undergoes regression, his individuality loses distinctiveness and he can therefore become what the
group wants him to become. At this level, he is an "automaton" and
suffused by the emotions generated by the primitive drives of the
group. For both Foulkes and Bion, in a therapeutic group it is the
therapist who is the natural leader of the working group, even though
he may abrogate this role and, in both instances, he receives his backing from the underlying unconscious vitality of the group.

The classic picture of the psychoanalyst is depicted by Freud as
someone remote, shadowy, neutral, and emotionally uninvolved, and
it is this image that was carried by the psychoanalyst into the group
therapeutic situation. There was also a tendency on the part of the
group analyst with this heritage to behave as if he were in the analytic
situation. Thus, he will be prone to making individual interpretations
and influencing the individual members of the group. It is only too
easy for the individual interpreter to become the leader, especially if
the interpretations have an impact on the group and generate feelings
of uncanniness. Unless the therapist has a good sense of the group
and its potential, he will succumb to the individual viewpoint and
inevitably become the group leader in the most overt fashion.

Bion has pointed to the dangerousness of leadership, especially
within the therapeutic group. On the level of basic assumptions, the
situation is a positive minefield in which the therapist can succumb
to the inveiglings of the group. Unless he is aware of himself, his
indistinctiveness will lead him to become what the group wants him
to become, even if this reaches messianic proportions.

THE DEVELOPMENT OF LEADERSHIP SELF-EFFACEMENT

It can be taken for granted that the group is ambivalent to leadership.
It both wants it and rejects it in ways not too dissimilar from that of

the therapeutic leader. The group is ambivalent toward the leader and the leader is ambivalent toward leadership. The leader may develop the idea that the quality of leaderlessness related to a capacity for leadership that is not used may be the essential factor that leads to success in group treatment. Another Lao-tzu aphorism indicating that the best leader is the one who does not lead or who knows how to follow may generate a very special type of group climate, loaded with doubt, unsureness, and tension. It is the climate of questioning and confusion in which therapy seems to flourish. The leader who withholds leadership is potent in generating therapeutic curiosity, exploration, self-examination, and group inquiry. The answers are located in the group, not in the leader, and are rarely clear-cut. What works for the therapeutic group may, however, be detrimental to other types of collective organizations.

When Foulkes (1964) speaks of the group therapist as someone who "submits his own function completely to the interests of the group," he is essentially a Lao-tzu leader who keeps in the background, follows the lead of the group, and lets the group speak in preference to himself. As a member of the group, he is tolerant, receptive, and open to new experiences. Most of all, he acts as a projective screen for all the feelings and fantasies of the group. As a gray eminence he silently and passively and unobtrusively builds up an internal model of group functioning that is insidiously imparted to the members and becomes a part of their vision. The inexplicable aspect to all this is how the therapist does so much by doing so little, but by doing so little, he makes it possible for the other members of the group to do much more. The startling insights and the mutative interpretations derive from the group but the master builder has been at work to construct a therapeutically active group.

Of the two psychologies, the follower is to some extent a mirror image of the leader in reverse. The leader should be able to look into the mirror and see the follower, and the same is true of the follower given the right conditions. It seems that not only are leader and follower closely related to each other, but that they can also vary, the one with the other. The more the personality lacks distinctiveness, the easier does alternation become.

Like all other human attributes, the quality of leadership starts in childhood and can be observed in the nursery. The first observation to be made is that leadership and followership seem interchangeable in toddlers. There are bullies of whom the nursery group are scared, but there are also others who attract subgroups into their orbit for reasons that vary with the individual. Erikson would refer to this type of protoleader as possessing "sending power"; it may in later years be summarized under the rubric of "popularity" and the attractiveness is not always on the manifest level. There are some children who seem to have no overt drawing power and are described by the teachers as modest, diffident, unpretentious, and yet eager to get things done, tasks accomplished, without pushfulness or taking over the situation. These young ones seem bent on harmony and will attempt to modulate extreme affects, or, when possession of a toy is at stake, will mediate between rivals. On sociograms, other children often wish to sit by them or choose them as friends, but for reasons which are not easy to discern, except for the fact that they represent no threat to anyone. Teachers will often describe them as self-effacing, but effective. They certainly do not seem to be beset by counterphobias or reaction formations. They manifest no Napoleonic strivings and no Machiavellian manipulativeness. For children they are "nice guys" and for adults they are "decent kids." The more sophisticated group observer, watching them in operation, concludes that they are interpersonally competent and remarkably insightful for a child. On further evaluation, it often transpires that their parents have run democratic establishments in which conciliation and mediation are frequent and familiar processes. The background and development is quite different from the controlling, asserting, and power-based leader who can also emerge as a dominant force in children's groups, but whose term of office is generally short lived.

In adolescence, these differing leadership and followership roles are consolidated and the dynamics of this new development have been described by Erikson (1968).

> But youth also makes an important step toward parenthood and adult responsibility in learning to take *leadership* as well as to assume *followership* among peers and to develop what often amounts to an astonishing foresight in the functions thus assumed. Such foresight can be, as it were, ahead of the individual's overall maturity precisely because the prevailing ideology provides a framework for an orientation in leadership. By the same token, the common "cause" permits others to follow and to obey [and the leader himself to obey higher leaders] and thus to replace the parent images set up in the infantile super-ego with the hierarchy of leader-images inhabiting the available gallery of ideals—a process as typical for delinquent gangs as for any highly motivated group. Where a youth can neither obey nor give orders, he must make due with an isolation which can lead to malignant withdrawal, but which also, if he is lucky and gifted, will help him respond to guiding voices who speak to him [as if they knew him] over the centuries, through books, pictures, and music [p. 187].

I particularly wish to call attention to this type of individual who appears to belong neither to leadership nor to followership roles and appears not to need one or the other. They are gifted adolescents with heightened self-consciousness that makes it difficult for them to locate themselves in categories, and who regard such labeling with uncertainty and dubiousness. For a while, they isolate themselves (and this is not infrequent in the lives of group therapists) and are able to learn from books and running brooks without absolute commitments. They emerge as leaders who will not lead and followers who will not follow, but who remain open-minded and flexible in both thinking and behaving. When the group pushes them needfully in the direction of leadership, they develop followership characteristics and model the good follower who lends body and strength to the group; and when the group pushes them in the direction of followership, they begin to evince elements of leadership that are subtly attuned to the group in question. Between the poles of leadership and followership, these individuals practice a modulation and mediation that suggest an extraordinary capacity for compromise. Although they have not fixed their propensities in the direction of leading or following, it is clear from their group behavior that they have undertaken both roles in play or practice.

Play is where all life's roles begin. A common game of childhood, follow-my-leader, requires appreciable degrees of modulation, mediation, and tact to be successful. After some preliminary negotiation, a self-selected or group-selected child runs ahead, but followed in line by the rest of the group. He will lead them into all kinds of hazardous and difficult situations and the group must imitate him in every detail whether his behavior is hazardous, difficult, or clownish. With every change of leadership, the tasks carried out become more and more adventurous and the group tends to follow the more exciting type of leadership. In my own childhood, I can recall a few glorious moments of leadership, but, for the most part, I was a follower until I discovered the almost equal pleasure of being the tailman. I acquired a number of insights from this group game: first, that it was just as exhilarating to be a follower as to be a leader, although the tough work of generating new behaviors has to come from the leader; second, that the tailman was tantamount to being a leader in reverse and completed the work of the group since all group behaviors stopped with him. Without the followers, of course, there would be no game at all and it was clear that the leaders needed their followers as much as the followers needed their leaders. The tailman had a peculiar aura that drew others to this position. There was a uniqueness about it that matched the leader's, and it was not uncommon for the group to turn upon itself with the connivance of every follower and thereby transform the tailman into the leader.

It was with such group games that I began my career in therapeutic leadership. There were many other group games similar to this that informed me that any type of leadership that I undertook would be based on my understanding of the tailman psychology. Thus, I would follow the leader and the followers to complete and integrate the group organization; I would follow so closely and tactfully that the group would hardly know of my existence; I would tail the group so well that they would think that they did it all by themselves, and I would say so little that they nicknamed me "dummy" because I was one who was habitually silent but only pretending to be so: I might have all the cards in my hand! I eventually became so convinced that the tailman was the crucial member of follow-my-leader that I began to refer to myself as the leader of the tail, signifying perhaps that the best place for the leader to be was at the tail end of things; that is, the position of the Lao-tzu leader. But can the tail wag the dog, or will the tail, under such circumstances, become so powerful that it is the occult leader and practices leadership without the responsibility of leadership? Are we again verging on a semantic quibble? But what can we call a leader who will not lead?

THE THERAPEUTIC LEADER AS MEDIATOR

If one thinks of a continuum of therapeutic interventions ranging from the nondirective to the directive, the process of mediation can belong to either pole. In this presentation, I am concerned with the nondirective type of mediation and I would like to extend the concept of mediation to include its more unconscious aspects. Psychoanalysts, such as Anna Freud, have placed the psychotherapist in an intermediate position between the functioning of the ego, the superego, and the id. For Erikson, the mediation includes the ego, the superego, the id, and the environment. The mediator has all the characteristics of the psychotherapist. He is impartial and neutral and reaches conclusions dispassionately. In the therapeutic group, the mediating process is even more complex. He mediates between the different parts of the individual member and mediates between different members in the group. The mediations are much quieter in tone and slower in pace than in industrial negotiations. The mediator remains outside the conflict but is able to present aspects of conflict to the different members of the group involved in it.

The difference between industrial mediations and the mediating process in therapeutic groups is that the mediation does not have a specific goal that can be accomplished within a given period of time, and the conflict is interpersonal and intrapersonal. The process continues between members of the group and the group therapist, between members of the group and the outside world, and between any group member and his own internal intrapsychic agencies. The group becomes aware of mediation and not of leading, manipulating, and controlling. They become aware of the mediating process that goes on inside themselves and between them and the other group members. Each member becomes a mediator mirroring the therapist. The mediator not only clarifies the dimensions of the conflict, but, with the help of the group, brings different points of view to bear on it. The group perceives his job as clarifying and facilitating and is therefore less ambivalent in its response to him. It is part of the mediator's skill to obliterate the more intrusive parts of his personality, so that mediation does not become a power struggle between the members and himself. The unconscious aspects of mediation are interpreted to the group and later by the group, while the manifest aspects are clarified.

Thus I see mediation as a continuous process in group psychotherapy because I am referring to both interpersonal and intrapersonal conflicts in which the members are helped to recognize the dynamics that move them to come to terms with one another and accept reasonable compromises.

Other group psychotherapists such as Pines (1988) have regarded mediation in group psychotherapy as mainly episodic. At times, they point out, the mediating role can act negatively. "Group members would put pressure on the conductor to be a leader and to be a mediator. It is through his refusal of this role that conflict is generated and this sets in motion a process whereby group members' capacity to contain and understand the dynamics of conflict occurs" (p. 58). Pines also insists that the free-floating discussion of the analytic group, which reveals hidden aspects of individual and group dynamics, is not relevant to the mediation situation, but here, I feel, he is using the limiting notion of manifest mediation, and drawing conclusions from that. He sees mediation as important in crisis situations in group therapy which borderline patients, with negative mirroring responses, leading to head-on clashes. The group-as-a-whole then becomes enmeshed in a disastrous situation in which the therapist has to function as a mediator. Before mediation can bring conflict into the open and delineate its different parts, a phase of analysis is required so that the members can understand the counted out parts of negotiations before accepting them. At such times, in skillful therapeutic hands, mediation and analysis go hand in hand as a group indicator without the more controlling and aggressive impingements of leadership.

EPILOGUE

On one of my visits to London to see Foulkes, he took me for a walk to the Golders Green Cemetery where the ashes of Freud lay surrounded by the burial urns of other leading psychoanalysts, not all of whom had remained "classical!" I asked Foulkes what he thought about having a similar pantheon for group psychotherapists, and he smiled with amusement and said that this was not the group psychotherapist's way to solve group schisms. Conflicts needed to be resolved for the living.

REFERENCES

Bion, W. R. (1959), *Experiences in Groups.* New York: Basic Books.

Erikson, E. H. (1968), *Identity, Youth and Crisis.* New York: W. W. Norton.

Fenchel, G. (1983), Interview of Saul Scheidlinger. *Group*, 7:47–56.

Foulkes, S. H. (1964), *Therapeutic Group Analysis.* New York: International Universities Press.

Keats, J. (1947), *Letters*, 3rd edition, ed. M. B. Forman. London: Macmillian.

Pines, M. (1988), Mediation papers: A group analytic response. *Group Anal.*, 21/1: 57–59.

Redl, F. (1942), Group emotion and leadership. *Psychiat.*, 5:573–596.

Reik, T. (1948), *Listening with the Third Ear.* New York: Farrar, Straus & Co.

Scheidlinger, S. (1982), *Focus on Group Psychotherapy.* New York: International Universities Press.

Shils, E. (1965), Charisma, order and status. *Amer. Sociol. Rev.*, 30:199–213.

Winer, J. A., Jobe, T., & Ferrono, C. (1984), Toward a psychoanalytic theory of the charismatic relationship. In: *The Annual of Psychoanalysis, XII/XIII*:155–175. New York: International Universities Press.

Yablonsky, L. (1976), *Psychodrama Resolving Emotional Problems through Role Play.* New York: Basic Books.

Chapter 6

The Moral Dimensions of Leadership

OTTO F. KERNBERG, M.D.

What follows is a contribution to the psychoanalytic study of group processes, with a particular focus on the psychological pressures that may induce or reinforce corruption in organizational leadership. Such corruption is manifest in practices that clearly negate the ethical principles of leadership, that tolerate gross contradictions between public and confidential practices in leadership functions, and/or represent significant injustice to the members of the organization or to those who depend on the organization's products or tasks. A secondary effect of such corruption is a deterioration of the task-oriented function of groups, task systems, and the entire organization within which such groups and task systems function. I am interested in the forces that tend to undermine the moral dimension of leaders in organizations, and the counterforces, including the leader's personality, that may control and reverse this process.

My point is that even in the absence of gross corrupting factors there is a risk of moral deterioration derived from the two major dimensions of narcissism and paranoia. This is so even when a relatively normal, mature, intelligent, and capable leader assumes leadership that he might leave without undue threat to his self-esteem, or where the nature of the job offered no occasion or temptation for financial or power corruption, or where even the prestige he obtained might not exceed that which he might obtain in other areas.

Psychoanalytic theorizing about group functioning, starting with Freud (1921), has explored the psychology of the followers rather than the leader. Bion's basic assumption groups (1961)—the dependency, fight–flight, and pairing assumptions—focused on the characteristics of small groups of followers.

Bion pointed to the potential temptation for the leader to be seduced into a complementary role to that of the regressed group's momentary need, but he did not describe the group leader's personality as a causal factor of this situation. There is an implication, however, in Bion's work, that narcissistic personalities may be easily "seduced" into leadership functions when faced with the regression of the dependency group, and that paranoid personalities may be "seduced" into leadership functions under prevailing conditions of fight–flight assumptions.

Rice (1969) and Turquet (1975) complemented the basic psychoanalytic studies of mass phenomena by Freud and of small-group processes by Bion with their study of large-group processes and, particularly, of regression in large groups. Once again, the personality functions of leaders were remarkably absent from their analysis. In fact, as Katz and Kahn (1966) first pointed out, the functional analysis of group processes, organizational structure, and their interaction derived from psychoanalytic models typically leave out the influence of the leader's personality as a crucial codeterminant of the organizational structure.

It was only natural that, once the basic psychoanalytic theory of group processes stemming from these fundamental contributions became integrated into actual research on organizational functioning, the previously ignored (or denied) role of the personality of the leader was brought back into focus. Thus, Levinson (1972), Chasseguet-Smirgel (1975), Zaleznik (1979), and Anzieu (1981) focused on personality aspects of the leader that foster or may control the regression in groups within organizational functioning. Zaleznik concentrated on the respective impact of the "consensus" and the "charismatic" leader. Levinson focused on the mutual relationship between transference regression in followership and the personality of the leader. Anzieu and Chasseguet-Smirgel focused on the "merchant of illusions," the narcissistic, self-indulgent leader of regressed groups who gratifies the group's search for an all-giving, grandiose, yet nonthreatening, pseudopaternal leader, and who protects them from reality and the higher level of oedipal conflicts.

Rangell (1974), in describing the syndrome of "Compromise of Integrity," pointed to the corruption of superego functioning induced by unbridled narcissism, and the facilitating function of regressive group processes in bringing about such superego deterioration in leaders. He stressed that the superego was more open to environmental influence than the other psychic structures, and that group processes affecting the leader typically would pressure him into adopting moral stances that are mutually contradictory.

In my own work in this area (1978, 1979, 1980, 1984a) I have stressed the specific effects of obsessive, schizoid, paranoid, and narcissistic aspects of the personality of the leader on social organizations and groups within them, and pointed to the importance of analyzing the ways in which the channels of gratification of the leader's narcissistic, dependent, sexual, and aggressive needs were played out within and outside the organization. In exploring the respective interaction between paranoid leaders and fight–flight groups, narcissistic leaders and dependency groups, and seductive–hysterical leaders and pairing groups, I reached the conclusion that the essential ingredients of the personality of the leader that determine the impact of his personality on organizational functioning are his level of narcissistic integration, the degree of his paranoid tendencies, his intelligence, and his moral integrity. I turn now to an examination of the factors favoring the corruption of leaders in organizations, particularly those factors emanating from regression in the group they are leading.

THE INFLUENCE OF COLLECTIVE TRANSFERENCES ON THE LEADER'S FUNCTIONING

Even in the optimally functioning organization, where task groups are organized efficiently and the administrative structure is attuned to the organizational tasks so that a minimum of group regression develops, regressive pressures surround the leader. These derive from the universal transference dispositions of all the members of the organization, transference dispositions that might be classified—in a perhaps too simplistic but at least comprehensive way—as preoedipal and oedipal longings. The preoedipal longings for dependency and nurturance are accompanied by preoedipal types of idealization, on the one hand, and preoedipal types of envious resentment, and paranoid projections of this envy onto the leader, on the other. The effect of these preoedipal trends is a change of the leader's image in the followers' mind into one that fulfills (and consequently frustrates) magical expectations for protection, guidance, nurturance, and personal affection and love. Preoedipal idealization also defends followers from negative preoedipal transferences and may foster or reinforce the leader's narcissistic tendencies while potentially frustrating his own dependency needs.

Unconscious, and conscious, envy of the leader tends to blend with oedipal conflicts in relation to him. At the level of oedipal transferences, the leader–follower relationship may vary for male and female members of the organization. In the case of men, oedipal idealization of the father as an omnipotent and omniscient protector blends with the preodipal need for dependency and an implicit temptation for unconscious homosexual submission. These needs are balanced by oedipal competitiveness expressed as rivalry, the wish to rebel against and triumph over the oedipal father with its corollary of projection of aggression onto the leader and corresponding paranoid fears of him. Insofar as leadership implies the exercise of authority over followers, the realistic aspects of leadership strengthen these trends. Oedipal rivalry and submissiveness strengthen the paranoid features of the transference reaction toward the leader. Dissociative tendencies in followers may emerge, an alternation between paranoid fearfulness, on the one hand, and idealizing, submissive playing out of the homosexual dynamics of the negative Oedipus complex, on the other.

The relationship of female staff members to the male leader may carry the transference implications of oedipal sexualization with its complement of seductive submissiveness, direct erotization of the relationship, and the temptation for masochistic behaviors as an expression of unconscious guilt because of the oedipal aspects involved. In general, in women, the idealization of the oedipal father usually predominates over the aggressive conflicts related to the negative Oedipus complex, to envy and resentment of men, and to the temptation for pseudoaggressive interactions derived from masochistic tendencies.

These oedipal relationships tend to be inverted in organizations with female leaders, with the additional complication that, insofar as female leadership runs counter to profoundly ingrained, traditional patterns, complex compromise formations between cultural stereotypical behavior and deeper transference dispositions tend to develop—an important subject that extends beyond the confines of this essay.

The cumulative effect of all these transference dispositions is pressure in the direction of idealization of the leader which stimulates his narcissistic tendencies, and of paranoid fearfulness in relating to him. Even the cautious expression of paranoid developments on the part of followers tends to evoke counterparanoid tendencies in the leader. Projective identification is probably the mechanism most responsible for inducing behavior related to repressed or dissociated object relations between leaders and their followers. Thus, even under optimal organizational circumstances there are powerful trends in the direction of narcissistic and paranoid stimulation of the leader. The net effect of these transference dispositions is to stimulate the leader's narcissistic self-aggrandizement and his paranoid disposition, frustrate his dependency needs, amplify his aggressive responses as perceived under the influence of the followers' paranoid dispositions, and lend a subtle sexuality to his relations with members of the organization, which may lend erotic quality to institutional life, but which may destroy administrative relationships by infiltrating them with sexual conflicts.

When the organizational functioning is less than optimal—a development that, given the nature of human functioning, is the rule rather than the exception—the regressive potential is immediately magnified. This increase of the narcissistic, paranoid, and/or sexual dimension of organizational regression may simply be a response to an organizational structure that is less than functional and is moving into a direction of either authoritarianism or chaos. We are still talking only about the consequences of transference dispositions for the administrative structure. We are not yet addressing the complications derived from the development of regressive group processes.

THE EFFECTS OF NONFUNCTIONAL ADMINISTRATIVE STRUCTURES

The administrative structure may be considered functional when the distribution and delegation of authority, task definition, the carrying out of tasks, and task monitoring are matched by appropriate, that is, sufficient and stable, but not excessive or insufficient, investment of authority of managerial leaders at all levels. I shall not explore in detail the characteristics and the "checkpoints" of such a functional nature of distribution of authority here. What interests us is that, when excessive authority is vested in the leader of the organization or in any level of leadership within it, it tends to distort administrative relationships throughout the entire organization. When I speak of authoritarian administration I mean administration invested with power beyond what is functionally required for carrying out organizational tasks.

One immediate consequence of authoritarian leadership is a reduction in the flow of information throughout the organization, the reduction of feedback from followers to leaders, and an immediate increase of the dependent–idealizing–narcissistic dimension of the leader–followers' relationship and of the rebellious– submissive– paranoid dimension as well. If the leader seems actually to take on the functions of the fantasied oedipal father whose will is almighty, who cannot be questioned, and yet who tempts the son to rebel against him, the dynamics of transference regression are exacerbated. Under these conditions, the erotization of immediate relationships around the leader may defensively protect the organization from excessive regression into the narcissistic and/or paranoid dimensions by involving the leader in an isolating erotic network. This development, however, is the exception rather than the rule. An authoritarian leader is usually strengthened in his authoritarian tendencies by the intense idealization, admiration, and submission that he evokes, as well as by the subtle or not so subtle hatred and rebelliousness he also evokes. An authoritarian administrative structure, in short, fosters narcissistic and paranoid regression in the authoritarian leader simultaneously with transference regression along the same lines among the members of the organization.

A similar regressive process occurs if the degree of authority vested in the leadership is reduced rather than increased in comparison to functional requirements—in other words, if there is insufficient or inadequate authority vested in leadership to define and establish priorities for organizational tasks, to direct their carrying out, to monitor these tasks, and maintain viable organizational boundaries. The reduction in the authority of functional leadership reduces the clarity of task systems, weakens leadership functions throughout the organization, blurs the boundaries of functional, task-related groups, and immediately tends to bring about regression in the group processes of the organization. The result is an activation of the unstructured small- and large-group processes referred to earlier. Typically, small-group regression arouses fight–flight and dependency group assumptions, a process that affects the task systems (which are typically small groups), while the characteristics of large-group regression ("loss of morale") occur throughout the organization as a whole.

THE EFFECTS OF SMALL- AND LARGE-GROUP REGRESSION

In practice, the development of fight–flight group regression is characterized by organizational splits with subgroups strongly defending leadership while other subgroups attack it, a development that may coincide with that of other groups whose regression into dependency shows in a generalized sense of passivity, helplessness, and "deskilling," while hopes for magic solutions from above are kept alive. If primitive idealization of the leader, punctured by frustrated, angry helplessness because he is not forthcoming in his leadership functions characterizes the dependency group, intense anger, rage, attack, and desperate fears of retaliation from the leader characterize the fight–flight group. The reduction in functional leadership activates the paranoid and narcissistic dimensions of leader–follower relations that are characteristic of authoritarian developments. We now may add that the loss of functional group structure that gradually evolves under authoritarianism also brings about group regression, particularly small-group regression of the fight–flight type as staff splits into those who assume a passive, submissive, defensively idealizing attitude of leadership, on the one hand, and an angry, fearful, and suspicious outgroup on the other.

Simultaneously, under authoritarian extremism or chaotic loss of authority, large-group processes tend to become activated. The symptoms are a sense of disorientation regarding external reality, the loss of a clear sense of identity of the members of the organization, a pervasive fear of the potential for activation of aggression, and a search for some soothing, banal, nonthreatening, self-indulgent figure of authority who will calm the waters—in other words, narcissistic regression typical of static large groups (Kernberg, 1987). If the organization is naturally split into opposing camps—management and labor, for example, or doctors and nurses, or teachers and students—the large group may be transformed into the dynamic mass described by Freud (1921) with a search for a powerful, aggressive leader who will organize it and the organization in the context of a fight against external enemies. Here the search for a paranoid type of leadership for organizational "warfare" replaces the search for a narcissistic type of leadership of the static large group of organizational "bewilderment."

In summary, any loss of an optimal administrative structure, particularly when it manages to trigger regressive group processes throughout the organization as well, will generate powerful tendencies of a persecutory–paranoid as well as an idealizing–narcissistic type in the organization, with enormous pressures on the leader to become either paranoid, autocratic, and aggressive or self-indulgent, self-idealizing, and soothingly narcissistic. A sexualized "privatization" of the leader's immediate environment is an infrequent and usually inadequate defense against these other powerful processes affecting the organization. Jaques (1955, 1976) has coined the term *paranoiagenesis* to refer to paranoid regressions as a constant potential in organizations. We might add that such paranoiagenesis usually runs parallel to primitive idealization, both processes being kept separate by a generalized splitting of object relations in the context of organizational regression.

There are, however, corrective forces that may be activated in what I have described as the potential for regression in social organizations. These corrective forces constitute potential tools that may protect the leader from regression and, particularly, from the deterioration of the moral dimension of leadership that is our main subject. If the leader can continue to analyze the main tasks of the organization and their constraints, the relationship between developments in the environment and the mission and the capabilities of the organization, the monitoring and protection of organizational boundaries, time may be available to analyze the organization's internal constraints and conflicts and resolve them in a functional fashion. In addition, the use of certain basic principles of organizational management may counteract group regression. These include reinforcing the functional aspects of the organization's administration, of the formal channels of communication, and of ordinary channels for redress of grievances, all as a protection against excessive paranoid tendencies, and to provide opportunities for analyzing the organizational conflicts within clearly structured meetings. Executive conferences may be set up, for example, in which information is shared, as opposed to executive meetings at which decisions are made; the "three levels" system of administrative checks and balances and of redress of grievances (involving a staff member, his supervisor, and the supervisor's supervisor) may be reinforced; and rational relations may be fostered among inside and outside control agencies such as legal structures, professional organizations, boards of trustees, labor unions, forums that permit rational analysis to counteract the rumors, institutional demoralization, and the sense of diffusion of decision making.

THE LEADER'S PERSONALITY

In an earlier paper (1984a), I concluded that, from the point of view of optimal resistance to the regressive pressures operating on leadership, the leader's personality characteristics should include a moderate quota of narcissistic tendencies, some paranoid potential, high intelligence, and a well-developed sense of morality. In what follows I expand on this proposal and bring it into the context of the temptations for regression in the organizational leader.

In briefly summarizing some generally accepted conditions for effective leadership I shall refer to what Klerman and Levinson (1967) call the leader's technical, human, and conceptual skills. Technical skills refer to the knowledge of the particular field in which his organization is involved. The leader's technical skills tend to become less important the greater the number of levels of functional hierarchies his organization has, and the higher the level at which he operates. In fact, one might say that, while conceptual skills become increasingly important at the higher levels of hierarchically complex organizations, the technical skills are more important at the lower levels of hierarchy, and in organizations having few levels of hierarchies. Again, I am stressing the functional level of hierarchies that correspond to significant discontinuities in the span of administrative authority, an issue carefully discussed by Jaques (1976, 1982).

The leader's conceptual skills correspond, I believe, to his intelligence, and Jaques has convincingly proposed that the leader's conceptual skill is reflected in his capacity for an extended "time span of decision making," which means, in practice, the capacity for developing realistic long-range planning with its implicit absorption of multiple levels of information, and relative independence from short-term constraints on the decision-making process.

Technical and conceptual skills refer to knowledge and intelligence; human skills refer to the leader's personality. Obviously, there are an infinite number of individual personality traits that are commensurate with leadership functions, and a limited number of known, severe personality disorders that, for various reasons, may limit or severely cripple leadership capacities.

In earlier work (1979), I examined the damaging consequences of obsessive, schizoid, paranoid, and narcissistic character pathology on leadership functioning. Here I want to focus on the positive aspect of certain personality traits, particularly narcissistic and paranoid structures.

A high sense of personal security that is relatively independent of immediate social feedback, in other words, a modicum of normal (infantile or adult) narcissism embedded in a somewhat neurotic yet overall adaptive personality structure may provide a healthy insulation for the leader. All neurotic character pathology serves narcissistic functions; if an excessive degree of self-assurance, ambition, and a need to be admired and followed are part of a character structure that does not reflect the pathological narcissism of a narcissistic personality disorder, such narcissistic traits may protect the leader from narcissistic lesions ("insecurity") as well as from excessive paranoid reactions to not being loved "at all times by all people." The danger, of course, is that the leader's narcissistic tendency be reinforced by adulation. Such adulation may bring about a circular process wherein artificially inflated self-esteem derived from idealization and admiration in the organization gradually diminishes the leader's capacity for self-criticism and leads to a chronic narcissistic regression that may become maladaptive to leadership. This narcissistic regression fosters corruption in leadership, because the leader's emotional needs may now run counter to the demands of the organizational tasks. The protection of the leader's self-esteem and the reinforcement of his narcissistic gratifications take precedence over painful decision making, and favoritism may replace justice in dealing with colleagues and subordinates.

Here an integrated, autonomous superego may intervene as a protective structure that provides the leader with a capacity for self-evaluation and fairness, thus counteracting the danger of narcissistic deterioration. But it is very difficult for the leader with narcissistic tendencies, however benign, not to feel reassured in the long run by the friendly responses of those who know how to cater to his narcissism. It is very difficult for him not to gradually come to resent those who refuse to so cater. The leader's narcissism will convey his need to be loved, which will trigger the temptation in some of his followers to ingratiate themselves with him. An element of corruption inevitably enters into this interaction.

In contrast, the tolerance for other people's criticism, the mature narcissistic gratification at being able to tolerate criticism and to learn from it is an important corrective. Sometimes a leader's narcissism permits him to listen to criticism privately though not publicly. It is here that the responsibility for a realistic assessment on the part of followers begins: What are the limits of the leader's capacity to listen? Only the consistently responsible behavior of followers defines the objective boundaries of the leader's capacity to respond positively to critical feedback.

Also related to narcissism is the leader's potential envy of those of his followers whom, because of his envy of their capacities, he perceives as more gratified by their functions than he is, particularly more gratified in their dependency needs or their needs to be positively rewarded for their work; or his envy of those whom he perceives as more successful or more creative than he is, or those whom he perceives as a potential threat to his authority. This threat also relates to the paranoid aspects of the leader's personality, but conscious and/or unconscious envy of followers (and projective defenses against such envy) are important concomitants of narcissistic leadership. It cannot be repeated too often that, when organizational leaders have an independent area of their own technical, professional, or conceptual expertise their tolerance of the creativity of coworkers is much higher, which helps creativity within the entire organizational structure. The leader, however, whose main motivational goal is not that of the organizational leadership, who becomes an absent leader and experiences the organization as a constraint to his own interests, will have a negative effect on the organization and its staff.

The other major dimension that may protect, and also threaten, leadership functions is a certain degree of paranoid alertness. There is an enormous difference between a "normal" paranoid capability, on the one hand, and the leader with a paranoid personality, on the other. The latter feels constantly hurt, potentially persecuted, perceives all critical feedback as acts of insubordination, and at times may transform his organization into a "fortress" against the external environment, a fortress behind whose boundaries he also has to crush the ever-present danger of a fifth column. At the opposite pole, a total absence of concerned alertness and suspiciousness implies naiveté, that is, a denial of the ubiquity of aggression, of the ambivalence that is normal in all human relations, and one that is certainly typical of organizations.

The organizational leader cannot afford to be naive, because there will be objective aggression in the ambivalence toward him from all the members of the organization of whose collective transferences he is the target. We have already examined these transferences, and here it only remains to be said that they may express themselves in ambivalent behaviors that reduce the efficiency of the organization and that, unconsciously, also express indirect aggression toward the leader. The leader of the organization needs to be aware that he is the target of such aggression as well as of idealization, and that he is the focus of both narcissistic and paranoid temptations. Such an alertness may help him to diagnose early or even prevent potentially damaging actions against him and the organization, but, at the same time, his paranoid capability may also activate his own counteraggression and increase his suspiciousness beyond the reality of the situation.

In fact, one of the sources of authoritarian behavior in the leader is precisely the acting out of counteraggression spurred by paranoid sensitivity to staff ambivalence. The leader who needs to exercise "absolute" control in order to feel secure from the aggression of those he suspects may by the same token corrupt the organization because his authoritarian behavior will foster submissiveness and opportunism as it splits the staff into a narcissistic–submissive and a paranoid–withdrawn group. The "paranoid urge to betray" (Jacobson, 1971) is typically expressed in the leader's righteous indignation over real or imagined slights, with a subsequent, revengeful misuse of his authority to "punish" the culprits of the attack. Here it is the paranoid dimension of leadership that triggers organizational corruption, as the leader's "revenge" expands into the followers' shared gleefulness, colluding indifference, or attitudes of "innocent bystanders." The degree to which the leader's paranoid tendencies permit him to absorb the aggression of his followers rather than to return it in the form of authoritarian self-assertion marks the difference between the positive and negative effects of paranoid personality features in the leader. Thus, both narcissistic and paranoid trends in the leader may protect his leadership function or may bring about its deterioration. The deterioration of leadership in turn reinforces narcissistic and paranoid regression in the organization and fosters organizational corruption as part of the defensive processes triggered by such regression.

The narcissistic and the paranoid dimensions in the leader and in the followers enter into complex relationships. There may be a hidden grandiosity of the leader that is fostered by the idealizing and submissive tendencies of the followers, especially in relatively isolated organizations with very long-term leadership. By the same token, the hidden aggression of the followers expressed in chronic "passive" ambivalence may first bring about the leader's hypersensitive and eventually authoritarian reaction, and secondarily increase further and be successfully projected onto the leader himself, eventually tempting him into a paranoid response.

The narcissistic and paranoid tendencies in the leader may balance each other, so that optimally his narcissistic stability protects him from reacting with excessive aggression to challenges within the organization, and his paranoid tendencies may provide a relatively harmless channel for "balancing" angry responses to narcissistic lesions. But with more severe character pathology, narcissistic and paranoid tendencies may reinforce each other. Under extreme conditions, leaders with severely narcissistic and paranoid tendencies may exert a sadistic control over the organization, with devastating consequences for themselves and everybody else in it.

I have described elsewhere (1984b) the syndrome of "malignant narcissism," constituted by the combination of a narcissistic personality disorder, severe paranoid tendencies, ego-syntonic aggression, and antisocial features. In fact, the deterioration of superego functioning under the impact of narcissistic and paranoid regression is one of its most dangerous consequences. Revolutionary mass movements often fall into the hands of leaders with such a narcissistic and paranoid personality structure: the paranoid dimension provides the leadership needed for an aggressive challenge to the status quo, while the narcissistic dimension provides the certainty of a "radiant future" once the revolutionary group has triumphed. It seems to me that both Hitler and Stalin presented personality structures with features of malignant narcissism, which may be a characteristic common to many revolutionary leaders who end up as sadistic tyrants.

Still another combination of narcissistic and paranoid features is that of the leader with a totally self-indulgent, childlike narcissistic quality that permits him and those around him to deny all aggression in their interaction. One might say that this is the narcissistic leader of the static large group (Kernberg, 1987) who protects the large group from mutual aggression by a soothing set of clichés. This personality constellation in the leader, however, is damaging to the organization because it implies a lack of functional aggression in making the painful decisions that the organization needs, and it very often leads to the outbreak of severe aggression one or two levels beyond or below the leader's immediate entourage. Often the unconscious tendency to avoid conflicts by "projecting" them to lower levels of decision making actually fosters paranoid outbreaks at another hierarchial level: here the leader's pathological narcissism acts as a defense against his underlying paranoid constellation and its corresponding aggression, which are "exported" to other locations in the organization. This brings us to considering the "consensus leader" and the "charismatic leader."

The consensus leader, under optimal circumstances, has a healthy narcissism that permits him to work with a group, to tolerate and obtain feedback, to experience narcissistic gratification in the shared decision-making process, and in transforming his group into a functional task system. A consensus leader may, however, also evolve into the narcissistic "good guy" leader who tries to avoid conflicts and painful decisions, whose leadership function becomes overly politicized and opportunistic, and who eventually may foster corruption in the system. Similarly, the charismatic leader's self-assertiveness may result in firmness in the exercise of leadership functions and support of task performance and of the organizational structure. On the negative side, it may lead to excessive idealization and submission on the part of followers, fear over their own rebelliousness and a paranoid projection onto him, and thus lead secondarily to a reinforcement of the paranoid dimension of the leadership and an authoritarian regression of the organization. My point is that what really counts are the underlying nature of the narcissistic and paranoid equilibrium, and that particular leadership styles do not necessarily protect the organization from major lines of regression.

THE LEADER'S VALUE SYSTEMS AND ORGANIZATIONAL CORRUPTION

Three dimensions of organizational functioning are intimately connected with carrying out leadership roles. These dimensions present

us with the paradox that what is most useful for the organization is
also threatening to its functioning, and particularly to the moral aspect
of leadership. I am referring here to (1) the political dimension of
negotiation across task–system boundaries and organizational boundaries; (2) the exercise of power as part of legitimate authority; (3) and
the activation of an ideological superstructure on the basis of the task
sentience of the members of the organization.

The political dimension of leadership refers to the leader's capacity
to "win friends and influence people" in the service of task performance. Given the contradictory aims and motivations of competing
segments of the organization and the different constraints within it,
conflicts of interest are to be expected and are inevitable aspects of
organizational functioning. To convince those who have conflicting
loyalties and interests that it is necessary to compromise in order to
achieve broad institutional goals cannot be done simply on the basis
of rational argument, but requires what might best be called tactful
lobbying.

The danger is, of course, that expediency may run counter to the
overall organizational interest, and that, for example, in order to gain
the good will of one sector of the institution some basic task requirements of the organization are sacrificed. Here the alternative is between the strength of the leader's commitment to overall institutional
goals that will protect him from "deals." The risk here, however, is
of rigidity in the decision-making process that will alienate those he
needs to carry out institutional tasks, on the one hand; and to compromise against overall organizational interests, on the other. An obsessive leader in such a situation may create unnecessary constraints
and even paralyze organizational decision making. At the other extreme, necessary flexibility may shade into opportunistic deals that
may end up corrupting the leader's stance for the organization as a
whole.

Financial compensations of leading figures in the organization are
a typical illustration of the temptation for "deals" that may end up in
gross unfairness and a general sense of corruption in the setting of
financial rewards, as opposed to the alternative extreme of a bureaucratic system of rewards that protects the organization against arbitrariness but at the cost of damaging the organization's capacity to
compete effectively for leading staff with other organizations.

Another avenue for potential corruption, as well as self-defeating
rigidity, also has to do with the leader's reward system. It is almost
unavoidable for strong pressures to build up around the leader for
preferential rewards to those with whom he has a personal relation-

ship, as well as to those he must engage in political discussion regarding organizational interests. But there are also those who are several organizational levels removed from him. Here the leader's narcissism might tempt him to reward the former and may foster opportunism and corruption.

The exercise of power is an essential, unavoidable part of leadership, and it requires a leader's capacity to draw comfortably on the aggressive aspects of his own personality. Power, the capacity to carry out organizational work, and, in the case of leaders, to lead organizational staff in this process, stems from many sources: the authority legally vested in the leader; the authority derived from his personality characteristics, and his technical and intellectual skills; the authority delegated to him by professional and/or other sentience groups; the projection onto him of aggression as part of the paranoid dimension of organizational functioning; and the idealization of him as part of the narcissistic-dependent dimension of organizational functioning.

As I mentioned earlier, the functional exercise of authority occupies a middle range between excessive exercise of power that transforms authority into authoritarianism, and inadequate exercise of power that is a cause of deterioration and failure in leadership function and leads to organizational chaos and immediate regression in its group processes. What I have said about power implies that I adopt an eclectic position that differs from the traditionally opposing views that power resides in the personality of the leader or power results from the organizational structure.

The concentration of power in the leader and his exercise of it tends to vary, or, rather, there are varying conditions that tempt the leader to increase the exercise of power and that increase or inhibit his capacity to do so. The successful functioning of the organization provides a sense of satisfaction and triumph for all those who carry out its tasks, and tends to bring about a sense of power in individuals and groups reflecting such task systems. Organizational success increases the capital of credibility invested in the leader and increases his power and authority. Such increase in power and authority, however, may reinforce the narcissistic dimension of leadership, an unrealistic self-aggrandizement of the leader, simultaneously with a temptation to exercise power in authoritarian ways.

By the same token, organizational failure tends to reduce the authority of the leader and to activate regressive group processes—the activation of fight–flight conditions and aggression secondary to the frustrated dependency that comes with a sense of failure. These regressive developments in turn tend to generate a search for paranoid leaders as part of fight–flight conditions, and random aggression as part of large-group processes reflecting organizational failure and loss of morale.

Typically, organizations with failure in top leadership develop powerful currents of conflicts among subsystems and the emergence of leaders who enact the paranoid demands of regressive groups. These are organizational preconditions that may foster the ascendance to power of leaders with inordinately strong paranoid and narcissistic personality characteristics. Or else, in response to general group regression and loss of morale, the paranoid and narcissistic dimension of leadership is activated to an extent that fosters a secondary paranoid regression in the leader. This is the time, he feels, to search for culprits responsible for organizational dysfunctioning; he is tempted to replace rational analysis with an attack on scapegoats and/or a radical bureaucratization or ritualization of organizational functioning in an effort to control the diffused aggression that seems to permeate it.

Unconscious or conscious guilt over the aggression triggered in the organizational life, however, may be expressed in the temptation to protect an incompetent leader at any organizational level. Somebody who in every responsible organizational manager's mind is clearly incompetent is "chosen" to expiate the guilt over the organizational aggression, and a shared effort evolves to save this failing member. At times, very strong and authoritarian, even sadistic, leaders have a "weakness" for an incompetent hierarchial subordinate while clearly acknowledging their awareness of his failings. There may even be an undertone of satisfaction (or moral self-congratulation) in the tolerance of this situation in the face of complaints about the incompetent person. Paradoxically, the aggression against which the protection of the incompetent is an unconscious expiatory maneuver may reemerge in the injustice done to all those who suffer under the incompetent leader. Personal morality and unconscious guilt may thus also be subverted by institutional processes.

What is corrupting in such regressive activation of power struggles throughout the organization is the development of the urgent need to "protect one's skin" under conditions of organizational failure, authoritarian threats, and paranoid and narcissistic regressions. Task sentience deteriorates, and concern for one's personal interest takes precedence over organizational goals. Leaders uncertain in their functions and in the stability of their jobs may become prone to decision making that is no longer based upon organizational interests but their efforts at survival, which clearly indicates the corruption of their task.

In addition to the political dimension of leadership, and the varying degrees of concentration of power in the leader, the development of an organizational ideology (or of competing ideologies) tends to affect the leader's decision-making process. By ideology I mean a system of beliefs, convictions, fantasies, and myths shared by members of a social group. Ideology becomes of interest insofar as many organizations are subject to competing ideological currents, some of which may be realistically at the service of the task while others only pay lip service to the task and may actually constitute a constraint upon it.

The interests of teachers as a professional group, for example, may actually run counter to the educational goals of their institutions: should the teachers' be paid according to the institution's educational effectiveness? Teachers' unions would be apt to oppose such a linkage; but the school system involved may find it an excellent way to achieve its overall goals. In hospitals, the interests of, say, medical faculty and mental health workers may clash significantly while both sectors pay lip service to the hospital's clinical goals.

My point is that rational leadership should encourage and identify with a task-oriented ideology that corresponds to organizational goals. This is another way of talking about the leader's responsibility for maintaining morale. The danger here is that this task-oriented ideology may run counter to other human needs and value systems that may be irrelevant to the specific goals of the organization, but are crucial to the members of the organization maintaining a sense of well-being and dignity. If the needs of individuals and groups in an organization are a basic constraint to optimal organizational functioning, in other words, if one has to consider human factors as limiting the degree of efficiency of an organization, then it is important for the leader to be able to identify with ideologies or socially accepted value systems that are tangential to the interest of the organization itself. In other words, it is a function of the leader to protect individuals from poor working conditions, from arbitrariness in job assignment, from risks connected with the work, regardless of the impact of such protective measures on work efficiency.

Under ideal conditions, such ideological contradictions may be minimal, but under less ideal conditions the leader's identification with a complex system of values may actually protect his decision-making process from the expediency of exclusive identification with rarified organizational or other goals. For example, there may be systems of treating patients in hospitals that are financially highly efficient but are run counter to the human needs of the patients. Menzies (1960) described a social system of nursing in a general hospital that protected the nursing staff from excessive anxiety, but ran counter to the emotional needs of severely ill or dying patients. For practical purposes, the director of a university hospital must identify with the value systems of the medical school interested in optimal clinical and academic work, but also with the legal system and its corresponding ideology in terms of the legally required preconditions for the hospital's functioning and accreditation purposes, with the professional ideology specific to physicians as a profession, and with his own personal value system activated under conditions in which personal ethics influence decision making (e.g., regarding when not to resuscitate).

All organizations, in order to function, must develop bureaucratic structures that protect task systems from arbitrariness, that solidify lines of authority and boundaries of subsystems, while protecting the organization from regression into unstructured large- and small-group processes. These bureaucratic requirements, as we have seen, also protect individuals from arbitrariness and may counteract organizational paranoiagenesis. But these same protective bureaucratic structures may express dissociated organizational sadism in senseless rigidities. The sea of bureaucrats may consciously or unconsciously obstruct creative developments by sadistic insistence on procedures, and it is a function of leadership to counteract such subtle yet persistent expressions of aggression. With an authoritarian leader in control of an inflexible bureaucracy, the danger exists of a deadening of functioning throughout the entire system, of the kind that has, for example, so successfully damaged and paralyzed the economic life of the Soviet Union (Zinoviev, 1984).

One corrective against such bureaucratization is the flexibility of informal arrangements that circumvent bureaucratic requirements, but at the cost of corruption ("personal deals") infiltrating the entire system. In fact, bureaucratic rigidity together with a compensating corruption of the system characterizes many dictatorial and totalitarian states.

This brings us to the crucial importance of the extent to which the leader's value system reflects a mature rather than a primitive superego; in other words, the extent to which he can critically explore the contradictory value systems, ideological cross-currents, and task requirements of the organization. If a moderate degree of narcissism and a paranoid potential are essential ingredients of an effective leadership, it also needs to be underlined that these very personality characteristics tend to undermine individual morality and a firm commitment to value systems. The favoritism to opportunistic followers who stimulate the leader's narcissism, the rejection of honest criticism on the part of those who seem to threaten that narcissism, carry with them the danger of moral corruption. The need to defend against potential enemies has the same effect: survival becomes a major "moral" goal.

The need to punish those who dare to rebel may not imply any dishonest behavior on the part of the leader's conscious behavior; the effect of his inappropriate aggression, amplified in the paranoid atmosphere of organizational regression, is in itself devastatingly corruptive. The leader's capacity for ideological commitment, an expression of his individual value system, may protect him against organizational corruption, but also tempt him to attempt compromises running against functional organizational goals or against his general commitment to a humanistic quality of interpersonal interaction in the organization.

As Zinoviev (1984) has pointed out, in large groups where authority is projected outward or upward, onto the hierarchical superiors, there is a tendency for corrupt behavior that individual members would not carry out in their private, personal life. In agreement with Zinoviev, I believe that an authoritarian structure in an organization fosters the projection of superego functioning onto external or hierarchically superior authorities; then group regression occurs in the narcissistic–dependent and/or paranoid direction, and corrupt behavior can be observed to increase. As Zinoviev says, such conditions promote careerism, selfishness, neglect of tasks, the enjoyment of other people's failures, hostility to those who advance, a search for propitiatory sacrifice of selected victims to the leadership, a tendency to general abandonment of moral values and individual differentiation, with resentment toward those who seem particularly autonomous or courageous. Finally, there is a tendency toward a blind egalitarianism and a paradoxical reinforcement of the authority of authoritarian leaders as a defense against mutual envy. These conclusions dovetail with Chasseguet-Smirgel's (1975) and Anzieu's (1981) ideas concerning regressive group processes, previously mentioned.

It might be said that what has been described here is the human condition in general, but the fact that the same individuals who can behave morally under more differentiated circumstances present such behavior patterns under conditions of organizational regression makes it of interest in terms of organizational management. Also, the leader should not be seduced by conventional demands for a primitive sense of justice and punishment, but should maintain his individual moral judgment in the light of such temptations.

The personal moral integrity of the leader, predating his assuming leadership functions, is the best protection against the consequences of narcissistic and paranoid regression in the organization. A social system that invests a leader with accountability to the organization as well as to supraordinate social, economic, and political institutions within which the particular organization functions, provides external guarantees for an adequate structure that will protect leadership functioning. The leader's professional sentience to the profession within which he was trained, his human sentience to the staff who will work for him, and his general sense of social responsibility regardless of the particular task of the organization should go a long way to protect his individual moral integrity.

My principal point is that the careful analysis and setting down of organizational guidelines in all areas of conflicts that affect leadership functions may protect the leader against times of acute regression when the narcissistic and paranoid dimensions are activated and his internal freedom for guidance by his own ethical systems becomes challenged.

REFERENCES

Anzieu, D. (1981), *Le Groupe et L'Inconscient: L'Imaginaire Groupal.* Paris: Dunod.

Bion, W. R. (1961), *Experiences in Groups.* New York: Basic Books.

Chasseguet-Smirgel, J. (1975), *L'Idéal du Moi.* Paris: Claude Tchou.

Freud, S. (1921), Group psychology and the analysis of the ego. *Standard Edition,* 18:67–143. London: Hogarth Press, 1955.

Jacobson, E. (1971), *Depression.* New York: International Universities Press.

Jaques, E. (1955), Social systems as a defense against persecutory and depressive anxiety. In: *New Directions in Psycho-Analysis.* New York: Basic Books, pp. 478–498.

——— (1976), *A General Theory of Bureaucracy.* New York: Halsted.

——— (1982), *The Form of Time.* New York: Crane, Russak.

Katz, D., & Kahn, R. L. (1966), *The Social Psychology of Organizations.* New York: John Wiley.

Kernberg, O. F. (1978), Leadership and organizational functioning: Organizational regression. *Internat. J. Group Psychother.,* 28:3–25.

——— (1979), Regression in organizational leadership. *Psychiatry,* 42:24–39.

——— (1980), Regression in groups: Some clinical and theoretical implications. *J. Personal. & Soc. Sys.,* 2:51–75.

——— (1984a), The couch at sea: The psychoanalysis of organizations. *Internat. J. Group Psychother.,* 34/1:5–23.

——— (1984b), *Severe Personality Disorders: Psychotherapeutic Strategies.* New Haven, CT: Yale University Press.

——— (1987), Las tentaciones del convencionalismo (The temptations of conventionality). *Revista de Psiconanal.,* 44/5:963–988 (Buenos Aires, Argentina).

Klerman, G., & Levinson, D. J. (1967), The clinical executive: Some problematic issues for the psychiatrist in mental health organizations. *J. Study Interpers. Proc.,* 30:3–15.

Levinson, H. (1972), *Organizational Diagnosis.* Cambridge, MA: Harvard University Press.

Menzies, I. E. P. (1960), A case study in the functioning of social systems as a defense against anxiety. *Hum. Rel.*, 13:95–121.

Rangell, L. (1974), A psychoanalytic perspective leading currently to the syndrome of the compromise of integrity. *Internat. J. Psycho-Anal.*, 55:3–12.

Rice, A. K. (1969), Individual, group and intergroup processes. *Hum. Rel.*, 22:565–584.

Turquet, P. (1975), Threats to identity in the large group. In: *The Large Group: Dynamics and Therapy*, ed. L. Kreeger. London: Constable, pp. 87–144.

Zaleznik, A. (1979), Psychoanalytic knowledge of group processes. Panel report. *J. Amer. Psychoanal. Assn.*, 27:146–147, 149–150.

Zinoviev, A. (1984), *The Reality of Communism*. New York: Schocken Books.

Part IV

The Mother-Group and Preoedipal Pathology

INTRODUCTION

Howard Kibel (in chapter 7) describes effective group treatment for functionally impaired patients. He examines their underlying pathology in terms of character structure and personality organization. He clearly illustrates how the group modality provides a needed opportunity for such individuals to work through difficulties in differentiating self and object representations and other manifestations of blurred ego boundaries. He believes that the group situation (by providing a matrix, a holding environment, what Scheidlinger calls a "mother group" milieu) offers the safest opportunity for working through unconscious primitive fantasies for disturbed patients who might not otherwise succeed in growing. In the group atmosphere catharsis, ventilation, and emotional resonance make for meaningful affective experience with others (rather that producing conscious awareness or intellectual insight which is often insufficient to generate meaningful change in patients).

While acknowledging the here-and-now interaction in the group, Kosseff (chapter 8) focuses on another aspect: how the group situation arouses the deepest underlying promptings (and memory traces) dealing with both union and separate "selfness" in each of us. Kosseff hypothesizes that the group atmosphere does this catalytically by tapping the unconscious intrapsychic roots of each participant's proto-memories, and banked engrams which began to register vaguely as the neonate emerged from mother–infant fusion; and grows more specific as the child develops interconnections and symbiotic promptings; and becomes still clearer and more specific as there is movement toward autonomous selfhood. Kosseff proposes that the "mother-group" properties, and the group matrix, arouse memories and bring out feelings that are probably universal (when facilitated by leadership and group cohesiveness), and these can be utilized on behalf of emotional development.

Ramon Ganzarain, though valuing good-mother group factors,

nonetheless finds it essential to balance the therapeutic equation by encouraging a focus and working through of the split-off sadistic primitive psychodynamic forces within group members. These he calls the bad-mother group factors. His paper (chapter 9) contains many examples of these fantasies and underlying preoccupations.

Ganzarain explores and clarifies how he works as group leader, mainly through active interpretation, dealing with the aggressive and sexual impulses and hostile affects which operate both from intra-psychic and group dynamic sources within the group.

Priscilla Kauff (chapter 10) describes the conditions inherent in the therapeutic group situation which facilitate treatment of tenacious preoedipal pathology. After describing why it is so difficult to treat character disorders, she focuses on the unique features afforded by group interaction which can be of help in treatment. Among the many factors deemed therapeutic, she also acknowledges and examines the important concept of the "mother-group" as elaborated by Scheidlinger (1974).

Ganzarain, Kibel, Kauff, and Kosseff all appreciate how vital it is that their preoedipal and borderline patients work through unconscious primitive fantasies and affects. Indeed, these issues need to be explored in most, if not all, psychodynamic groups.

The authors in this section agree that polarized unconscious archaic mental representations and their related impulses and emotions must be taken into account. They consider the group to be an invaluable instrument which can help patients (who often only receive limited help in these areas in individual treatment) overcome early life deficits and longings which get reactivated in the course of regression and progression in the "facilitating" group.

REFERENCE

Scheidlinger, S. (1974), On the concept of the mother group. *Internat. J. Group Psy-chother.*, 24:417–428.

Chapter 7

The Therapeutic Use of Splitting: The Role of the Mother-Group in Therapeutic Differentiation and Practicing

HOWARD D. KIBEL, M.D.

Treatment of patients with severe psychopathology has been a continuing source of interest in the psychiatric literature. All too often the patients are described from a diagnostic vantage point rather than a functional one. They may be called borderline and narcissistic, on the one hand, or schizophrenic, on the other hand. Yet within these diagnostic categories, a range of disabilities may be found. For example, Grinker, Werble, and Drye (1968) noted some time ago that the borderline condition embraces a wide range of pathology, with some patients falling close to the neurotic end of the boundary while others function closer to psychosis. This paper will address the group of functionally impaired patients whose score on the Global Assessment of Functioning (GAF) Scale (American Psychiatric Association, 1987) would consistently range between 31 and 50. These patients carry a variety of diagnoses, are likely to have a history of one or more hospitalizations, but generally are not actively psychotic. These are the chronic patients who flood ambulatory care clinic facilities.[1]

The thesis will be presented that group psychotherapy is an effective form of treatment for most of these individuals. Once these people are engaged in the treatment, the group serves to maintain their current level of functioning and offers them possibilities to change.

---

[1]Recently, the term *Severe and Persistent Mentally Ill* (SPMI) has been applied to these patients. Unfortunately, a more precise definition of the SPMI is lacking.

While the group experience provides them with support, the treatment is conducted along psychodynamic–psychotherapeutic lines. The method does not resemble counseling nor the style of a "rap" group. It requires clinical proficiency to run this type of group, as well as both a dynamic understanding of the members' pathology and of group process. It is psychoanalytically informed group psychotherapy.[2]

STRUCTURAL PSYCHOPATHOLOGY

Object relations theory has enriched our understanding of these patients. While descriptive diagnosis has many implications for treatment, structural diagnoses of their ego functioning offers a broader understanding of their relatedness in a group (Kibel, 1980). Patients with borderline and psychotic personality organization (Kernberg, 1984) may show considerable differences in symptoms, identity diffusion, and reality testing. But they show striking similarities in defensive operations, particularly for those patients in the functional range under consideration here.

Patients with psychotic structure have an impaired ability to differentiate self and object representations and hence have a blurring of ego boundaries. The more functional ones possess rudimentary or partial differentiated internal self and object images, specifically in the realm of pleasurable, rewarding, and hence libidinally linked experiences (Kernberg, 1976). The basic "good" self–object constellation functions as an organizer around which the individual can negotiate the environment, albeit in a somewhat stereotyped, primitive, and egocentric way. In contrast, a nondifferentiated, aggressively linked, self–object unit is split off, extruded, and primitively denied. Those whose egos are organized at the borderline level of character pathology have a different, but specific intrapsychic structural defect. The integrative capacities or synthetic functions of their egos are seriously impaired. As a consequence, primitive division of the ego into its libidinal and aggressive components is maintained defensively to protect that ego core built around positive internalizations. Primitive dissociation of contradictory ego states is reinforced by the use of denial, projective identification, primitive idealization, devaluation, and omnipotence.

---

[2]This term is a derivative of the one used by Chessick (1977) to describe a method that combines empathy, support, receptivity, selective transference interpretation, and exploratory work.

In both groups of patients (i.e., those with psychotic structure and severe borderlines), there is a predominance of primitive defensive operations centering on the mechanism of splitting (Kernberg, 1984). In both, there is a preponderance of pregenital aggression or, at least, an inability to incorporate and master aggressive derivatives, so that the ego core or central experience of the self is fragile. Sadistically contaminated images threaten to infest all internalized object relations of these patients and their external counterparts. Primitive denial, projective identification, and persecutory anxieties occur regularly.

Needless to say, these patients have an impoverished sense of self resulting from either a dispersal of identity in those with psychotic structure or identity diffusion in borderlines. Notably, within this functional range, the self-reflective capacity of the ego is virtually missing (Kernberg, 1986). This means that in psychotherapy these patients have little or no capability for introspection and self-observation and are vulnerable to those regressive aspects of group that further threaten to disrupt their fragile sense of individuality and autonomy. All this dictates, as we shall see, the use of special techniques in treatment.

Central to the considerations here are these patients' difficulty in tolerating regression, their use of splitting as a core defense, their lack of a self-reflective capacity, and their fragmented identifications. These very qualities and defects that make such patients poor candidates for individual psychotherapy are the very same ones that make group psychotherapy an optimal treatment, but only when it is constituted along homogeneous lines and carefully structured. Many of the important theoretical contributions to the thesis of this paper come from the work of the scholar to whom this volume is dedicated.

REGRESSION

It has been claimed that patients with chaotic, amorphous, and fragile egos do best in groups (Freedman and Sweet, 1954; Stein, 1963). This is because, with appropriate supportive technique, the group helps them to forestall unwarranted regressive reactions. Specifically, it alters the transference (Stein, 1964), diminishes the demand for active participation, allows each member to titrate his own level of tolerance for involvement, and is reality orienting (Horwitz, 1977). These aspects of group are well known and have been said to limit regression even with more integrated patients. This is not to suggest that treatment in a group need be merely supportive or even superficial. In fact, a seemingly contrasting view was offered by Bion (1959), namely that psychological group formation in therapy reactivates regressive levels of even greater depth than individual analysis (Scheidlinger, 1968).

This apparent contradiction about regression in the psychotherapy group can be reconciled. Many theorists have confirmed Bion's contention that group-as-a-whole experiences stir developmentally early layers of psychic functioning, even in relatively well-integrated patients. A number of regressive forces propel members into acting and reenacting primitive object relationships. These include the contagious effect of group emotions, the presence of envy, rivalry, and competition, but particularly the threat of the loss of one's individuality and autonomy (Horwitz, 1983). Yet across the board, regression in groups need not be profound. It is simultaneously mitigated by certain factors in groups, such as the social context, the reality-orienting influence of feedback, and the actual gratification that members provide one another (Stein and Kibel, 1984). Consequently, the group becomes a medium for the contemporaneous expression of both advanced and primitive object relationships, each reflecting a different level of ego organization (Kernberg, 1975).

The notion that members show variable ego functions in groups was initially advanced by Scheidlinger (1968). He brought concepts from modern ego psychology to bear upon traditional psychoanalytic thinking about regression. He noted that autonomous ego functions and those related to "regression in the service of the ego" can be mobilized in individuals for adaptive and growth-promoting purposes. This occurs, as we shall see later, whenever the group is structured in a way that allows it to function as a "holding environment," in the sense noted by Winnicott (1960) with respect to the parent–infant relationship and certain dyadic transferences. Group cohesion creates the conditions that enhance latent synthesizing and controlling functions of the ego, as the members' sense of mutuality produces a merging of their separate self-images into a more coherent sense of self-in-the-group (Kibel, 1987).

It is important to bear in mind that the members' level of ego integration and the group's level of functioning need not be equated. For example, in a typical Tavistock-style group, the impassive style of the leader can produce groupwide regressive reactions in well-integrated individuals. Conversely, a supportive, cohesive group can contain the primitive tendencies of patients with severe psychopathology and enhance their adaptive functioning precisely because of the phenomenon of transient merger of their separate, fragmented egos.

In this instance, the group-as-a-group can function at a level above that of any of its individual members.

This view of regression in groups is a derivative of Scheidlinger's notion that groups have two broad process levels (or dimensions) that operate simultaneously (1960). One, the *contemporaneous–dynamic* level pertains to conscious needs, ego-adaptive patterns, group roles, and the social network of member relationships. Behavior here is primarily reactive to realistic group-situational factors and brings into play the more external aspects of personality. In contrast, the *genetic–regressive* level refers to unconscious and preconscious motivations, and particularly to defensive patterns and conflicts. At this level, phenomena emerge in response to those situations in which defenses have been loosened so that repressed or contained emotionality is revealed. Operationally, members' functioning within each dimension depends upon both the group's composition (e.g., diagnostic mix) and the leader's style. Consequently, a structured, cohesive group can maximize the first level (the contemporaneous–dynamic), while minimizing the second (the genetic–regressive level).

IDENTIFICATION

Scheidlinger (1964) noted that members' identification[3] with the group as an entity serves a variety of genetic and contemporaneous needs. Early childhood experiences with caretakers, siblings, and even physical surroundings are retained as memory traces of self-in-relation-to-object representations. These are always at play, to some degree, in the perception of contemporary situations, but more particularly so in patients with severe ego pathology. Their sense of self is so fragile that they must call upon past experiences in order to make the present less confusing. This strong need to reestablish parallel linkages in a current context accounts for these patients' so-called "object hunger." This is at the root of their yearnings for belonging, emotional support, need-gratification, and, in group, participation in the social collective. Once established as a cohesive body, the group then serves various defensive needs and much more. Specifically, the group's culture becomes fundamental to each member as an organizer

---

[3]Identification here refers to an endopsychic process in which there is individual involvement with a real or symbolic object. In the developmental hierarchy of object relationships, it falls far short of identity formation, which refers to the consolidation in the ego of coherent attitudes, values, style of relating, and defenses; in short, an enduring self-concept.

of experience. Its level of predictability remains greater than in ordinary social relationships, since the group is molded under one powerful and consistent influence, namely, the leader (Stein and Kibel, 1984).

As mentioned previously, membership in a group poses the threat of the loss of one's individuality and autonomy. This is inherent to the demand for membership, namely, the giving up of the sense of I for that of We. Yet eventually this process of transient giving up of some aspect of oneself to the group-as-a-group is welcomed because of the attendant increase in self-esteem that comes from being part of a larger whole. This happens more readily when the group is perceived as a benign, comforting, and accepting entity. Such an observation led Scheidlinger (1964) to conclude "that, on the deeper genetic-regressive level, the group entity becomes for the individual the symbolic representation of a nurturing mother" and, in a broader sense, advanced the hypothesis "that the universal human need to belong, to establish a state of psychological unity with others, represents a covert wish for restoring an early state of unconflicted well-being inherent in the exclusive union with mother" (p. 294). Indeed, this tendency is especially marked and fundamental in groups of people who have notable ego disturbances along the lines of identity dispersal or diffusion (Scheidlinger and Pyrke, 1961).

Identification with the group provides each member with a transient pseudoidentity of the self-in-the-group. This can appropriately be viewed as a so-called "group identity" (Scheidlinger, 1964), in that in a group with stable structure there is a common perception of one's self-sameness and continuity in time, together with a consistent perception of the group entity and therapist, and the perception that all these meaningful people (and entities) recognize this self-sameness and continuity. This is exactly what is meant by theoreticians who speak of the group entity as a "container" or "holding environment" (James, 1984), or as a protective "group envelope" (Day, 1981). For these patients, it functions as a sanctuary within which the individual feels secure.

The practical consequences of identification with the group entity are twofold. First, attachment to such a powerful object provides a sense of belonging, enhances each individual's self-esteem, and, because of this ego support, maximizes latent potential. These include such functions as adaptation to reality, the sense of reality, reality testing, the sense of self, relatedness to others, the capacity for concern, and flexibility or receptivity to new experience. In other words, group participation, with the resultant sense of being valued, promotes optimal functioning and prepares one to change.

The second derivative of group belonging relates to the ability to take in information, attitudes, and all that is usually involved in feedback. Through group identification, each member relates to others as if they were an offshoot of the group itself and then reacts to this and other attributes of the group as if these were also his own. This is the basis of incorporation. Over time, as feedback is digested, its introjection allows for the formation of new personal, but, as will be discussed, enduring identifications.

SPLITTING

The need to belong is inherent to human nature. Granted, its expression is thwarted in patients with severe psychopathology because of their impaired object relationships. Its development can be traced to the earliest phases in the evolution of object relations, specifically, those that follow the normal phase of autism. Normal symbiosis extends from the second month of life to somewhere between six and eight months of age. At that time, there occurs consolidation of the basic "good" self–object constellation, which soon becomes the nucleus of the self system and the basic organizer of this primitive ego (Kernberg, 1976). Pathological function at this level is characteristic of patients with psychotic ego structure.

The next stage of development extends from this one of normal symbiosis to at least the eighteenth month. At that time, there occurs differentiation of self from object representations and, hence, the establishment of stable ego boundaries. Pathological functioning at this level is characteristic of the more impaired patients with borderline personality organization.

These two levels of ego development correspond respectively to the symbiotic phase of development and the earliest subphase of the separation–individuation process described by Mahler (1971, 1972). Anna Freud (1965) initially postulated that this period of development was characterized by egocentricity, coupled with a symbiotic perception of the mother as a gratifier of needs. Scheidlinger (1974) used these notions to explain attachment to the group entity. However, he went further and explained how defensive operations characteristic of these early phases of development, namely, those grounded in splitting, operate in groups. Accordingly, he stated that, "in the face of the individual and collective stresses and anxieties induced by group formation," attachments, primitive patterns of relatedness are activated, particularly the search for a need-gratifying relationship with a maternal image. As a result, "while the group entity is . . . perceived in a positive and benign . . . [vein], the group leader and the other members become almost immediately the objects of a gamut of partially ambivalent but largely hostile and fearful attitudes" (pp. 424–425).

This formulation, from the group literature, regarding the concept of the mother-group has much to commend it. It explains the profound attachment individuals have to groups, even in the face of negative treatment results. It accounts for the influence of group norms, group pressure, and persuasion on the members. It explains why termination from group psychotherapy is almost invariably erratic, too abrupt with some patients or interminable for others. It explains how a cohesive group can manage intragroup conflict and even strife. More important, it states that this very perception of the group as an entity "is progressively utilized by both the members and by the therapist in the service of the 'therapeutic alliance' or of group maintenance and cohesiveness so that the intragroup conflicts and personal problems can be subjected to analytic scrutiny in the context of an anxiety level which is not too threatening to the equilibrium of individual patients and of the group entity" (p. 425).

For the patients under consideration here, the implications are twofold. First, a supportive group atmosphere is a necessary precondition for exposure of aggressively linked, internal object relationships. In other words, libidinal attachment to the group entity permits splitting to operate in a planned, organized manner. Second, the more cohesive the group, the more secure the patients will be in exposing these noxious aspects of themselves. A benign, maternal group image facilitates the acting-in the group of these elements. They then become available for treatment. In this way, the group truly functions as a sanctuary, much as the nursery does for the toddler, where aggressively tinged relatedness can be exposed, tolerated, explored, practiced, and worked out.

For such therapeutic splitting to occur a group with a nurturing atmosphere is presupposed. Opposing conditions are possible and need to be avoided. Scheidlinger (1974) noted several references in the literature to the group being perceived as a threatening, engulfing object. It is frequently the case that fears of abandonment by and fusion with the group are activated in patients with severe ego pathology. This can be observed in hospital settings with large groups composed of such patients, as one typically finds at poorly run community meetings. Both inpatient and outpatient groups with such patients can deteriorate along these lines, if the group remains unstructured and the therapist (incorrectly) assumes a detached, impassive, reflective stance. Then these patients project aggressively linked introjects, namely persecutory fantasies, into the "void" of the group, which functions as a screen for their fantastic imagery. Under such circumstances they experience the group or "the meeting" as a terrible place, but fail to blame the leadership or each other. In other words, the group is perceived as "bad" when the split operates in reverse.

The ultimate goal when conducting psychotherapy groups of such patients should be to put their natural tendency to use splitting to therapeutic advantage. This is done by creating a supportive group atmosphere and then reinforcing it throughout the course of treatment. The technique for this will be discussed below. The danger in this approach is that cohesion and the attachment to the group entity become overly sustaining for these patients and, thereby, makes eventual separation from treatment difficult. However, this may be a small price to pay for patients with such severe impairment of functioning. They may be "lifers" in treatment in any event.

Immediate advantages accrue when splitting is put to therapeutic advantage, even before formal work is done on aggressively linked, internal object relations. Each member's sense of self is reinforced through assimilation with others in the development of a common group identity. More important, there are particular benefits to having split object relationships coexist, in a compatible way, in a controlled environment such as the therapeutic group. To some degree, the usual disabilities of splitting are mitigated. Specifically, ambivalence is tolerated better, affects seem less intense, frustration tolerance is improved, impulsivity is lessened, reality testing is less subject to distortion, and oscillations in self-esteem are decreased. All this occurs because aggressively dominated introjects are offered a sublimated channel for expression under the benign aegis of the mother-group. Thus, in a substantive way, the group experience is inherently supportive.

TECHNIQUE

The therapist's technique is crucial to the creation of the mother-group and its maintenance. He must constantly and repeatedly work to help these patients master the inclusion phase of group development. For them, inclusion is associated with fantastic notions of merger and fears of loss of autonomy. For this reason, developing group cohesion is an arduous process, one that waxes and wanes. It is as if once the therapist has pulled the group together, it remains so only briefly while aggressively linked introjects are reenacted. Then, the patients pull away from one another, disperse if you will, and the therapist has to effect the whole thing over again. During these transient phases of togetherness, intrapsychic change becomes a possibility, as will be described below. The therapist's job seems somewhat repetitive and is quite taxing.

Establishment of substantive cohesion in the group is opposed by the potential for development of a dependent group culture. These patients, in the face of the multiple stresses of group life and in an attempt to provide their chaotic egos with a semblance of coherence, gravitate toward a relationship with an external object that is perceived as powerful. The therapist can readily fill this role. Patients have the proclivity to become dependent on him or her. Yet, the group entity alternately can serve a similar purpose. The therapist's task, then, is to gently deflect attention away from himself and to enhance latent trends toward group coherence.

Cohesion is promoted when the therapist focuses attention on the common concerns of the members, both inside and outside the group. A supportive group-centered technique, which stresses the commonalities of experience, fosters a sense of mutuality. So do groupwide suggestions, directions, and clarifications. Coalescence of the members into a supportive unit, such as the mother-group, is the product of a bonding together of their separate "good" self-images.

In this kind of group, the therapist must assume a fairly active role. He needs to take an energetic part in helping the patients interact with one another. He should guide them in helping each other (i.e., by giving mutual support, advice, feedback, and opinions). These patients can be shown how to make a variety of "meaning attribution" statements (Scheidlinger, 1987) to each other. Moreover, he should examine all the material of the treatment from a group-centered vantage point. First, he must consider how each group event, no matter how seemingly insignificant, relates to the group as a whole. Second, he must bring this to everyone's attention and let them see how together they are affected by every element of group life. By doing this, he maximizes the members' sense of being in a collective and thereby strengthens latent elements of their group identity. Groupwide clarifications do the same.

Like a symphonic conductor, the therapist must orchestrate the flow of the group. He must take the initiative to encourage discussion and even occasionally introduce topics. He must bring in relevant material from previous sessions and pick up on the subtler aspects of their conversation and behavior. He cannot leave too much for the patients to do themselves. Yet, he should refrain from doing individual treatment in the group, even though these patients will unwittingly pull for this. If he needs to talk to one member, he should do so only in order to stimulate the others' interest and the group interaction. Lastly, major interventions should be made to the group-as-a-whole, recognizing that, like an orchestra, it is composed of divergent elements. He should recognize each of these (e.g., deviant members, excluded material, repudiated aggression, etc.), but emphasize the cohering elements in the group. The overall goal is to synthesize disparate features of group life. A few brief vignettes will illustrate these points.

During one session, the conversation was initially slow and halting. Two members discussed recent changes in their living situations, while others appeared disinterested or distracted. The therapist tried to get them involved, but to no avail. Finally, the therapist asked if they were preoccupied with thoughts related to the end of the previous session. One young woman had said, at that session, that she felt as if she did not "fit in" with the group. The focus on this brief comment yielded contradictory responses from the members. Two patients had thought that her statement signaled an intention to prematurely terminate. One man believed that she had been brooding about and objecting to a suggestion that he had given her several weeks previously. The woman in question now reported that she had merely meant that she doubted whether she was capable of being of help to the others, while she considered each of them to be effective with one another. Next, primitive denial took hold (which is typical in such groups). The members minimized their reactions to the end of the previous session, despite evidence to the contrary. Yet, following this interchange, the tempo of the session quickened and the members became animated.

In a clinic, a group with cotherapists was delayed momentarily in starting. The therapist who was present was called to the telephone to receive a message that was intended for the absent, senior therapist who was on vacation. Once the session was under way, the patients talked about the one absent member, who was in the hospital for a major physical ailment. While this was not the first week of his hospitalization, more conversation revolved around him at this session than at the previous ones. Some of it, while focused on other members, indirectly related to this man. Interspersed were oblique references to each of the therapists, culminating in pointed concerns, namely doubts, about the emotional involvement of the present therapist with the group and its membership.

All of this puzzling material was motivated, it turned out, by the collective fantasy that the initial telephone message was a notification for the absent, senior therapist that the absent patient had died (which it was not). Realistic concerns about the absent member and projected fantasies that were stimulated by the absence of one therapist crystallized upon a routine event, namely, the task of the junior therapist to receive a message for his colleague. Its importance initially went unnoticed by the therapist since in this case the function had little to do with the group.

In another group, Mrs. L. opened the session by referring to an interchange of the previous week. She said she was upset that the members had misunderstood her comments concerning a former group member. She perceived them as having been overly curious and perhaps semicritical of her references to him. Now, she wanted to clarify for them that she mentioned him merely because she missed him. The group members reassured her that she had misunderstood their comments and intentions. Then Mrs. L. proceeded to ask the members for some advice. She had been requested by her ex-husband to attend a conjoint session with his therapist. She wanted to know their opinion as to whether she should go.

The members' responses were sparse. One woman asked a few questions and hinted that she believed further contact with the ex-husband was unwise. One man seemed intrigued by the possibility of a marital session, but did not state so explicitly. Another man merely tried to be solicitous with his questions, as if attempting to draw her out further. But she revealed little else.

This was a group of eight members. Mrs. L. had asked for advice from all, but received responses from only three. These responses, in fact, were rather meager in substance. The group was at an impasse. What had happened was apparent to the therapist. Mrs. L. had "double-binded" her peers. Her complaints from the previous week showed them how she could harbor a grudge if feedback was not in line with her expectations. The members retaliated by withholding their reactions to the proposal of a conjoint, marital session.

The therapist broke the impasse with the following intervention: "I see that no one is able to give Mrs. L. the feedback and advice that she requested. Perhaps you [the other seven] are worried that there will again be miscommunication and that your intent will be misperceived, as it was last week. This kind of situation must be frustrating for all of you [all eight], particularly since you [the other seven] are interested in her situation and appear to want to help." In this instance, the therapist recognized the resistance, alluded to the underlying anger, but supported and emphasized the positive aspects of the members' behavior, i.e. their efforts to cohere with one another (Feilbert-Willis, Kibel, and Wikstrom, 1986). This intervention is prototypical of the kind recommended above for groups of such low functioning patients.

Further explication of technique is beyond the scope of this paper. Suffice it to say that, once cohesion is established and the mother-group is functionally operative, members will respond to each other in a therapeutic way. Specifically, under the guidance of the therapist they will confront each other's distortions, clarify interactions, and in other ways diminish projective trends.

MECHANISMS FOR CHANGE

Horwitz (1974), in his review of the Psychotherapy Research Project of the Menninger Foundation, reported that a number of patients, one-third of whom had borderline personality organization, showed substantial improvement in a treatment which emphasized consolidation of the therapeutic alliance. These patients were able to achieve significant and stable structural change through a method that promoted the beneficial aspects of the dyadic transference relationship including its need gratification, rather than through its interpretation. Put simply, the treatment alliance not only served as a prerequisite for therapeutic work, but often became the main vehicle for change. It is postulated here that, by the same token, over the long haul in group, patients with severe ego pathology can be maintained and even grow through participation in the treatment, because they form new partial identifications by incorporating elements of the group alliance.

Identification in groups, in its most general sense, is a multilayered phenomenon. On a surface level, members identify with one another because they are mutually in strife and sense certain similarities in each other's symptoms, attitudes, and conflicts. This is the well-known phenomenon of universalization. In a more fundamental way, mutual identification emanates from sharing the same relationship with the therapist. In a similar vein, by virtue of the technique described above, they identify with the group as an entity. Through these new relationships in the group, the patients develop a special kind of identification with the therapeutic attitude of the leader. This includes his encouragement of the expression of intrapsychic difficulties, tolerance for aggression and intragroup conflict, the conviction that these will be worked out, and even his self-investigative approach. This myriad of identifications forms a basis for change.

The entire process of change is built around an internalization of supportive aspects of the group combined with the work on inter-personal relationships. The term *internalization* is used here in the manner defined by Schafer (1968), namely, it "refers to all those processes by which the subject transforms real or imagined regulatory interactions with his environment, and real or imagined characteristics of his environment, into inner regulations and characteristics" (p. 9). In other words, in a supportive group, a new, more benign, and more gratifying relationship occurs between the self and other, namely the group, along with its members and leader, which then becomes as-similated into the individual's internal world of object relations.

In the group, being accepted and valued despite the expression of social attitudes that derive from unacceptable instinctual wishes heightens self-esteem. The group's and the therapist's ability to accept the "badness" of each member reduces pressure from sadistic super-ego forerunners. In effect, the patient is given the opportunity to internalize more benign attitudes toward aggressive drive derivatives, to regard them tolerantly as part of the human condition and, there-fore, to expend less psychic energy defending against them. In this way, there occurs partial neutralization of a noxious self–object re-lationship.

Salutory experiences in the group become the foundation for in-ternalization of the remedial self–object relationship. This becomes the kernel of the corrective emotional experience in treatment. New introjects then influence one's behavior in the group. They act in a reciprocally enhancing manner within the group, so as to contribute to further growth of the therapeutic alliance. Stability of change occurs because improved attitudes and behavior induce positive reinforce-ment. Development of a gamut of protherapeutic attitudes is moti-vated by the fantasy of winning the therapist's love and respect. Thus, both internal and external rewards serve as potent forces in the main-tenance of change.

The individual's emotional bond with the group, its members, and leader, form the matrix upon which these altered identifications de-velop. This dynamic is akin to the ordinary maturation and devel-opmental processes of infancy and childhood when crucial internalized self and object representations become imprinted upon the ego. Group psychotherapy, in a way, provides a second chance to correct the earlier state of conflict between contradictory aspects of the per-sonality. The overall process of the corrective emotional experience, when viewed from a structural perspective, involves the strengthening of libidinally linked object relationships with a concomitant partial neutralization and repression of their aggressively linked counterparts. More specifically, an altered view of the self in relation to an altered view of a significant other (the group, its members, and leader), as well as the affective bond between these two representations, becomes assimilated into the person's internal world. As Horwitz (1974) noted with respect to individual treatment, "the latter involves not only new and more accepting perceptions of the self, including those based upon identifications, but also includes more realistic and benign views of the attitudes of others" (p. 262).

This entire formulation is in accord with Horwitz's (1974) findings *"that varying degrees of stable structural change occur in all successful treatments depending upon the extent and quality of the internalization process"* (p. 264). It argues that integration of good and bad, self and object representations, which happens in the most expressive psychotherapies, especially psychoanalysis, is not the only means for growth. More specifically, identity formation, which implies that there has been a synthesis of libidinal and aggressively invested self representations into a cohesive self (Kernberg, 1986), does not need to occur for change to be substantive and stable.

Even apart from internalization, the group, at the very least, serves a supportive function by reinforcing splitting mechanisms (Kibel, 1978, 1987) in that the ego core is shored up and is unfettered by the aggressive counterpart which has been partially detoxified (Kibel, 1987). This permits adaptive functions to emerge. In this instance, balance is maintained between opposing forces in the personality. However, the exploratory aspects of group psychotherapy, that is, the systematic scrutiny of the reenactment of internal object relations, promises more. Here, there is opportunity for the development of ego mastery and an altered experience of oneself in the group. The resultant internalization of remedial self–object representations produces a reorganization of conflicted internal representations in their relationship to one another, so that the central ego core dominates, more or less, the sense of self. Put simply, good introjects are enhanced and bad ones diminished. The quality and degree of this internal realignment determines the stability of the change.

Overall, change occurs in three basic ways. First, the group experience serves a supportive function in several respects. Members provide each other with acceptance, sympathy, approval, encouragement, advice, and guidance. Relatedness is encouraged through the group interactions, which also serve to gratify object needs (Stein, 1970). Second, when splitting is put to therapeutic advantage, internal object relationships are reenacted in a protected environment. The resultant interactional patterns are exposed, explored, and discussed. Clarification by the members of their bonds to one another and of each other's array of relationships promotes ego mastery over them. Third, because projective identifications occur in a controlled and manageable way, the beneficial aspects of projective–reintrojective relatedness occur. This will now be explained.

Ogden (1981) observed that "projective identification is one of the few psychoanalytic concepts that bridges the intrapsychic sphere of thoughts and feelings and the interpersonal sphere of real object relations occurring in the context of a given social system" (p. 331). As a theoretical construct, it explains how individuals with severe ego pathology manage aspects of themselves which are perceived as dangerous and unwanted, namely, their chaotic and primitive impulses. Projective identification is used continually by these patients to induce others to feel, think, and behave in a manner consonant with the ejected fantasy. Usually in life, significant individuals respond to the patient in a corresponding manner. While this also happens in group, in the long run, opportunities are provided for the projected fantasy to be processed in the group matrix, toned down, or even corrected. The therapeutically crucial element here is the feedback process.

Energetic, aggressively associated interchanges are inherent to group life. For these patients, any expression of anger, or merely an encounter that contains some measure of discord, causes anxiety. This, in turn, activates aggressively linked internal images, which are then projected into the group matrix. The reintrojected object often assumes a persecutory-like quality. Because of its primitive, sadistic origins, it is connected to fantasies of criticism, admonition, disgust, and retaliation. Witness the reaction of Mrs. L. in the clinical example above. Usual social interactions activate these processes and the associated distortions. The goal in treatment is ultimately to correct the reintrojective aspect, in terms of the way these patients experience themselves in the group. For this to occur in a salutary way, the therapist must treat the group, as noted previously, in such a manner that it comes to function as a benign, reality-based object, one that can become the source of constructive feedback.

Feedback functions both overtly and in subtle ways as part of the reintrojective process. For example, in the vignette above, over time, repeated clarification of Mrs. L.'s misperceptions of others will help to correct a faulty introject. Additionally, she will find out that anticipating criticism and being poised for discord are contrary to reality. This will help her to modify her defensive stance with others, much like the "mirror reactions" described by Foulkes and Anthony (1965), which help developmentally in the differentiation of the self from the not-self. As they noted:

> The reflections of the self from the outside world lead to greater self-consciousness, so that the infant . . . eventually learns to distinguish his own image from that of other images. . . . The mirror reactions in the group help . . . by externalizing what is inside and internalizing what is outside, the individual activates within himself the deep social responses that lead to his definition . . . as a social being [pp. 150–151].

Reintrojection in group is influenced in three ways which process and alter the members' aggressively contaminated projections. First, by tolerating them or merely by example, the therapist helps the patients to tolerate their own and each other's aggression. Second, by facilitating mutual exploration of the reenactment of aggressively linked internal object relationships, the therapist shows members how to live with their projections and manage them via acceptance, mastery, or assimilation. Third, through group interactions, noxious projections are "soothed" prior to reintrojection by virtue of their association with the mother-group image. Overall, the bond to the group entity, its members and leader, through mirror reactions improves reality testing by helping patients to distinguish actual feedback from the distortions caused by their own projections. Thus, the totality of projective–reintrojective relatedness within the group matrix proves therapeutic. Stated simply, when the group environment is experienced in a benign, nurturing way, interpersonal feedback will be used by these patients in a constructive manner, rather than in the usual distorted, noxious way.

All this can be stated in another way, again drawing upon the analogy between the patient in the group and the toddler in the nursery. Group interactions function as a special kind of play (Kosseff, 1990) through which the members learn how to relinquish symbiotic needs; in the group they "hatch" and then "practice" relationships (Mahler, 1972). Play is the opportunity to make trial relationships, where there is relatively little fear of consequence or of being held forever to what one has said or done or to the responses of others. Play allows one to project parts of oneself into the immediate world, place them into others, yet recover them at will. It permits individuals to confront and accept split-off parts of their egos on a trial basis, or more substantively, to experiment with new, trial identifications. All this occurs under the protective aegis of the mother-group, once that has been formed and shaped by the therapist. For this reason, Kosseff (1990) correctly noted that group psychotherapy is experienced in the area of transitional phenomena.

Thus, through identification with the group entity, projected fantasies are reprocessed and then internalized. The newly formed introject initially serves as an internal object representation. However, because of the sustained, consistent atmosphere of a supportive group, over time it becomes absorbed into the patient's self representations, yielding new ego identifications. The reintrojective process is the essential part of the treatment that proves palliative. In short, pathological identifications are superseded by more mature, realistic relationships in the group (Belinkoff, Bross, and Stein, 1964). There is a more useful realignment of intrapsychic forces as these healthier identifications strengthen the ego core or central experience of the self. This occurs without the need for any basic alteration in the ego's general dynamic structure to sustain it. More specifically, identity formation, which implies the integration of libidinal and aggressively invested self representations into a cohesive self (Kernberg, 1986), does not need to occur for change to be substantive and stable.

There is an implication in this thesis that the basis for change is experiential, as opposed to the acquisition of knowledge or the development of insight. Decidedly, in these groups, clarification and confrontation do occur, but interpretation, in its classic sense of exploring the origins of dissociated split ego states, need not occur. This method does employ the use of meaning-attribution techniques for the promotion of ego mastery. But, the observing ego is not the mediator of change; the experience of the treatment is.

REFERENCES

American Psychiatric Association (1987), *Diagnostic and Statistical Manual of Mental Disorders*, 3rd ed., rev. (DSM-III-R). Washington, DC: American Psychiatric Press.

Belinkoff, J., Bross, R., & Stein, A. (1964), The effect of group psychotherapy on anaclitic transference. *Internat. J. Group Psychother.*, 14:474–481.

Bion, W. R. (1959), *Experiences in Groups.* New York: Basic Books.

Chessick, R. (1977), *Intensive Psychotherapy of the Borderline Patient.* New York: Jason Aronson.

Day, M. (1981), Process in classical psychodynamic groups. *Internat. J. Group Psychother.*, 31:153–174.

Feilbert-Willis, R., Kibel, H. D., & Wikstrom, T. (1986), Techniques for handling resistances in group psychotherapy with severely disturbed patients. *Group*, 10:228–238.

Foulkes, S. H., & Anthony, E. J. (1965), *Group Psychotherapy: The Psychoanalytic Approach*, 2nd ed. Baltimore: Penguin Books.

Freedman, M. B., & Sweet, B. C. (1954), Some specific features of group psychotherapy and their implications for the selection of patients. *Internat. J. Group Psychother.*, 4:355–368.

Freud, A. (1965), *Normality and Pathology in Childhood*. New York: International Universities Press.

Grinker, R. R., Werble, B., & Drye, R. (1968), *The Borderline Syndrome: A Behavioral Study of Ego Functions*. New York: Basic Books.

Horwitz, L. (1974), *Clinical Prediction in Psychotherapy*. New York: Jason Aronson.

—— (1977), Group psychotherapy of the borderline patient. In: *Borderline Personality Disorders*, ed. P. Hartocollis. New York: International Universities Press, pp. 399–422.

—— (1983), Projective identification in dyads and groups. *Internat. J. Group Psychother.*, 33:259–279.

James, C. (1984), Bion's "containing" and Winnicott's "holding" in the context of the group matrix. *Internat. J. Group Psychother.*, 34:201–214.

Kernberg, O. F. (1975), A systems approach to priority setting of interventions in groups. *Internat. J. Group Psychother.*, 25:251–275.

—— (1976), *Object Relations Theory and Clinical Psychoanalysis*. New York: Jason Aronson.

—— (1984), *Severe Personality Disorders: Psychotherapeutic Strategies*. New Haven, CT: Yale University Press.

—— (1986), Identification and its vicissitudes as observed in psychosis. *Internat. J. Psycho-Anal.*, 67:147–159.

Kibel, H. D. (1978), The rationale for the use of group psychotherapy for borderline patients on a short-term unit. *Internat. J. Group Psychother.*, 28:339–358.

—— (1980), The importance of a comprehensive clinical diagnosis for group psychotherapy of borderline and narcissistic patients. *Internat. J. Group Psychother.*, 30:427–440.

—— (1987), Inpatient group psychotherapy—Where treatment philosophies converge. In: *The Yearbook of Psychoanalysis and Psychotherapy*, Vol. 2, ed. R. Langs. New York: Gardner Press, pp. 94–116.

Kosseff, J. W. (1990), Anchoring the self through the group: Congruences, play, and the potential for change. In: *The Difficult Patient in Group: Group Psychotherapy with Borderline and Narcissistic Disorders*, ed. B. E. Roth, W. N. Stone, & H. D. Kibel. Monograph 6. Madison, CT: International Universities Press, pp. 87–108.

Mahler, M. S. (1971), A study of the separation–individuation process and its possible application to borderline phenomena in the psychoanalytic situation. *The Psychoanalytic Study of the Child*, 26:403–424. Chicago: Quadrangle.

—— (1972), On the first three subphases of the separation–individuation process. *Internat. J. Psycho-Anal.*, 53:333–338.

Ogden, T. H. (1981), Projective identification in psychiatric hospital treatment. *Bull. Menn. Clin.*, 45:317–333.

Schafer, R. (1968), *Aspects of Internalization*. New York: International Universities Press.

Scheidlinger, S. (1960), Group process in group psychotherapy. *Amer. J. Psychother.*, 14:104–120, 346–363.

—— (1964), Identification, the sense of belonging and of identity in small groups. *Internat. J. Group Psychother.*, 14:291–306.

—— (1968), The concept of regression in group psychotherapy. *Internat. J. Group Psychother.*, 18:3–20.

—— (1974), On the concept of the "mother-group." *Internat. J. Group Psychother.*, 24:417–428.

—— (1987), On interpretation in group psychotherapy: The need for refinement. *Internat. J. Group Psychother.*, 37:339–352.

—— Pyrke, M. (1961), Group therapy of women with severe dependency problems. *Amer. J. Orthopsychiat.*, 31:766–785.

Stein, A. (1963), Indications for group psychotherapy and the selection of patients. *J. Hillside Hosp.*, 12:145–155.

—— (1964), The nature of transference in combined therapy. *Internat. J. Group Psychother.*, 14:413–424.

—— (1970), The nature and significance of interaction in group psychotherapy. *Internat. J. Group Psychother.*, 20:153–162.

—— Kibel, H. D. (1984), A group dynamic–peer interaction approach to group psychotherapy. *Internat. J. Group Psychother.*, 34:315–333.

Winnicott, D. W. (1960), The theory of the parent–infant relationship. In: *The Maturational Processes and the Facilitating Environment.* New York: International Universities Press, 1965, pp. 37–55.

Chapter 8

Infant and Mother and the Mother-Group

JEROME W. KOSSEFF, Ph.D.

It is my hypothesis that therapeutic group membership draws upon the very taproots of personality—that which was laid down from the very beginning of life—through the interactions of mother and child. This interaction created the very first internal environment for each; the body ego was the second (Fliess, 1961, p. 97). From this interaction between mother and child there emerges a sense of self which becomes psychic foreground, while the relation with the interactive other becomes background. In similar fashion, we might conceive of the individual in the group as psychic foreground, while the whole group becomes background. This background consists of a precipitate of shared experiences, a "matrix."[1] As the child is held and draws upon the relationship with the mother for his growth, so also is the individual group member contained and evokes what he requires from the group matrix. Both child and group member, being held thus in a physically enclosed space, sooner or later incorporate that holding into an inside psychic space, a "potential space" (Winnicott, 1971, pp. 1, 5), where creative interplay between reality and fantasy can flourish.

Consequently, it would seem that the group may be a potent therapeutic vehicle especially—but not only—because it is providing both a conscious social interactional level, while simultaneously evoking an unconscious isomorphic level of interaction, the latter level consisting of protomemories from that very first mother–child interactional process. These memories are so deeply imprinted in us that they can

---

[1]"Matrix" derives from the Latin for "womb." It has been defined as "the silently active containing space in which psychological and bodily experience occur" (Ogden, 1986, p. 180).

never be erased. They are so central that they become the foundation of character structure. They are so deeply rooted that they are automatically reverted to when the self becomes threatened or otherwise unsure of its continuing existence. It is this "fallback" position for the individual in the group whenever anxiety and/or change is imminent that provides the security necessary for continuing growth. Whatever the vicissitudes of growth, traces of this lost original and fundamental relationship remain. The mother and child and their internalized counterparts of ego and object never become truly and completely separate. The search for an even more complete re-union, especially if that original relationship was absent or has been lost, goes on throughout the life cycle (Hermann, 1936, p. 262). It is this abiding threnody of "mother-need" that I shall focus on in this paper, as it is manifest in the life cycle and as it emerges in the psychodynamic group.

Green (1972) says "the importance of the analytic setting arises from the fact that it allows the development of a *metaphoric* regression which is . . . an analogue of infantile regression. In the same way, the response of the analyst, comparable to holding, it itself only a double of maternal care" ([p. 294]; see also Stern [1985, pp. 106, 219]). Similarly, the psychodynamic group has an isomorphic structure intrinsic to it, in that group-as-a-whole responses, and individual interactions also, have both holding and confronting aspects. Thus both the group and the individual analytic relationship evoke the mother–child developmental schedule (Bollas, 1978, p. 106), a schedule *which has to do with group formation in the first place, and which affords an enduring motive power for the group along the way.*

THE CONVERGENCE OF THE TWO WORLDS: THE GROUP AND THE INFANT WORLDS

Two issues about the group confront us and tie in with the mother–infant schedule: first, there is the cohesiveness of the group. Group members somehow seem to make their group cohesive (Frank, 1957, p. 57). Identifications[2] with the leader result in identification of each with the other. Those who are not comfortable with peers can sometimes belong nonetheless by being help-seekers or help-providers. It is not necessary for mutual liking to take place, although frequently regard and respect seem to develop as a result of earned membership and

---

[2]Aristotle described man as *mimetikon zoon*, translated as "an animal that identifies with other" (Padel, 1985, p. 275).

participation in the group. It often follows that an attack or confrontation by other members is therapeutic in such an atmosphere of tolerance and valuing of self-knowledge especially when made in the name of the group. If group cohesiveness is regularly found in the group, is it a phenomenon of intrinsic human behavior? Does it relate to a wish to belong to a group, and a group that is the kind for which one longs? And, if so, what makes such behavior operational (Frank, 1957, p. 57)?

Second, regression occurs in psychodynamic groups, often quite rapidly. Why does this happen perhaps more readily or more often than in individual therapy? These issues have been addressed frequently, and a variety of explanations have been proposed (Scheidlinger, 1980b).

Perhaps these issues can be further understood as we examine recent detailed studies on infant development and correlate them with data from the psychodynamic group. Although many facets of group interaction are operative at the same time, we shall focus on one unconscious dynamic that seems central to group therapy and that illuminates the issues of cohesiveness and regression and the whole sense of "groupness," the notion of the "mother-group" (Scheidlinger, 1982).

This aspect of group phenomena has been noted by Schindler (1966) as a basic unconscious sense of the group-as-a-whole which conveys feelings of safety and regard, while yet providing a non-mother space and play through which the creative reexperiencing of "I-ness" can once more unfold. Scheidlinger (1980a, 1982) has focused on the reactivation of the search for a "need-gratifying relationship to the mother," during group formation (1982, p. 83). This paper will further explore how, from these early modest beginnings of "dual union" (Deri, 1984, p. 6) of mother and child, the capacity for group formation and group function perhaps arises.

Foulkes (1948) approaches these issues of cohesiveness and regression: "The deepest reason why patients . . . can reinforce each other's normal reactions and correct each other's neurotic reactions is that *collectively they constitute the very Norm from which, individually, they deviate*" (p. 29). Each member contributes a part of the self which constitutes a reaching out to others, "the most enormous extension of vision of which life is capable: the projection of itself into other lives" (Eiseley [1946, p. 46]; Winnicott [1971, p. 151] also makes a similar point). Thus there is in the group a self-holding, a reaching to and into others, and in response to others, a taking from them into oneself, or an ejecting of parts of self or others from oneself.

The group then becomes the "environment mother," a securely

holding, unobtrusive mother of provision and nurturance which can silently contain and hold all the group members, thereby affording to each reparative possibilities to identify, to reexamine, and to reorganize the "self-and-mother" parts of self. The group provides opportunities to identify that which is valuable and that which is deleterious, to refind the "me" parts of self that had been lost. Such loss often occurred when there was disruption of the original mother–child unity, through sacrifice of parts of the self to the "object-mother," the kind of mother whose own needs may have prematurely taken precedence over the infant's needs. Now there is the possibility of reclaiming those parts through the good-mother aspect of the group as the safe haven, wherein each can unravel the tangled skein of self and mother parts that are troublesome, and overcome conflict-laden, or competitive, or repetitively compelling aspects of the experienced mother.

This process may also be viewed as a gestalt process, in which now one, now another, part of the self becomes figure or retreats into ground; now the group member gives over part of himself to the group-as-a-whole, now focuses more exclusively on his own self. Of course, both processes go on simultaneously, but the emphasis changes (Ashbach and Schermer, 1987, p. 247). The group, where a "we" has been relatively securely established by the joining of its members, becomes a dependable mother-group serving as safe container for the anxieties of each, in which it is possible for each to go on searching further for missing parts of the "me."

THE INFANT WORLD AND THE BEGINNINGS OF "GROUPNESS"

More sophisticated infant research in the past two decades has brought out data that had not been envisioned before and that has moved the timetable of psychic development considerably earlier than had been believed, when it had been based more on adult retrospective recollections (Beebe and Lachmann, 1988, p. 306). Our discussion of these new data will be limited to two major areas which are common to both group behavior and to mother–child interaction: (1) the earliest evidences of self and (2) the precursors of empathy.

The Earliest Evidences of Self

Stern (1985) and others provide data suggesting how very early in life a beginning sense of self seems to form. By the end of the first two months, infants are in the process of forming an organization of self, using cross-modal sensory experiences. They already seem to begin to experience a world of perceptual unity. Where object relations theorists "have postulated a very active subjective life, filled with changing passions and confusions," researchers have added empirical observational data to document this. They have "asked" the infants directly what they are experiencing and have devised laboratory methods for ascertaining this by studies of headturning, sucking, and scanning (Stern, 1985, pp. 39, 44, 52). For example, researchers found that blindfolded three-week-old subjects, sucking a specially shaped nipple, could later distinguish that nipple visually from other nipples. Beebe and Lachmann (1988) have summarized a host of very detailed empirical infant researches that appear to validate and enhance psychoanalytic observations. These researches deal with mother–infant mutual interactions and mutual regulation of behavior in the first year of life, and seem to demonstrate that these interactions form an important basis for later self and object representations. Many of these studies were made by painstaking frame-by-frame microanalysis of videotaped mother–infant exchanges, which would not be otherwise observable. These studies revealed exquisitely detailed reciprocal matching and/or mismatching of response between mother and infant. From these researches they concluded that:

> The dynamic interplay between the actions . . . of infant and caretaker, as each influences the other, creates a great variety of mutual regulatory patterns. The infant is capable of comparing the nature of the inter-action pattern at the moment with a stored model or representation of how the interaction typically goes, and evaluating whether the two are similar or different. The infant is organizing a representational world, in the first half of the first year, prior to the emergence of symbolic capacity. This interactive "process model" of early representations implies that *the experience of self and object are structured simultaneously* [Beebe and Lachmann, 1988, pp. 326–327; emphasis added].

This conclusion from infant research seems to confirm Fairbairn's (1952) classic psychoanalytic insight that self and object are not merely externally bound, but also become internally connected in relationship to one another. He proposed that split-off aspects of the ego become and remain intensively affectively identified with internalized objects, providing both psychic structure and motive power for change (Ogden, 1986, pp. 147, 149, 150).

Thus, these very early "emergent-self" behaviors suggest that the infants are not only in touch with their world, but from birth on they begin to organize it.[3] Spitz (1955) has focused on these first two months in the life of the newborn in "The Primal Cavity." "Taking-in" involves the mouth, the grasping hand, and visual tracking all at the same time. This is a total gestalt of perception and affect; any part of this nursing experience may stand for the total experience. Since interoceptive and exteroceptive perceptions are united in the oral cavity, *inside* and *outside* are at this time interchangeable, and with no distinction of "what he sees with his eyes from what he feels with his mouth." This "mouth-self" is "the place of transition for the development of intentional activity, for the emergence of volition from passivity (Spitz, 1955, p. 253). It is also a dividing line later, for self from nonself, self from objects and acceptance from rejection; additionally, the oral cavity becomes the prototype for all bodily and other spaces" (Spitz, 1955, pp. 222, 226, 237, 238).

The infant's mouth sucks at the nipple, the hand grasps the breast, the skin is warm in contact with the mother's body. The child is rocked rhythmically and passively through *space,* and the eyes are riveted on the mother's face. It is a *shared experience* in which the mother's sensory reactions and perceptions reflect back an image of the infant that signals the mother's feeling toward the infant. The child is nestled in her embrace as he nurses, the postpartum equivalent of the womb (Modell, 1976, p. 295). As he nurses he "takes her in" with all of himself; meanwhile, she responds by her own enchantment with the child. *The child is internalizing the mother who has internalized him* (emphasis added) (Spitz, 1955, p. 225, 230; Solomon, 1963, p. 72).

This is the "harmonious interpenetrating mix-up" of mother–infant (Balint, 1959, p. 114). At the same time, it is the joining of a mature psychological organization with a primitive one. This is akin to Foulkes's description of the group's dynamic organization. Indeed, Ashbach and Schermer (1987, p. 87) see the seeking for this lost grandiose symbiosis of the mother-self union as a basis for joining a group. This interchange with mother confirms a primordial sense of himself, that he *is*, that he *exists*, as an object in his mother's eyes; he also gets some sense of importance from this role, and he shares in her power (Solomon, 1963, p. 69). At the same time, he is being *held,* so he is in a place where he *belongs.* "Confidence in the mother's love of him and of her acceptance of his love becomes the foundation of his capacity to keep experience, thought and understanding *contin-*

---

[3]Although there is some question about Stern's and other investigators' design and conclusions, evidence mounts in support of their contentions.

uous" (Sutherland, 1983, p. 530). See also Balint (1959, p. 65); Ogden (1986, p. 198); Blatt and Behrend (1987, p. 285).

This mutuality is also the basis for the internalization of a "good inside," a positive sense of his self as a valuable entity, along with a concept of the world as a friendly and fulfilling place (Deri, 1984, p. 252), possibly instilling a rudimentary optimism, hopefulness, and reliance on self during the symbiotic phase which is preparatory for later experimentation in the world (Kramer and Achter, 1988, p. 572). Only if the infant's illusions of the breast being there correspond in time and space to the actual presentation of the breast (or its equivalent) can the infant generate an internal image of a powerful, "good" self, able to tolerate reality assaults on this initially valuable omnipotent feeling. Ultimately, such positive experience gradually leads to the capacity to moderate omnipotence with more realistic self-appraisal (Winnicott, 1971, p. 88). Matching of behavior between mother and infant (especially of interpersonal timing and affectional direction) leads to expectation that this matching will go on; if it does not, infants can be derailed from their play and disrupted in their growth, with consequences for the emerging self. For example, Peto (1955) describes two primordial contrary events: the baby who loses the nipple and the baby who rediscovers the lost nipple. In the first case, when losing the nipple, there is an integration of that lost nipple into the ego as an internal object that was previously gratifying, but is now ungratifying. This leads to feelings of emptiness and strangeness and disturbance of the primitive body schema of mouth–nipple, possibly provoking intensified efforts at omnipotent control. In the second case, the nipple refound and contact reestablished with the external object (the real nipple) leads to restored feelings of a whole self but with doubt about its continuity in the future (p. 381); see also Stewart (1987, p. 204). In both cases, unconscious doubt about the integrity of the self arises. As a result, there may be precursor feelings of castration anxiety and a tendency to use projection, seeking to rid oneself of the disappointing internalized "bad" nipple (Bychowski, 1952, p. 78). Under such circumstances, there may result a fear of nothingness, neither nipple nor self-attached-to-nipple. In turn, this could induce the terrifying alternative of nonexistence, a "taste of death" (Solomon, 1963, p. 70).

Earlier, we noted that the nursing infant, held in his mother's embrace, is in a near-womb situation. But, as interaction proceeds, specificity of perception occurs. The nipple lost and refound has also positive growth potential. "The infant's helplessness in its pain (hunger) acquaints it with limitation—a lack in the self . . . taken up . . . and experienced as the *gap* between its present state and its past (satisfaction) . . . impels the infant beyond itself toward an other . . . this intuition of lack is an awareness of the implicit otherness *within* the self. . . . This is the paradox at the heart of desire: interiority runs through an other" (Opatow, 1989, pp. 653–654). Thus as the infant is enlarging and solidfying his primitive self, he is at the same time accommodating within this self a place for future internal and external interaction with an other, which is—paradoxically—part of him and not part of him. The intricate changes by which this "oneness" becomes "I-ness" occur in the body ego, wherein "the mouth which gripped the nipple, the skin which was warmed by the mother's body, the hand which grasped at the breast and the smiling face, they preserve and symbolize these experiences of oneness" (Peto, 1959, p. 230) in the infant's transitional elaboration of his own self and differentiation of the other. For example, Peto (1962), in describing the consequences of losing and refinding the nipple, is describing the earliest instance after the birth process itself, of disruption between mother and child; that is, he pictures the opening of a space, however dysphoric, between the two (p. 384). Beebe and Lachmann (1988, pp. 323–324) describe additional mismatching experiences by the mother with her infant. As early as two weeks of age, infants regulated such "impingement" (Winnicott, 1971, p. 47) defensively by gaze aversion, head aversion, bodily aversion (e.g., pulling the hand out of mother's grasp, shutting of eyes, and limp head-down postures). Videotape studies show that these are compromises of moment-by-moment sensitivity to maternal pressure, the infant vigilantly coping by responsive engagement and disengagement but with relatedness maintained nevertheless (Bower, Broughton, and Moore, 1970). For example, in averting his gaze, the infant may be needing to take "time out," to be able to hold onto a *continuous* image of mother when her expressions may be changing too fast for his limited integrative capacity (Leon, 1987, p. 150).

Again, the effect of such derailments creates "a space between," "increasing *the visual-spatial boundaries in relation to the mother*" (Beebe and Lachmann, 1988, p. 324; emphasis added).

Thus, even in this first year of life, matching and mismatching experiences have already established presymbolic organization of self and object representations which, once structured, tend to resist restructuring, creating early unconscious "rules" that govern and circumscribe later behavior, and tending to become self-perpetuating (Beebe and Lachmann, 1988, pp. 330–331; see also Beres and Arlow, 1974, p. 187). These empirical studies and observations do not assert that self and spatial concepts in the infant arise only by negative and avoidance experiences, but rather demonstrate how processes of developing internal structure and space begin very early and simultaneously with external spatial relationships and attitudes, ultimately leading to the sense of a separate self. At first, psychological space is equivalent to actual physical space between mother and infant. As internalization proceeds there develops a "within space," a metaphorical location in which self and object representations come to be held side by side, but separate from each other over time (Bergman, 1978, p. 329).

Noshpitz connects the self, its space, and the group: he views the self as having the quality of occupying space, of creating a presence in space, a territory with a core of self, but with fluid boundaries, which may exclude or contain other people (1984, pp. 21, 25, 33); also Bergman (1978, p. 148). At two months the infant is in a peculiarly helpless and cognitively undeveloped state, but is already vigorously and affectively experiencing all that goes on with him, in him, and around him.

> Just as there is an adhesive quality to the mother–child basic unity, so there is the surprising sense of attachment to any group of substantial meaning for that person . . . the sense of personal space . . . indeed, the issues of boundary are closely identified with those of survival, both individual and group (or species), and it makes sense that these be attended by intense emotional investment and passionate defensive action [Noshpitz, 1984, pp. 18–19, 25, 29].

Thus, the dual unity of mother and infant, and the group and its members, have each a nurturing matrix. For the group, the matrix is that "network of interpersonal relationships which contains the tensions of the group's emotional climate. . . . In this 'space between the individuals' is where individual fantasies and interpersonal interactions take place. The group, therefore, is not a social body formed when individuals come together, but is formed out of the pre-existing matrix in each member" (Ammon, 1977, pp. 15, 18). Each member is already a more or less stable configuration of internal objects formed from interpersonal interaction and maturational provision, an "inner group" (Ashbach and Schermer, 1987, p. 71) and a beginning self.

These empirical researches on the origins and vicissitudes of the sense of self in the first year have also proved predictive of issues of attachment, cognition, and vocalization in the second year and beyond. There are implications for subsequent self and object representations, even to determining the sense of self in later triadic groupings and in the quality of larger scale social interactions with others as well (Beebe and Lachmann, 1988, pp. 327, 328, 331).

In summary, these evidences of the developing primordial self suggest that an indelible imprint of otherness is present in the self from the beginning of life. This enduring dialogue between self and other goes on throughout life, in one fashion or another, and can by externalization become a basis for group interaction and for empathy.

The Precursors of Empathy

Winnicott (1971), speaking of empathy, noted that the precursor of the mirror is the mother's face. "What does the infant see when he looks at his mother? He sees himself or herself" (p. 112). If he mostly sees himself reflected in mother's eyes, development goes on apace. If he must focus on her, to the neglect of his own self, he may not be able to get or take in what he needs from her for the development of his own psychic structure, his energy being spent more in defensive than in self-absorbing internalization.

But precursors of empathy begin during the symbiotic phase when children examine adults' behavior and affect with utmost concentration and penetration, especially moods, tones, and expressions. When they discern pleasure in the adult, there is basis for empathy. As compared to merging, empathy "depends on cues from the subject to the observer about the inner state of the subject, compared then by the observer with the latter's own similar experience, leading to inferences about a match between the two," or, more simply, being able to know in a meaningful way the affective experience of another person (Freud, 1913, p. 320; 1921, p. 110; Jaffe, 1986, p. 233). The hypothesis most often given in explanation of this phenomenon is that emotional contagion follows closely on the communication of a shared unconscious fantasy, and that this process holds for all human experience, from the dyad to the formation of a group (Beres and Arlow, 1974, pp. 45, 47; Jaffe, 1986, pp. 231, 235).

Empirical mother–infant studies have demonstrated that before there are clear internalized representations of self and object, "matching experiences provide each partner with a behavioral basis for knowing and entering the other's perceptions, temporal world and feeling state, and may contribute to later experiences of being attuned, known, tracked, or on the same wave-length" (Beebe and Lachmann, p. 331). In treatment, empathy "gives the patient a sense that his feelings and experiences have a logic and coherence that can be understood and accepted by another person. It also involves sharing what the patient is avoiding experiencing" (Blatt and Behrend, 1987, p.

287). These definitions of empathy certainly apply to intragroup interactions, as when one member voices what others are feeling.

Where does empathy come from, and how is it elicited in the receiver? Matching kinds of behavior in both adults and infants may hold answers that are especially cogent for the functioning of the therapy group. Adults whose dialogue with each other had similar bursts and pauses tended to be more like each other, perceived each other as warmer and more alike, choosing each other as dinner partners. Similarly, "as mother and infant match each other's temporal and affective patterns, each recreates in himself a psychophysiological state similar to that of the partner, thus participating in the subjective state of the other. There is external matching by visual awareness and by the invitation of the other's affectivity, while simultaneously there is a reciprocal proprioceptive accompaniment . . . This is a cross-modal transfer . . . in the first months of life; . . these mechanisms have specific relevancy for the origins of empathy" (Beebe and Lachmann, 1988, pp. 321–322).[4] Noshpitz (1984) adds that "early feelings of unity and connectedness have a curious capacity to persist, and can dominate interpersonal experience for a lifetime" (p. 28). Based on these and other clinical and empirical research, it seems highly likely that empathy, which serves as a "connective tissue" in group organization and function, has its origin in the earliest mother–infant exchanges.

These vital areas, the burgeoning sense of self and the precursors of empathy, correlate with group formation and functioning. They have profound importance for understanding healthy and pathological personality development, and group interaction, be it social or therapeutic.

A MOTHER-GROUP SESSION

In order to highlight the pervasive, lifelong place which the mother-need has in the psyche of the individual, and how the mother-need leads to group-seeking, I shall describe part of a single group session briefly, and its aftermath. The overt theme is of one group member's man–woman conflict, arising out of an unfinished mother–child separation–individuation problem. This session highlights how adult *conscious* preoccupation with residual mother–child conflicts (and their

---

[4]On the other hand, Beres and Arlow do not seem to accept such early precursors of empathy, positing it as developing only after the separation of self from nonself (1974, p. 33).

derivatives) are contained in an *unconscious* matrix, that of the mother-group (Bion, 1962, p. 90).

Just before a recent session of this ongoing group (composed of four women and three men in combined treatment), John had announced dramatically in the waiting room that he would be splitting up with his girl friend, Lisa, immediately after the group session. John was an executive, with a good income. He had many affairs of short duration. The current affair after four years of treatment is the first one of significance. He had been told in the group that he was rigid, critical, self-righteous, and selfish. He usurped the focus of the group very often to justify his actions outside the group. He had also been told that his interpretations of other group members' behavior were often invalid, but he nevertheless proceeded to employ them. He was an obsessional "organization man," consumed with an utterly logical and precise ordering of his life. His looks, articulateness, and money had more or less carried him along in his outside life. But he had become somewhat alarmed as his friends married and had children, while he was still alone. He had begun to feel a bit of a freak. Yet, he countered these feelings with the belief that he had but to find the right woman and all would be well, that nothing was "wrong" with him. He fought treatment intensely, while appearing acquiescent.

He was of Italian background, an only child of a nonreligious family. His mother, dominant in the household, had used John to satisfy her ambitions for status and financial stability. His father, apparently displaced by John's birth, had a few affairs during his wife's pregnancy and just after John's birth. John quoted his father as advising: "don't ever trust women." His father had a heart attack while John was in his twenties, but continued to drink and smoke in spite of John's expressed anxiety, and later died. John had a mother who could never admit to being wrong, even when she was (much like himself). Categorical positions of "right" and "wrong" for both ruled their psychic world. Since the father's death John supported his mother, who was living in a retirement village in California. She seemed to be a chronically depressed woman, who had been hospitalized for depression sometime after the father's death. For John these events generated feelings of being abandoned and lonely, and he recalled his mother's hospitalization poignantly as the first time that he had cried as an adult. Until this relationship with Lisa, much of John's focus had been on his relationship with his mother; in some ways his preoccupation with Lisa had a familiar ring to it. There was an unswerving attempt by John to bend both mother and Lisa to his life-style and needs. Similarly, it seemed that his mother had repeatedly refused to see John as a real person, but rather as someone destined to transform her own life, a deliverer–child. To some extent, John tried to be this for Lisa too (Bollas, 1978, p. 101). In the group, he sought to be the hero–seducer (Gibbard, 1974, p. 254).

At present, John was under considerable tension; because of a merger of two advertising agencies his job was at stake. In his two previous jobs during treatment he had great friction with his immediate male superiors. He competed with them enviously and vigorously (just as he did with me in the group). Before the current job, he had seriously considered a business of his own, but dared not undertake it alone. Now, for the first time in his working life, he had come to feel that his superior had given him carte blanche, "was noncompetitive with him," and most appreciative of John's initiative-taking and managerial ability. Perhaps the different personality in his superior, as well as some relaxation of competitive vigilance in himself, made this job different. Now with the merger imminent, it seemed his superior was impotent to help save John's job. Once again, it seemed that the father figure had failed him, and was the impotent figure John rather expected. Some time after starting this job John also began his relationship with Lisa, which was tempestuous from the start. Lisa had a history of dedication to her medical career. It was the reason she gave for the breakup of her marriage, as well as of a previous, long-term affair. She was also extremely judgmental, very critical of a group of friends John had carefully garnered recently; she was critical of his treatment with me as well. He had become desperately upset by her diatribes.

In our group session, after his preliminary announcement, he went into a lengthy account of how selfish Lisa was, detailing his disappointment at neither getting gifts from her, nor thanks for gifts given her. He was still essentially buying love by the gift of himself, his time, and his devotion, with the unconscious demand that his gift-giving would change this self-preoccupied professional woman into the accepting, giving, self-immolating, and completely compliant woman about whom he fantasied. His underlying demand was that she "change," by virtue of his devotion to her, and become the docile woman he envisioned, despite knowing that her previous relations with men had foundered on just those issues. In his need to picture her as thoroughly unregenerate, he did not tell the group that she planned a surprise birthday party for him, and was giving up a prized tennis weekend to do so, even if a bit reluctantly.

The group had a history with John, which is of significance for our thesis about the functioning of the mother-group. Early on, he had sought to be dominant in the group, but had been somewhat rebuffed, especially—among other things—because of his impatient and demanding ways. Also, he had complained at length about his mother's demandingness. It was only very slowly that he was able to accept the group's help in freeing himself from overinvestment in his widowed mother. During this session, he musingly remarked that he was now more able to heed the group about Lisa than he had been about his mother. He described his recent surprise at finding his mother had become less demanding, less depressed, and less hypochondriacal! He expressed his gratitude for this help from the group, and then went on again about Lisa. It is noteworthy that it was after he was able to accept the group's help with his mother that his affectivity had become more available to him, and that his relationship with Lisa began. We might surmise that the group served an empathic mothering function that his own less empathic mother had not satisfied. John responded to the group by a good-mother transference, as he and his mother relinquished their mutual dependence. Perhaps as a result, John had begun to dare attempt, for the first time, a longer-term, more involved relationship with Lisa. Now his self-doubt, teariness, and psychic pain were listened to carefully and compassionately, without overt antagonism or impatience by the remainder of the group, despite his assumption of entitlement.

At this point, another member, Richard, reacted to John's complaints about Lisa, saying that gifts were not the issue between John and Lisa, but rather whether John wanted to continue the relationship on *any* terms. Richard noted that his own stormy marriage was beginning to settle down after four years, but that it had taken much thought, patience, and perseverance. Richard also said he had felt pushed away by John when he asked John if, despite the issue of gift-giving, John cared for his girl friend. Richard wondered if Lisa might be feeling similarly pushed away by John, adding that from John's description there was considerable similarity between John and Lisa, both very intelligent, ambitious, fiercely determined to have their own way and neither one able to give ground to the other.

In this session, the group members grasped the sense of desperation in John's efforts to win Lisa over. John was becoming aware, after the intense affair of the past eight months, of his dread that he would once again be without a continuing relationship if he gave up on this woman also. At the same time, he was determined that Lisa change and conform more to his rather rigid expectations of her. He especially deplored her smoking and drinking (which he associated with his father's illness and death). She was a hard-bitten professional woman, easily his match in perfectionism and demandingness and obduracy, in fact rather a mirror-image of him in many ways.

Thus, John, in his powerful misery and fury, resonated throughout the group. In his intensity and neediness, his was "the voice of the group by virtue of empathy, projective identification and the channeling and regulation of communication, a conduit for the group's emotionality" (Rioch, 1970, p. 170). The image of his mother–and–himself was in his own and other group members' thoughts as he talked of Lisa and himself. In this same session, other group members also dealt with conflictual roles with each other, with outside persons, and with their own mothers.

It seemed to me, during this session, and I summed it up, that the group had reached into depths of feeling, the communal thread being the terrible dilemma that one could suffer humiliation, suffocation, even annihilation if one stayed in an intimate relationship, but that not to stay was equally frightening. The group sat quietly thinking this over. By the end of the session, John announced that he had decided to give the relationship with Lisa more time.

In this session, John's was the agonized voice of the group's present-day conflicts, expressed during the session. Richard typified the regressive pull of the group by a dream he had that same night after group, with its interweave of group and family, child and adult, passive longing and active coping. Both men, it seems to me, were empowered by the group's acceptance to search within themselves.

Newest in the group, Richard had initially suffered shock when, in his first few sessions, he was told by three of the women members that he was being "pushy" in asking so many highly personal questions of them. After a bit, he was able to accept this as deriving from his anxiety to belong, and connected it up with outside experiences. By now, after six months, he had become the barometer of the group's emotional climate. His verbatim dream and associations are presented here because they seem to epitomize the group's capacity to activate early sense of self and primordial feelings of empathy.

THE DREAM

"I was with some people, and I was reproducing an old fashioned song. I didn't know if others were singing, but it seemed to be a Victor Herbert melody (possibly 'Babes in Toyland') and somewhere there was the injunction: sing, sing. As I sang, I not only sang the song, but also reproduced in the song a momentary scratchy sound as if the recording was an old wax cylinder, like an old Edison phonograph, and had skipped a groove, as if the recording was imperfect, and I was very proud of how I had done it. I was suddenly aware I had left my youth behind, and suddenly I was a child again. The fact that childhood was gone was very frightening. It was the singing that had gotten me to it.

"After I awoke, I felt that the song in the dream was a 'window' into my feelings, and explained why I had trouble doing music currently. It takes me to the loss of when I was a child. The paradox was that I felt my childhood in the dream and lost it at the same moment. Part of being in therapy is to keep hold of childhood, and not lose it, like taking photographs of beautiful moments with my three-year-old daughter, Jennifer, wanting them to stay that way. It is important not to lose the thread to childhood—a source of strength. But I had turned my back on childhood because I was angry at my parents, mixed up, trying to be like my adored older brother Charles and not myself—a lot of my childhood I didn't like. Jennifer sings 'Daisy, Daisy' and drops a line at the end that makes it even cuter. This is like my dream. The intensity of the fear, really terror, terror of loss, not something bad that was happening, but that I had been pretending that I was a child. Not so anymore, I used to like to sing a lot as a kid, for my parents, my singing was completely my expression of love of singing, and nothing else involved.

"I couldn't pinpoint anything in the group that had triggered that dream except at the end, when you said the theme of the group was the fear of being obliterated in relationships. In the dream, I don't feel obliterated at all. I felt like this perfect time was gone. It used to be in the present and now it is a memory. Kind of an underlying feeling of becoming aware of my mortality.

"Because of the dream, I want to do something—the dream is telling me something—also feel reconnected with something as a result of it and don't want to let go of it. The feeling was for an instant, only an instant, but the fact I could feel it at all was rewarding.

"I don't know why I was so terrified—maybe feeling I was on my own, away from my parents. Also, time, in feelings about the dream: I wasn't concerned about what other people thought, and I was totally involved with what I wanted to be involved in. I must have connected with the pre-Joan time [younger sister] when I felt very loved, when I was just trying to be just like this, like a wax cylinder—not just the song—but like it was on this old-fashioned phonograph in the dream, I would sing the music exactly, didn't have to guess at it. The phonograph was my friend, a door to another world for me, saw *Babes in Toyland*, saw that once or twice on TV, wanted to see the toys *come to life*."

(Here I asked him if *he* is coming to life?)

"Maybe the terror of finally letting go of my parents is very frightening to me—and really being on my own—and while pretending to be a kid and not—and no way back to being a kid—and I want to go back.

"In the group, it reproduces that situation, for me and for others, of being a child again and you the father. The terror is feeling that I can't go back again and I suppose feeling vulnerable in the world. Not the whole thing, but that I'll lose that thing in myself that I like so much, that singing.

"It was a *very intense dream*—this frightened me although it was not a nightmare. It was because the subject matter was so important; childhood, music, and being there again. I feel this dream is a message—I don't completely understand the force of it—I feel compelled to do something and to stay connected to myself, as an adult, because that's what I am now. To keep connection to the part in a realistic way, not as a child. The big message from the dream is that I always wanted to be and stay a child. But all I accomplished was to pretend. It's a strange thing to get into more contact with being a child. Music is the unbroken connection, at least there's that, something I've loved and always have and still do. So I haven't betrayed myself by turning my back on music, a lot of strands and directions."

(I remarked that music was a statement of Richard's continuity as a person and that a year before he had had an "aha" experience while describing his high-chair behavior as a very young child, and I had suggested that the way he described waving a spoon was an early evidence of his interest in rhythm and music.)[5]

DISCUSSION

My understanding of a group member's dream is not to be construed as a mystical conception of a "group dream." Rather the dream seems to represent regressive and reintegrative movement induced by the group in a group member. It is a focus on the past as it pertains to current life and self. There is a central unconscious use of the group as a containing mother figure. For Richard, the group was taking him back to an awareness of his hungry yearning for the lost mother of his childhood; perhaps the yearning was triggered by John having ignored Richard's overtures, as his mother had done after his sister's

---

[5]It may well be that Richard's interest in music arose from unconscious connection to his early untrammeled contact with the sound of his mother's voice (Solomon, 1963, p. 69; Bollas, 1978, p. 102; Jaffe, 1986, p. 592).

birth. But at the same time he was unconsciously using the group matrix to differentiate himself once more from his infantile "I'm-singing-dancing-as-fast-as-I-can-for-you-mother" self, as now the adult regretfully accepting the conditions of current life and the conversion of old desire into new beginning. It might be argued that the inter-action with John was rebuff enough to have set off the dream. But the parallels for Richard in the rejection experienced with his mother, the nostalgic cast of the dream, the sense of loss, and especially the terror aroused by the dream, as well as the beginning healing in the split between his childhood and current self, took the immediate ex-change with John back to early life feelings. I believe this all came about because he also now had the whole group in his corner, as a good-mother image, much as John had felt about the group's help earlier in this session. When several group members had rebuffed Richard at first as being "too pushy," his anxiety about belonging was aroused. Now he seemed to feel secure, a member respected for his intuitive forthrightness, perspicacity, and insightfulness. He could use me as a good father figure, the group-as-a-whole as the loving mother, while John was for him the mother of rejection. All three transferences seemed to combine after this session, freeing Richard to "dream up" aspects of his whole closed world of inner relationships for exami-nation. In effect, Richard was "singing" once again, after all these years, this time in the group, as he both confronted and supported John, and at the same time contested for the group's attention. The dream and its associations took him back to his sense of self before his mother had turned away toward his younger sister. Now he was refinding the exuberance of early childhood, using it in this group session, and before long in confrontations with his wife, then in a radical creative career change the following year.

John too had apparently profited from this session. He had proj-ected several derivatives of mother feelings into female members of the group, seeing one as helpless without him, another as desirable but unavailably depressed, and a third as frighteningly angry at him. What he was less conscious of was the beginning awareness of the introjected abandoning mother inside himself. He had also listened somewhat less rejectingly and less competitively to Richard. John's overall functioning seemed to have been facilitated by the unexpected warmth and help the group had given, with regard to both his mother overinvolvement and his love affair with Lisa. For this rather lost and jaundiced woman-rejecting Don Juan, desperately seeking the missing parts of himself in the many women he had slept with but did not really accept, the group as a mother-group was releasing for him. It enabled him to experiment with himself, trust himself more, and open up efforts to reach out to a woman who seemed remarkably "well chosen" as a composite of aspects of both his mother and himself. The transformational possibilities that he saw with Lisa seemed to have had their origins in the hopefulness that had grown in him, partly as a result of the group's help with his mother, and in the courage that group acceptance gave him to dare offer somewhat more of himself than he ever had before invested in the relationship with Lisa. While there had been enough trust of me in the individual sessions to enable him to get under way in his treatment, it seemed that his rivalrous oedipal feelings had kept him from the fuller kind of intrapsychic and interpersonal exploration of himself that was now becoming possible with me too, once he felt assured of the backing of the group. And, although this current affair with Lisa may eventually prove to be the further pursuit of an illusory transformational object to put right what he felt was missing in him, it had at least affectively centered him more in himself than ever before (Bollas, 1978, p. 99). He had begun to find for himself a *me* in the *we*.

As we saw with Richard and John, the group offers provision for splitting transferential focus among the leader, the group, and its several members. This process may facilitate regression, the self in turn splitting into subselves allied with these various transferential, often archaic, objects. As these multiple perspectives about the self become more evident, some gratifying, some disquieting, the mother-group functions to maintain and reassure one's sense of subjective aliveness, of a self among other selves (continuity), while struggle ensues with other possibly conflicting perspectives (contrast) about one's objects and one's self. Ego splits ultimately rejoin into one self representation, affirming "the existence, integrity and primacy of the self's *subjectivity*, which, ironically enough, paves the way for a decentered objectivity" (Ross and Dunn, 1980, p. 337).

Additionally, the mother-group may serve another function, as it evokes the unconscious affective image of the very first transformational relationship, not of the (mother) object itself, but rather of the sense of psychosomatic fusion and transformation of the self ("the associated proprioceptive response") through early intense affective experience. This is the everlasting search for the mother, or its symbolic equivalent in current life, which the group as mother-group somehow fulfills. Bollas notes that transferences generally derive their idiosyncratic qualities from this basic paradigm of mother–infant (1978, p. 103). Indeed, the term *archaic transference* refers, in adult analyses, to "the archaic nature of the regulatory process that was unique for the (mother–infant) system *as it was consolidating*" (Sander, 1977, p. 98). These infantile experiences may also be the start of "groupness," in that suckler–suckling protomemories become the basis of all subsequent relationships, but afford the possibility of choice, flexibility, and change.

> At one extreme, the individual may identify with mother and so enter on relationships in which he is more giver than taker; at the other extreme, he may identify with infant self and be receiver or taker rather than giver. . . . But the very fact of being able to choose to identify with the one *or* with the other means that he also adopted a third position, from which he could observe self-and-mother as a couple and be for a while identified with neither. . . . Pathology would start from an inability or from a lessened ability to take up any one of the three positions; the normal ego is able to move between them [Padel, 1985, p. 275; see also Ogden, 1986, p. 213].

This beginning proliferation of the mother–infant unity leads to "splitting away of the observing self from the participating self, the internal from the external, the self-as-seen from the self-as-felt; and there is interaction among all these identification aspects of self, as if they were separate individuals" (Peto, 1962, p. 206). This is the "inner group" of subselves which becomes a template of later interaction with others.

Emerging from primary oneness into a primitive I–You relatedness, the lingering traces of this rudimentary social unit remain a permanent feature of the need for various adult support systems. While it is imperative for human beings to hold onto their sense of separateness and autonomy, they forever require a sense of being incorporated into a realm of relatedness. The complex process of empathy, we surmise, may serve this adult-to-adult search for re-union and relatedness much as its antecedent "attunements" did for the mother–infant duo (cf. Ferreira, 1961). Just as the child must solve the dual tasks of fostering a sense of himself as the center of his thoughts, his feelings, and his actions, and at the same time view himself as one self among many, so must the adult in the group also. The group's potential for change is partly contingent on this dual function of the group as mother-group, on its "holding" and in its role as transformational object. Ultimately, it becomes a transitional object, serving as a bridge that both joins and separates group and member (Kosseff, 1975; Tuttman, 1980; James, 1982) on the way to maturity.

SUMMARY

1. Recent empirical infant research seems increasingly to validate that the self begins to emerge early in the first year of life; the infant

is not only in affective contact with his world, but is also beginning to organize it. His emerging sense of self, it seems, develops in concert with the sense of the object, both in a climate of "mother-need."

2. This interactive, mutually regulating union of mother–infant, later self and object, seems to become the paradigm for later ways in which the individual shares himself with others, and seems to carry its own idiosyncratic stamp into triadic and larger social interactions.

3. Psychoanalytic observations and theory correlate with these empirical infant researches, on the pervasive unconscious lifelong role that the mother-need plays in coping with life tasks at any point in development.

4. The psychodynamic group has a peculiar capacity for evoking early aspects of mother-need through:

a. The embracing of the group members in the matrix of the group, akin to the fetus in the womb and the infant in his mother's embrace, the "mother-group" (Ashbach and Schermer, 1988, p. 184). This is akin to "the child internalizing the mother who had internalized him" (Solomon, 1963, p. 72): it is not only a "holding" that is provided externally, by group and by mother, but the internalizing of an internalizing other, of incorporating a sense of self that is a composite of one's own reaction to the other which is a reaction to oneself. This is to say that the group can therefore provide multifaceted feedback loops of self-searching in a unique therapeutic milieu.

b. The resonating interactions among group members which seem to echo and reactivate reciprocal behaviors of mother and infant, such as gazing, scanning, and holding in an affective climate (Beebe and Lachmann, 1988, pp. 305–307). The emphasis in both group and infant situations is on intersubjective *continuity*.

c. The group members' empathic or discordant responses to each other or to the group-as-a-whole which seem related to earliest matching and mismatching of psychophysiological and affective states in mother and infant (i.e., entering the state of the other, their attunement, later empathy).

These seem to be the ways in which the group's functioning can be understood; they are the means by which an individual can become more a self of his own by his intersubjective involvement with others. The group is Janus-faced, one side looking to the interactions among the members, the other to the internal dialogues that get stimulated and, ideally, resolved, by virtue of the group's unconscious affective approximation to mother–child internalizations. This is the group functioning as a "mother-group."

In conclusion, there is reason to believe that further investigation of primordial group behavior in infant life may offer leads to a more comprehensive theory of group dynamics and therapy. As well, it might lead to greater emphasis on group influences in psychoanalytic developmental theory.

REFERENCES

Ammon, G. (1977), Ego-psychological and group dynamics: Aspects of psychoanalytic group psychotherapy. In: *Group Therapy 1977*, ed. L. R. Wolberg & M. L. Aronson. New York: Stratton Intercontinental.

Ashbach, C., & Schermer, V. L. (1987), *Object Relations, the Self and the Group*. London, New York: Routledge & Kegan Paul.

Bach, S. (1984), Perspectives on self and object. *Psychoanal. Rev.*, 71:145–168.

Balint, M. (1959), *Thrills and Regressions*. New York: International Universities Press.

Beebe, B., & Lachmann, F. (1988), The contribution of mother–infant mutual influence to the origins of self-and-object representations. *Psychoanal. Psychol.*, 5:305–338.

Beres, D., & Arlow, J. (1974), Fantasy and identification empathy. *Psychoanal. Quart.*, 43:26–50.

Bergman, A. (1978), From mother to the world outside, the use of space during the separation–individuation phase. In: *Between Reality and Fantasy*, ed. S. A. Grolnick & L. Barkin, with the collaboration of W. Munsterberger. New York: Jason Aronson, pp. 145–166.

Bion, W. R. (1962), *Learning from Experience*. New York: Basic Books.

Blatt, S. J., & Behrend, R. S. (1987), Internalization, separation–individuation and the nature of therapeutic action. *Internat. J. Psycho-Anal.*, 68:279–297.

Bollas, C. (1978), The transformational object. *Internat. J. Psycho-Anal.*, 60:97–107.

Bower, T., Broughton, J., & Moore, M. (1970), Infant response to approaching objects. *Percept. & Psychophys.*, 9:193–196.

Bradlow, P. A. (1973), Depersonalization, ego splitting, non-human fantasy and shame. *Internat. J. Psycho-Anal.*, 60:97–107.

Bychowski, G. (1952), *Psychotherapy of Psychosis*. New York: Grune & Stratton.

Deri, S. K. (1984), *Symbolization and Creativity*. New York: International Universities Press.

Eiseley, L. (1946), *The Immense Journey*. New York: Vintage Press.

Fairbairn, W. R. D. (1952), *Psychoanalytic Studies of the Personality*, London: Tavistock.

Ferreira, A. J. (1961), Empathy and the bridge function of the ego. *J. Amer. Psychoanal. Assn.*, 9:91–105.

Fliess, R. (1961), *Ego and Body Ego*. New York: International Universities Press.

Foulkes, S. H. (1948), *Introduction to Group-Analytic Psychotherapy*. London: Heinemann.

Frank, J. D. (1957), Some determinants, manifestations and effects of cohesiveness in therapy groups. *Internat. J. Group Psychother.*, 7:53–63.

Freud, S. (1913), The disposition to obsessional neurosis. *Standard Edition*, 12:311–326. London: Hogarth Press, 1958.

———(1921), Identification. *Standard Edition*, 18:105–110. London: Hogarth Press, 1955.

Gibbard, C. (1974), Individuation, fusion and role specialization. In: *Analysis of Groups*, ed. C. Gibbard, J. Hartman, & R. Mann. San Francisco: Jossey-Bass.

Green, A. (1972), *On Private Madness*. New York: International Universities Press.

———(1978), Potential space in psychoanalysis: The object in the setting. In: *Between Reality and Fantasy*, ed. S. A. Grolnick & L. Barkin, with the collaboration of W. Munsterberger. New York: Jason Aronson, pp. 167–190.

Grolnick, S. A. (1978), Dreams and dreaming as transitional phenomena. In: *Between Reality and Fantasy*, ed. S. A. Grolnick & L. Barkin, with the collaboration of W. Munsterberger. New York: Jason Aronson, pp. 221–231.

———Barkin, L., with the collaboration of Munsterberger, W., eds. (1978), *Between Reality and Fantasy*. New York: Jason Aronson.

Hermann, I. (1936), Clinging-going in search. *Psychoanal. Quart.*, 45:4–36.

Jaffe, D. S. (1986), Empathy, counter-identification, counter-transference. *Psychoanal. Quart.*, 55:215–243.

James, C. (1982), Transitional phenomena and the matrix in group psychotherapy. In: *The Individual and the Group*, Vol. 1, ed. M. Pine & L. Rafaelson. New York: Plenum, pp. 645–663.

Kardos, E., & Peto, A. (1956), Contributions to the theory of play. *Brit. J. Med. Psychol.*, 29:100–112.

Kosseff, J. W. (1975), The leader using object relations theory. In: *The Leader in the Group*, ed. Z. Liff. New York: Jason Aronson.

Kramer, S., & Achter, S. (1988), The developmental context of internalized preoedipal object relations: Clinical applications of Mahler's theory of symbiosis and separation–individuation. *Psychoanal. Quart.*, 57:547–576.

Leon, I. G. (1987), Object constancy as a developmental line. *Bull. Menn. Clin.*, 51:144–157.

Modell, A. H. (1976), The holding environment and the therapeutic action of psychoanalysis. *J. Amer. Psychoanal. Assn.*, 24:285–316.

Noshpitz, J. (1984), Narcissism and aggression. *Amer. J. Psychother.*, 38:17–34.

Ogden, T. H. (1982), *Projective Identification and Psychotherapeutic Technique*. New York: Jason Aronson.

———(1986), *The Matrix of the Mind: Object Relations and the Psychoanalytic Dialogue*. New York: Jason Aronson.

———(1989a), *The Primitive Edge of Experience.*, Northvale, NJ; Jason Aronson.

———(1989b), On the concept of an autistic-contiguous position. *Internat. J. Psycho-Anal.*, 70:127–140.

Opatow, B. (1989), Drive theory and the metapsychology of experience. *Internat. J. Psycho-Anal.*, 70:645–660.

Padel, J. (1985), Ego in current thinking. *Internat. Rev. Psychoanal.*, 12:273–283.

Peto, A. (1955), On so-called "Depersonalization." *Internat. J. Psycho-Anal.*, 36:379–386.

———(1959), Body image and archaic thinking. *Internat. J. Psycho-Anal.*, 40:223–231.

———(1962), Terrifying eyes: A visual superego forerunner. *The Psychoanalytic Study of the Child*, 24:197–212. New York: International Universities Press.

Rioch, M. (1970), The work of Wilfred Bion on groups. *Psychiatry*, 33:56–66.

———(1975), All we like sheep (Isaiah 53:6): Followers and leaders. In: *Group Relations Reader*, ed. A. D. Colman & W. H. Bexton. Washington, DC: A. K. Rice Institute Series, pp. 159–178.

Ross, J. M., & Dunn, P. B. (1980), Notes on the genesis of pathological splitting. *Internat. J. Psycho-Anal.*, 61:335–349.

Sander, L. (1964), Adaptive relations in early mother–child interactions. *J. Acad. Child Psychiat.*, 3:231–264.

———(1977), The regulation of change in the infant–caretaker system and some aspects of the context–content relationship. In: *Interaction, Conversation, and the Development of Language*, ed. M. Lewis & L. Rosenblum. New York: John Wiley, pp. 133–156.

Scheidlinger, S. (1980a), Identification, the sense of identity in small groups. In: *Psychoanalytic Group Dynamics: Basic Readings*. New York: International Universities Press, pp. 213–231.

———(1980b). The concept of regression in small groups. In: *Psychoanalytic Group Dynamics: Basic Readings*. New York: International Universities Press, pp. 233–254.

———(1982), *Focus on Group Psychotherapy: Clinical Essays*. New York: International Universities Press.

Schindler, W. (1966), The role of the mother in group psychotherapy. *Internat. J. Group Psychother.*, 16:198–200.

Solomon, J. (1963), Alice and the red king. *Internat. J. Psycho-Anal.*, 44:63–73.

Spitz, R. (1955), The primal cavity. *The Psychoanalytic Study of the Child*, 10:215–240. New York: International Universities Press.

Stern, D. (1964), Adaptive relations in early mother–child interactions. *J. Acad. Child Psychiat.*, 3:231–264.

———(1980), The origins of empathy, report of scientific meetings, reported by D. A. Shapiro. *Bull. Assn. Psychoanal. Med.*, 20:1–9.

———(1983), The early development of schemas of self, of others and of various experiences of self with other. In: *Reflections of Self-Psychology*, ed. S. Kaplan & J. D. Lichtenberg. New York: International Universities Press.

———(1985), *The Interpersonal World of the Infant*. New York: Basic Books.

Stewart, H. (1987), Varieties of transference interpretations: An object-relations view. *Internat. J. Psycho-Anal.*, 68:197–205.

Strauss, M. S. (1979), Abstractions of proto-typical information by adults and 10-month old infants. *J. Experiment. Psychol. Hum. Learn. & Mem.*, 5:618–632.

Sutherland, J. D. (1983), The self and object relations: A challenge to psychoanalysis. *Bull. Menn. Clin.*, 47:525–540.

Symington, J. (1985), The survival function of primitive omnipotence. *Internat. J. Psychiat.*, 66:481–488.

Tuttman, S. (1980), The question of group therapy—from a psychoanalytic viewpoint. *J. Amer. Acad. Psychoanal.*, 8:217–234.

Winnicott, D. W. (1958), *Collected Papers: Through Paediatrics to Psycho-Analysis*. New York: Basic Books.

———(1965), *The Maturational Process and the Facilitating Environment*. New York: International Universities Press.

———(1971), *Playing and Reality*. New York: Basic Books.

Chapter 9

The "Bad" Mother-Group:
An Extension of Scheidlinger's "Mother-Group Concept"

RAMON GANZARAIN, M.D.

The group becomes a maternal object for its members. Scheidlinger's classic paper (1974) stressed the "good" mother-group functions. But he did not discuss fully or apply clinically the "bad" mother-group features. His presidential address on scapegoating (1982) examined instead that specific expression of groups' hostility. I shall inquire further into the "bad" mother-group phenomenon by focusing on the mental defense mechanisms against threatening maternal images, and on those clinical contexts in group psychotherapy which often elicit "bad" mother-related anxieties. Previous publications on the subject (Money-Kyrle, 1950; Durkin, 1964; Slater, 1966; Gibbard and Hartman, 1973; Bar-Levav, 1977) have only addressed such issues in part.

To idealize our mothers is a human need, protected by omnipotent denial and splitting. When we sometimes "see through" these defenses, we experience considerable anxiety and discomfort. There are consequently powerful resistances to observing and experiencing the "bad" mother images. Maternal bad aspects (sometime derived from real limitations, psychoses, or perversions) are denied, while splitting of ideal attributes promotes popular "all-good" maternal images, such as the caring "mother institutions" (church or country) or the goddesslike religious maternal images.

This paper is a synthesis and further elaboration of the ideas contained in three chapters of the book *Object Relations Group Psychotherapy* (Ganzarain, 1989).

157

Likewise, we defensively use splitting and projection, denying the "bad" aspects of "our" group, projecting them far away. Groups use yet another defensive unconscious maneuver: to promote confusion about "Who is bad?" whereby the "badness" is displaced from the group to either the leader, or to some scapegoated member, or sometimes to another group. There is consequently a tendency to limit the frustration with, anger at, and the hatred of the "negative" group attributes, by considering them as exclusively belonging to either the leader, to a cursed member, or to another group or subgroup, instead of accepting that the unpleasant qualities belong to "our group" and to every member, as well.

Groups can promote fanaticism—the "we-against-them" paranoid attitude—in any ideology. As is the case in religion or politics, "heretics" are violently condemned. Some groups demand their members' lives, by asking members to die for the group to which they belong. An extreme example of such demands was the mass suicide of the Jonestown, Guyana, community, requiring members to prove their loyalty to collective values by killing themselves. Through history, young men have been drafted to go to wars; at such times, some perceived their countries as overdemanding mothers expecting them to die in fighting of perhaps questionable moral or political value. However, the defiance of maternal possessiveness, under those circumstances, can be experienced as very threatening, evoking fears of retaliation.

The "bad" mother-group is perceived as overdemanding, devouring, intrusive, and lacking in reciprocity: overdemanding when imposing the group values on the individual, "leaving no freedom to be one's self" (Bion, 1961); devouring because it takes away the member's credits and possessions, thus threatening the member with a "loss of individuality" (Freud, 1921); intruding, when inquiring with hostile curiosity about secret, private affairs, attempting to influence members or ruthlessly subjecting them to public ridicule; and lacking in reciprocity. The infant requires maternal care for survival, but the mother does not need the infant in order to survive biologically herself. Similarly, the group can survive socially without any given member, while members need their reference, as group members, to define themselves. Each group member feels: "The group can do without me." And most groups do survive after losing any one member, in spite of the fact that they "will not be the same" without any one of its members.

LITERATURE REVIEW

The mother-group concept appeared relatively late in the literature, because early psychoanalysts placed emphasis on the paternal leader, as central in group psychology (Freud, 1921). Now, "the authoritarian . . . father seems almost gone. The new tyranny is that of the mother, who like the Goddess Kali presents a dual face: The source of love and life and the rival for love and life . . ." (Hearst, 1981a, p. 25).

Scheidlinger (1964) described group members' identification with the group-as-a-whole representing "a wish to restore an earlier state of unconflicted well-being in the child's exclusive union with mother, to counteract the fundamental fear of abandonment" (p. 218). He quoted Slavson's comment that while the group is a stand-in for the mother, the leader represents the father. For Foulkes (1964) "the group . . . frequently, possibly universally, represents the 'image of the mother,' hence the term 'matrix' " (p. 289). Grotjahn (1972) also asserted that usually the group is a truly good and strong mother.

Money-Kyrle (1950) distinguished three kinds of members' unconscious perceptions of their group: (1) as "good parents"; (2) like a "good father," who becomes mother's defender; and (3) like persecutory "bad" parents. Durkin (1964) postulated two separate group maternal transference manifestations: (1) the group conjures up the harsh, preoedipal image; and (2) "the therapist, in turn, is perceived as the good all-giving omnipotent mother," (p. 175). These different perceptions (or transferences) can easily be confused.

Slater (1966) wrote: the "mother-group is perceived as a source of succorance and comfort, even a refuge. At other times, this mother image is a frightening one" (p. 189). Gibbard and Hartman (1973) asserted that group members' "affective response to the group-as-a-mother is profoundly ambivalent. The 'Utopian fantasy' offers some assurance that the destructive aspects of the group-as-a-mother will be held in check" (p. 127).

Scheidlinger (1974) enhanced the protective "good" elements of the mother-group concept. For Bar-Levav (1977) instead: "The splitting of the transference between the therapist and the group-as-a-whole, both of whom represent different, rapidly interchanging aspects of the mother . . . proves most useful" (p. 460). He systematically described three major fears felt by patients when dealing with "bad" mother-group images: (1) of erupting rage; (2) of being swallowed, damaged, or mutilated; and (3) of starvation and abandonment. Probably Bar-Levav overemphasized anger and its catharsis, while overlooking the working through of sadness and loss.

For Hearst (1981a) the group functions as good mother through: life-giving (a group member becomes someone, "belongs" only within the context of the group's existence); confirming (being worthy for the narcissistic group self); sustaining (within the group setting); and accepting (everything can be expressed in and will be well received by the group). Hearst acknowledged that the good and the bad aspects of the mother are often in the group at one and the same time, "split between the therapist and the group." But she did not explore the bad aspects and how they interact with the good ones. Schindler (1981) discussed Hearst's ideas, commenting that to her the group offers unconditional acceptance, wisdom and strength, statements that seem "too optimistic and even questionable though desirable" (pp. 132–133).

"BAD" MOTHER-GROUP TRANSFERENCES

The "bad" mother-group images appear more clearly when oral and sadomasochistic conflicts prevail over genital group fantasies. The needs for nurturance and approval make members more vulnerable to the group's power to provide or to sadistically withhold what the individual needs. By contrast, when genital concerns predominate, the "bad" mother-group images are expressed in primal scene fantasies, often symbolically disguised, but occasionally verbalized in concrete genital transferential references directly involving the therapists. Understanding these various situations may help us to use them psychotherapeutically.

I shall systematically review the "bad" mother-group transferences activated by anxieties related to oral, sadomasochistic, and genital conflicts.

Oral Conflicts

Oral conflicts promote members' fears of being "smothered" or of being abandoned by their group. Some patients may experience being in a group as "damaging"; since their mothers offered them constant overprotection, they have always felt so understood and supported, that they have had no incentive to get out from the family into the cold world and survive there on their own. These patients experience being members of a psychotherapy group as paralyzing because it appears to postpone indefinitely their ability to take care of themselves. They therefore perceive the group help as threatening to "spoil" them.

Fears of abandonment by the group are activated when therapists miss meetings, or patients drop out, or new ones are added.

Therapists' Absences. When therapists miss group sessions, patients see them as unavailable or abandoning parent surrogates; the group is then often idealized as reliable, helpful, and "always available." The therapist's and the group's "badness" are meanwhile denied or confused. But there is an implicit concern with the consequences of the treater's absences on the group's future. Will patients start missing meetings also, until the group gradually dissolves?

Let us review what happened with *an unexpected absence*: I once asked my secretary to call the members of an advanced group, announcing with two days notice the cancelation of the coming session. However, Laura forgot the cancelation and showed up at the group meeting time, not finding anyone there. She described her reaction as an intense confusion, "feeling completely at a loss," in almost a derealization experience. She felt dizzy and needed to make a special effort to "put herself together" to drive back home. In the parking place, she could not recognize another group member's car in the lot. He had come to watch videotapes of their group sessions. But she could not see his car! Laura felt the *group's absence* as a dramatic *repetition* of her experience of coming home to learn that her mother had abandoned her, simply leaving behind a farewell note and an empty home, probably, Laura thought, because she had offended mother.

During the following session, the whole group responded with anxiety and anger. Laura then remembered that my secretary had called about the cancelation, and she added: "I know, Doctor, that your secretary does all your work!" Upon realizing what she just said, she burst into laughter. The patients elaborated their anger at the therapist's power to cancel group meetings. For Laura, my canceling a session turned the entire group into a bad mother: she believed "everybody missed because of being mad at her," since she had left the previous session furious with the entire group. Memories of her fight with mother, preceding the shock of mother's disappearance, came painfully back. Laura entertained the fantasy of the absent group resentfully deciding, after her fury with them, to teach Laura a lesson by not showing up when she needed the group the most. Such fantasies were intertwined with painful flashbacks, reexperiencing her surprise upon realizing mother had left home for good. Fear, pain, and anger were so intense that Laura briefly went through a dissociative state of "derealization." The condensation of paranoid fantasies and painful memories connected past experiences with current views of revengeful, unreliable mother images, personified in the past by Laura's mother and presently reexperienced in the way she felt treated by the group.

The reactions during the therapists' absence vary also according to whether there is no meeting during the absence or whether the group meets with the available remaining cotherapist. Meeting with the cotherapist, may provide the wrong impression that the group keeps going on as usual. Such a view denies missing the absent therapist. Angry patients may then get back at the absent leader by ignoring her or him. The absentee's complicity upon returning loaded with guilt for his absence may also deny the real importance of the absences. This collusion between helper and patients often means reactions to therapists' absences are underexplored.

The Arrival of New Patients. This situation can be compared to the birth of a new baby in a family, stimulating the siblings' ambivalence. It often enhances regression out of fear of losing the mother-group's attention, since the newcomer will probably get most of it. Some old-timers overidentify themselves with the newcomer's anxiety and tend to overprotect him or her, while others may attempt to scare the newcomer, telling horror stories about the group's past. Some members reassure the newcomer about how good it can be, while others discredit the group.

Old-timers also take an opportunity to evaluate the therapist's choice of newcomers and intensely approve or disapprove it, as a way of expressing their prevailing emotions toward the therapists; however, the timing chosen to add new patients is almost invariably not agreeable and resented because it takes away the group's attention from the older members' more pressing needs.

Sadomasochistic Conflicts

Sadomasochistic conflicts are based upon perceptions of the group as a maternal sadistic superego dictating norms, demands, and expecting specific responses. Members feel threatened with loss of individual identity, when they feel pressed to become "standard products" or "typical" members of a particular group. The group's "consensus" becomes a rigid punitive law.

Patients may fear the group as they might a domineering mother who would brainwash them and impose her values. For instance, George was afraid that the group would impose "Freudian values" upon him, "corrupting his Christian ethics." He feared that being in analytic group psychotherapy could "brainwash" him. He gradually discovered that he distorted the group's comments, that he "whipped himself" with sadistic distortions of what he assumed the group had told him. He realized he had been projecting his demanding attitude about himself, assuming the group would raise exaggerated demands of compliance with "Freudian values."

Maria shared George's mistrust of their group. She was a battered wife who managed to choose boyfriends who physically abused her. She had a knack for provoking people to attack her. Therefore, she soon became the group's scapegoat. She collected injustices and later on tried to induce guilt and sympathy for her suffering. She slowly realized that she had been using this same pattern with her parents, to extract their love, especially to get her mother's attention. Mother was a professional woman, who was emotionally unavailable to Maria. In order to get mother's attention Maria had to parade her sufferings. So, she devoted herself to collecting miseries. She engaged in all sorts of self-destructive behaviors: abusing drugs and alcohol, dropping out of school, belonging to vicious gangs, choosing men who seriously hurt her, and so on. After finally getting a divorce, she wore the "battered wife" label. She then went back to her parents' home. But they "forced" her to get some psychiatric treatment, as a precondition to accepting her back home. The group became for Maria her parents' ally or an instrument in punishing her. She tried to establish a tug-of-war, questioning "the group's values," as if they were "too straight," overrestrictive, and narrow minded. Maria, in her maternal transference to the group, engaged in defiant acting-out behavior repeating the same struggles she had gone through at home.

Group members also fear having to "confess" their shadowy, guilty deeds or fantasies, and dread "punishment" from the group, after exposing themselves to being criticized by or laughed at by group-mates. Some expressions of internalized sadistic superego struggles are sometimes dramatized in dreams. For instance, a group patient who suffered from confused sexual identity dreamed that she was on trial in an American Indian court, where the juror read the final verdict "all the half-breed defendants should be killed." Her associations were to herself as a sexual "half-breed" who would be condemned to death by her psychotherapy group not accepting her as a member.

The projection of sadistic internalized maternal superego to the group-as-a-whole, to the therapists, or other group members provides opportunities for mutative therapeutic exchanges, whereby the harshness of the superego can be modified. New definitions of the self, vis-à-vis internalized or projected bad mothers, become possible then, while the self learns and practices how to stand up to these overcritical maternal superego images. Such proactive, assertive movements on the part of the self produce significant therapeutic outcomes, while "supportive" comments from others are often overshadowed by harsh self-criticisms.

A year and a half after the beginning of a group that met twice a week for seventy-five minutes, Jill changed, during a session, from starting to complain that she was getting no support or positive feedback from the group, to dismissing, later on, her submissive need to comply with and to placate a demanding internalized mother. After expecting more positive feedback from the group, Jill slowly developed a conviction: "There is something good about me!" At this point she did not need as much support from the group as she had before. She was then able to express her wish to "get rid of mother!" Jill went through an "exorcism" of the "bad" mother. She first realized that she herself could be "vicious and demeaning like my mother." Later on, she became aware that she put herself "under excessive demands," concluding: "I am as sadistic as my mother and I don't want to be like that! There are also other aspects of myself which are loving, caring, loose, tolerant!"

In the process of realizing her identification with her sadistic mother, Jill transiently transferred to the group itself her bad-mother images, fighting then against the group's alleged sadism. Jill stood up and fought its overdemandingness, while redefining her real self beyond her imprisonment by or "cloning" of "bad" mother images. Daniel concurred with her, redefining their group's purpose as a *"growth group, not a support group."* He had overcome both his fears of a domineering mother and a similar wife, deciding to get a divorce. He had recently learned to grow up emotionally, in spite of his chronic difficulties as the family's younger child. Most of his many siblings had left the home during his growing years. Only his brother who was two years older was available. But this brother had been sent to a home for retarded children. At the time Daniel did not fully realize the problems of mental retardation and had believed that his brother was "kicked out" because of being "bad." He grew up in fear that he would be the next to be punished, were he not to please mother.

The whole group celebrated their "good riddance" of "bad" mother. All members commented on their mothers' attempts to control them, declaring they "would no longer put up with such hostility." Furthermore, they realized their own participation in such sadomasochistic interactions, by eagerly depending upon their mothers for support and reassurance; they planned to change such unrealistic dependency stances.

Genital Conflicts

Genital conflicts are activated by jealousy when feeling "postponed" or excluded by persons in the group who miss sessions. The assumption is that absent persons will be with somebody else, apparently more important to them than those attending the group meeting. Images are then unconsciously evoked about the absent person's possible activities while away, including making love to someone else.

In groups, absences may occur in a variety of ways: both therapists may be absent or only one is present. One or several patients may miss group sessions. When the cotherapists announced that both would be absent, group members responded with expressions of "primal scene" fantasies ranging from curiosity as to whether the cotherapists would be together, to wondering what they would be doing, to entertaining regressive fantasies assuming both would attend an office party during the group's meeting time. The members imagined hearing the therapists' loud drunken voices, while "having fun." The patients soon shifted to express their sensitivity about the differences between therapists and members, contrasting professional individuals with blue-collared, relatively less educated persons, thus displaying their envy and low self-esteem. They soon moved to criticizing authorities' abuses of power, while the common individual has to put up with them. When both therapists returned, the members tried to "turn the tables," attempting to stimulate the therapists' curiosity about alleged group secrets. Bad-mother images did not appear then as focused on the group-as-an-entity, but centered instead on the cotherapist couple, perceived as parents in intercourse or as contemptuous, privileged upper-class individuals.

The female cotherapist of a male incest perpetrators' group (Ganzarain and Buchele, 1989) was absent for two consecutive sessions. When she returned, a member started the meeting saying: "Finally I discovered why Sue has been out of town. She has been gone, trying to keep a secret, but I know why she was gone." He was unaware of any coincidence with the female therapist's recent "secret" absence. He had, he said, papers stating that "Sue had been out of town hiding a pregnancy and delivering a baby." When we commented on the group's curiosity regarding the female therapist's absence, the group shifted to talk about women's privileges at work, "simply because they are women." Women often go up the ladder of their companies' hierarchies, they said, using sex to achieve their success.

Intense anger at women's alleged privileges then became paramount: a woman can ruin a man's life, by accusing him of law-breaking sexual actions she provoked! Women at work get easily promoted! The bad-mother images were then centered on the negative transference to the female group therapist.

"Bad" mother-group images are activated when members have primal scene fantasies upon feeling, as witnesses, excluded from "secret" group interactions. Then they unconsciously compare their exclusion in the group to witnessing the parental couple in sexual intercourse; envy and jealousy stimulate their fantasied attacks against such a "bad" group, perceived as a persecutor, like the powerful, hostile, combined parental image. Consequently, the anxieties about the group's survival become paramount, fearing the group could possibly break apart and disappear.

Primal scene sadistic fantasies are anxiously defended against as threats to the group's survival. Powerful defenses are therefore mobilized. The destructive potential of possible sadistic exchanges needs to be denied, or avoided, by proclaiming the alleged omnipotence of Eros, and by engaging in pseudocaring interactions, thus creating an emotional atmosphere of hope in the group, characteristic of the "pairing" basic assumption (Bion, 1961). Concrete expressions of sexually sadistic images do not appear then; they instead exit silently, while group members defensively enjoy shared fantasies about the pleasant, fertile effects of love. I'll elaborate this point describing a group session with two main topics: "love hurts" (illustrated by a member's vaginismus) and "intimacy makes you vulnerable." These topics expressed fears about closeness possibly causing the disintegration of the group, after a vulnerable member was absent. Members defensively develop then an atmosphere of pseudointimacy by talking about sex and only implicitly exploring possible heterosexual couples within the group.

A Clinical Illustration. This is a description of a "pairing" atmosphere in the ninth session of an outpatient psychotherapy group, comprised of four women and four men. Rose was absent for the second time. During the first half of the meeting, Judith, the youngest and most attractive female, spoke about her sexual difficulties, vaginismus and frigidity, which had made her first two years of marriage almost impossible to endure. The group discussed her situation, asked pertinent questions, and suggested possible additional treatment measures. I will now focus in detail on the second half of this meeting. Roland shared he was having an extramarital affair, because his sexual needs were not satisfied with his wife. He proceeded to describe a Don Juanlike sexual life, adding his feelings of guilt for having to lie to his wife, but also his unwillingness to change his sexual behavior. Male members responded with criticism: "You are a philanderer! You are insecure about your masculinity and therefore try to show off, bragging about your harem." Judith responded with worried curiosity inquiring: "If you are not pleased with your wife, why do you stay married then?" For her, Roland's infidelity was exactly what she feared the most regarding her husband, that is to say, that he would walk out on her because of her dysfunctions.

Secretly, however, Roland had picked up this moment to talk about his promiscuous sexual life as a response to Judith's sharing her sexual difficulties. It was as if he were saying to her, "Do you need a sexual 'expert'? Let me introduce myself; I can help you." He had, as a matter-of-fact, preceded his statements about his sexual performances by recommending to Judith a bibliography of books on how to enjoy sex, obviously presenting himself, personally to her, as an alleged sexual expert. There was an attempt on his part to pair with Judith.

Cathy started asking Roland more details of his sexual adventures and in the process she revealed that she was also having an affair behind her spouse's back. Cathy elaborated on her emotional conflicts, feeling guilty and trying to push men away from her, by becoming overweight, while on the other hand starving for the emotional gratification of sexual intimacy. She stated, "I do it 'not for the sex but for the love,' my problem is with love not sex." She looked for intimacy to counteract her depression and loneliness. She didn't want to dump on her husband all the many "rotten things" that she felt she contained. There were further group criticisms for those cheating on their spouses. However, the group gradually moved to understand Roland and Cathy: What was the psychological explanation of their extramarital affairs? By now Roland and Cathy had become another "pair," united by their unfaithfulness and by the group's current attention to their sexual lives. Maybe they wanted to get back at their spouses because they were angry at them? Most certainly they were afraid of losing the spouses! Daniel, whose wife had threatened with divorce, was sure that was their case. Another member concurred. Judith thought they did it because of sexual frustration! The older male member took a grandfatherly role, advising them to "stop hurting themselves!" Daniel insisted: "I am afraid she will be gone any day!" Suddenly this brought up an ah-ha experience to Cathy's mind; she burst into tears and said, "That's it. I'm afraid of losing him as I lost my father! That's it!" She then proceeded to tell the group about her father's suicide. He killed himself when he was forty-two. He had been an alcoholic since adolescence and had gone to AA meetings, successfully achieving sobriety. His two sober months were interrupted by a relapse into drinking. He killed himself after this relapse. Group members gradually shared their feelings that loved persons could also abruptly leave them. They asked for details about the suicide and the life of Cathy's father. Roland said, "There is a curious parallelism: my father was a 'control-aholic' who couldn't relax, couldn't enjoy life, and was always tense. He saw me doing 'meditation-type' exercises and learning to relax myself; he wanted to learn them. I taught him, but he couldn't stand what he discovered within himself. He lost his mind and killed himself shortly after." Some member exclaimed, "Oh my God!" The group's "grandpa" then started reflecting about his vulnerability; he reported how he could manage his professional activities without feeling anxious and weak, but in his personal family life he felt tremendously vulnerable, particularly in his relations with his wife. He wanted to explore and understand how one can become so vulnerable. He pointedly addressed this question to the therapist.

This question marked a significant change in the style of interacting with the therapist during this session. In the second half of this session, the intensity of the interchanges among members didn't leave any opening for the therapist to intervene; in addition, once he tried to say something and nobody paid attention. He was literally excluded, silenced by the frantic rhythm of exchanges among members. When "grandpa" asked about his vulnerability, the therapist was in a dilemma. There were only three more minutes left to end the session, but very important material had come up; the group was now sending him messages that they wanted him to say something, maybe to prove to them that he was still with them, in spite of their having ignored him. He decided to intervene saying that becoming involved in the group was making them vulnerable to the fear of losing or missing each other and perhaps that was why they had not inquired about Rose's absence. He also reminded the group that upon convening the previous meeting, Roland had shared the information that psychiatrists are the professionals with the highest rate of suicide. Some members spontaneously interrupted, saying "the group will be gone too! Or you may be gone!" Judith was then crying. The therapist briefly added: "There is a fear of the responsibility of harming someone, maybe Rose, the missing member? Or perhaps driving me to become suicidal." A brief silence followed. Roland said, "When you (to the therapist) were talking, I had the impulse to stand up and start giving a hug to everyone in the room." Cathy responded immediately with loud laughter! and said, "Oh yeah!" Judith was still crying.

The therapist's comments brought first a brief moment of reflectiveness, with Judith crying and others acknowledging their fears that the group or the therapist might be gone forever. But shortly after, the group's hypomanic defenses were reinforced and there was again a brief plan to "become physically intimate," by hugging. It was significantly Roland who proposed it and Cathy who immediately endorsed it. The two "acting outers" had briefly "acted in" their defensive styles in dealing with depression! The group had previously indulged in pseudointimacy through "talking about sex," as if the topic would bring them closer, without having to pay attention to their fears of hurting each other. Significantly the subject of the meeting's second half was "casual sex," used to fill in the void of depression and to forget anxiety. Anxiety was, however, significantly present with unconscious worries about the group's survival; as if members were feeling: "If one patient starts missing a session will this mean that Rose will later on drop out and then others may do the same? Have we hurt Rose, the missing member?" Or the other way around: "If I get more involved here, would I be hurt here? I risk losing persons that I may need here." The group's anxiety about its survival was defended against by the pairing basic assumption, expressed as a hope that members could help each other to overcome the fears of love being hurtful. Similar expectations about the omnipotent "cure-it-all" magic quality of love had also inspired Roland's and Cathy's acting out.

During most of the session, the therapist was perceived as a threat. His treatment could make them face the truth about themselves, as the AA meetings and his inability to remain sober had killed Cathy's father, or as the truth discovered during meditation exercises had pushed Roland's father into madness and suicide! The therapist had become in their minds like the sphinx: a silent witness whose knowledge had killing powers. He was, off and on, perceived then unconsciously as the persecutor that group members had to eliminate because of his "knowing too much!" In other moments, they projected into him their own vulnerability, their potential for suicidal depression, and were fighting with a sense of guilt for wishing to lethally harm him.

The group's request for the therapist's intervention probably was an attempt to restore him, by innuendo, and thus relieve the patients' fears of him, by listening to his comments and implicitly realizing that he was intact, "all right." In addition, his references to their most intense anxieties soothed them, albeit briefly, making them feel understood.

DISCUSSION

A few notes on idealization are called for. Idealization is a defense against persecutory anxiety, a necessary way out of the schizoparanoid[1] position. Idealization makes it possible to develop the initial core of the good internal object. Idealization gradually may bring up a mastery over envy, since, without overcoming envy, idealization would not last.

A clear concept of idealization may prevent taking wrong, extreme positions in dealing psychotherapeutically with it, such as emphasizing the need to allow patients to unfold their idealizing transference, even at the risk that such transferences overdevelop, forming a blockade to further therapeutic progress. Stone and Gustafson (1982) wrote of that danger and made the important distinction between really cohesive groups and others in which overidealization leads to a group without any real healthy separateness among members or within each member. An opposite extreme view on idealization could be described as advocating "whenever you find idealization, wipe it out," assuming that to be the way to deal with the underlying persecutory anxiety. There is a middle-of-the-road approach between those two extremes. It considers the *timing* to interpret idealization. There is an initial stage, during which idealization needs to be developed as a defense, without having its growth disturbed; but in a later state it is necessary to deal with the hostility hidden beneath idealization.

Exploring the "bad" mother-group images can prevent the stereotyping of an idealized "good" mother-group, while the therapists or others are rigidly cast in "bad" roles. The mother-group functions, good and bad, should become instead interchangeable in psychotherapy groups, fluctuating among the group as an entity, the therapists, one member or another, or a different group. Achieving this fluidity of roles provides varied opportunities for the patients to meet and to solve their individuation difficulties. The group can be especially suited to contain and to receive projective identifications from its members, for holding, modifying, and eventually returning them to the projectors, helping their selves to blossom and to expand (Ogden, 1979). The patients often experience, while in group psychotherapy, for the first time, these essential "container" maternal functions

---

[1]The schizoparanoid position is "the earliest phase of development. It is characterized by the relation to part objects, the prevalence of splitting (in the ego and in the object) and paranoid anxiety" (Segal, 1974, p. 127). Splitting leads to the fragmentation of both the ego and the objects, weakening the former and making the latter appear as very threatening.

(Bion, 1964), since their dysfunctional mothers were frequently unable to provide them.

Bleger (1967) theorized that the psychotherapeutic setting can become a shelter for a mute symbiosis between patient and therapist, hiding a latent transference psychosis, through silently gratifying the patient's earlier dependency needs. The psychotherapist can detect and explore such a covert symbiotic gratifying arrangement. Otherwise, when ruptures of the psychotherapeutic frame alter such accommodation, the latent early psychoticlike anxieties can suddenly explode. I think the setting constitutes, on the one hand, a necessary health-promoting maternal, "holding environment" à la Winnicott, and what, on the other hand, Bleger correctly called our attention to possible unhealthy, mute transferential distortions of the setting. My discussion of idealization has a similar purpose.

While the group as an entity is cast in the role of a "bad" mother, therapists may feel relatively freer to perform supportive, "good" maternal functions (Durkin, 1964), responding more directly to patients' needs. Since focusing the anger and frustration on the group-as-a-whole takes care of the negative maternal transference, the therapist can interact with the patients, in caring ways, providing good and bad, although split, maternal experiences within the group. When the therapists are cast instead in the "bad" mother role, their behavior is perceived as a repetition of really depriving maternal attitudes, whereby mothers demanded (for their own survival) that their emotional needs be supplied by their child. These mothers used their children as self–objects. The child experienced afterwards a resulting self-estrangement (Miller, 1981). Family therapists have described, in this regard, the special role of the active father as the "helping third," whose family role is to reclaim the mother and make the husband–wife relationship the primary one, thus setting the children free for their own separation–individuation (Skynner, 1976). Cotherapists lend themselves to a replay of these families' struggles and solutions. Sometimes the scapegoated member becomes the recipient of a particular "badness," when cast in the role of an infantile introject of the needy, fragile mother, now displaced to this member. Subtle expressions of scapegoating may then be disguised as overprotection of a fragile, weak individual. It happens, for instance, with representatives of minorities, toward whom groupmates respond with lenient, apparent overprotection, while they are really contemptuous and jealous of these minority members, because they seem "too easily forgiven and protected from criticism."

From a psychological viewpoint the group is like a dream (Anzieu, 1966), insofar as both group and dream images are submitted (like fantasies) to the primary process functions of condensation, displacement, and symbolization. The "bad" mother-group images can therefore have multidetermined confusing meanings, undergoing disguising condensations and far-fetched displacements, across several group transferential targets. What unifies those multiple, "bad" mother-group images is a psychoticlike sadomasochistic, schizoparanoid style of relations between the self and the objects. By following the complex metamorphoses of the "bad" mother-group images and the defenses against them we can explore significant hidden negative transferences in group psychotherapy, thus overcoming the group schizoparanoid anxieties and defenses. We can also help the patients to achieve and work through the important maturing integrations brought up by the depressive position, allowing the reality of ambivalence to be fully experienced.[2]

REFERENCES

Anzieu, D. (1966), Psychoanalytic study of real groups. *Les Temps Modernes*, 242:56–73.
Bar-Levav (1977), The treatment of preverbal hunger and rage in a group. *Internat. J. Group Psychother.*, 27:457–469.
Bion, W. R. (1961), Group dynamics—A review. In: *Experiences in Groups*. New York: Basic Books.
——— (1964), *Attention and Interpretation*. New York: Basic Books.
Bleger, J. (1967), *Simbiosis y Ambigüedad*. Symbiosis and Ambiguity. Buenos Aires, Argentina: Paidos.
Durkin, H. (1964), *The Group in Depth*. New York: International Universities Press.
Foulkes, S. H. (1964), *Therapeutic Group Analysis*. New York: International Universities Press.
Freud, S. (1921), *Group Psychology and the Analysis of the Ego*. London: Hogarth Press, 1948.
Ganzarain, R. (1989), *Object Relations Group Psychotherapy*. Madison, CT: International Universities Press.
——— Buchele, B. J. (1989), Psychodynamics of incest perpetrators during group therapy. *Bull. Menn. Clin.*
Gibbard, G. S., & Hartman, J. (1973), The significance of Utopian fantasies in small groups. *Internat. J. Group Psychother.*, 23:125–147.

[2]The depressive position is "ushered when the infant recognizes his mother as a whole object. It is a constellation of object relations and anxieties, characterized by the infant's experience of attacking an ambivalently loved mother and losing her as an external and internal object. This experience gives rise to pain, guilt, and feelings of loss" (Segal, 1974, p. 126). Integration of the mother as a whole object and of ambivalence promotes ego development; hence, its acceptance of reality, internal and external, including both the "oral" as well as the "genital" mother.

Grotjahn, M. (1972), Learning from dropout patients. *Internat. J. Group Psychother.*, 22:287–305.

Hearst, L. (1981), The emergence of the mother in the group. *Group Anal.*, 14:25–31.

Miller, A. (1981), *Prisoners of Childhood.* New York: Basic Books.

Money-Kyrle (1950), Varieties of group formation. In: *Psychoanalysis and the Social Sciences,* ed. G. Roheim. New York: International Universities Press.

Ogden, T. H. (1979), On projective identification. *Internat. J. Psycho-Anal.*, 60:357–373.

Scheidlinger, S. (1964), Identification, the sense of belonging and of identity in small groups. *Internat. J. Group Psychother.*, 14:291–306.

—— (1974), On the concept of the mother-group. *Internat. J. Group Psychother.*, 24:417–428.

—— (1982), On scapegoating. American Group Psychotherapy Association Presidential Address.

Segal, H. (1974), *Introduction to the Work of Melanie Klein,* 2nd ed. New York: Basic Books.

Schindler, W. (1966), The role of the mother in group psychotherapy. *Internat. J. Group Psychother.*, 16:198–200.

—— (1981), Commentary on Hearst's (1981) paper. *Group Anal.*, 14:132–133.

Skynner, R. (1976), *One Flesh: Separate Persons.* London: Constable.

Slater, P. (1966), *Microcosm.* New York: John Wiley.

Stone, W., & Gustafson, J. (1982), Technique in group psychotherapy of narcissistic and borderline patients. *Internat. J. Group Psychother.*, 32:29–47.

Chapter 10

The Unique Contributions of Analytic Group Therapy to the Treatment of Preoedipal Character Pathology

PRISCILLA F. KAUFF, Ph.D.

INTRODUCTION

Character pathology, regardless of its origin, is notoriously resistant to analytic intervention. Whether manifested in persistent behavior patterns or in nonverbal bodily attitudes and attributes (Durkin, 1951), character pathology can produce the most tenacious forms of transference resistance. It is often so well disguised that it is as hard to detect as it is to treat. Consequently, it is a frequent culprit in the ultimate sabotage of treatment.

Over fifty years ago, in 1936, Anna Freud commented upon the problems of dealing with the "transference of defense," the process she later referred to as "character analysis," as follows:

> The repetition compulsion, which dominates the patient in the analytic situation, extends not only to former id impulses but equally to former defensive measures against the instinct. . . . It may happen in extreme cases that the instinctual impulse never enters into the transference at all but only the specific defenses adopted by the ego . . .[pp. 19–20].
>
> [Such cases are]: responsible for most of the technical difficulties which arise between analyst and patient. The latter does not feel the transference reaction to be a foreign body. . . . It is not easy to convince

This chapter is based in part on an earlier article, "Treatment Strategies to Deal with Oral Characteristic Resistance," *Issues in Ego Psychology* (1985), 8/2:32–35.

him of the repetitive nature of these phenomena. The form in which
they emerge in his consciousness is ego syntonic. . . . When the transference reactions take this form, we cannot count on the patient's willing
cooperation. . . . Whenever the interpretation touches on the unknown
elements of the ego, its activities in the past, that ego is wholly opposed
to the work of analysis [p. 21].

Anna Freud goes on to make the same point regarding "character
traits," a form of "permanent defense phenomena," calling their analysis a "peculiarly laborious process" (p. 33). It is tempting indeed to
wonder how Anna Freud might have felt about the treatment logjams
that character pathology can produce had she had group therapy as
an alternate or additional modality at her disposal.

Group therapists are frequently heirs to the incomplete or unsuccessful treatment of character pathology, whether in highly functioning individuals or in those more seriously ill. Such patients are often
the ones who are characterized as "difficult" when referred to group
therapy and indeed they can and do wear down even the most experienced and dedicated analyst. Yet these same patients often connect with their groups in a way that they may not have achieved in
individual treatment. They will often stick with group therapy for
long periods of time and eventually show improvement.

Analytic group therapy has shown itself to be uniquely suited to the
treatment of this highly resistant form of psychopathology. This chapter will explore several reasons why group therapy is successful, sometimes even more successful than dyadic therapy in the treatment of
character pathology.

PREOEDIPAL CHARACTER PATHOLOGY

While the whole range of character pathology presents serious stumbling blocks in treatment, that which is related to infantile fantasies
and affects of the preoedipal—especially oral—phase of development
is usually the most intractable. During this period, the ordinary developmental demands on the infant are staggering.

The infantile ego, without its later capacities of judgment, reality testing
and other critical functions, must struggle to deal simultaneously with
the conflict of the instincts, the pressures of the superego, and the
requirements of a complex reality which it is not fully equipped to
understand. . . . All sorts of compromises will be tried out as the developing ego attempts to cope with anxiety, whatever its source [Kauff,
1979].

Because these compromises occur early in development, within the limits of an immature ego, they are especially tenacious. They are also notably unsuccessful as modes of functioning later in life. Similarly, the attitudes, patterned behavior, and enduring traits which are often the outcome of these compromises are notoriously rigid, entrenched, and self-defeating.

Melanie Klein (1957) has richly detailed some of the processes that are typical of this early period of development. In defining the nature of the infant's experience of its world during this time, she has focused particularly on the function of the ego's primitive defenses, especially projective identification. Familiarity with these processes can help clarify the nature of preoedipal character pathology as it appears in the adult patient. According to Klein, the internal object world of the infant as well as its perception of the external world is largely determined by the early ego's efforts to deal with instinctual conflict:

> The infant projects his love impulses and attributes them to the gratifying (good) breast, just as he projects his destructive impulses outwards and attributes them to the frustrating (bad) breast. Simultaneously, by introjection, a good breast and a bad breast are established inside . . . the good breast—external and internal—becomes the prototype of all helpful and gratifying objects, the bad breast the prototype of all external and internal persecutory objects [p. 63].

She goes on to say that:

> When projection is dominated by persecutory fear, the object into whom badness has been projected becomes the persecutor *par excellence* because it has been endowed with all the bad qualities of the subject [p. 68].

Glatzer (1985) has further elaborated on these processes in her description of the preoedipal "witch-mother" fantasy. As the primary caretaker, the mother of the nursery is simultaneously the principal representative of reality, of frustration, and of prohibition. In this sense, it is she who deals the earliest and most serious blows to the infant's omnipotence, to its "fiction of self-sufficiency" (p. 7). The mother is at once the object of the child's projected aggression and the object of his reactive rage against her real or fantasized offenses. At the end, the child is faced with a malevolent, excessively powerful figure, largely of his own creation. The "persecutory breast" (Klein) has become the persecutory "witch-mother" and later reappears in the form of the dangerous, oedipal father.

The actual nature of the child's parenting experience may have little connection to the development and tenacity of these early fantasies. Real parents, after all, are often unrecognizable when compared with the child's fantasies, which, in turn, are shaped by the child's own projections. But nothing is more terrifying than the bad objects of the child's world with which the child is left to deal as a consequence of these projective processes. Kernberg (1975), for example, suggested that the main consequence of the projection of the "all bad" or aggressive self "is the development of dangerous, retaliatory objects . . . they have to attack before (as they fear) they themselves are attacked and destroyed" (p. 31). In other words, as the persecutory object becomes more and more dangerous, the stakes become higher and higher. The child feels himself locked into a life-or-death struggle. Thus the inner world can become all but impervious to reality even when that reality includes good or "good enough mothering" as Winnicott (1965, pp. 140–152) calls it. This impervious quality is reflected in the intransigence of the character pathology of which it becomes a part.

✓The part played by character pathology in the on-going denial of the negatively experienced parts of the self also contributes to its intransigence. Once externalized and embodied in the powerful mother imago, unacceptable aggressive and primitive sexual feelings and fantasies are safely removed from the self. As a result, the "bad mother" is at once a source of great danger, and at the same time, a *protection* for the child against the most undesirable or feared aspects of itself. As such, she will be as jealously guarded as she is profoundly feared. The dilemma then is that the individual must simultaneously protect—and defend himself against—the same bad objects, which are at their root largely of his own construction. It is little wonder that characterological mechanisms become as rigid and pervasive as they do with such a task to perform.

One mechanism which both preserves the bad object and defends against it is characterological masochism (Glatzer, 1985), a tenacious and sometimes lethal source of resistance in treatment. In his attempt to minimize the malevolent power of the "bad mother" and his feeling of being victimized by her, and in order to regain lost control and shattered fantasies of omnipotence, the patient will find ways to provoke his own deprivation. He will, in effect, become his own "bad parent." In their lives, patients with marked oral masochistic character pathology will repeatedly look for water from stones, consciously seeking nurturance where only deprivation is actually available. Or they will wrench defeat from the jaws of victory, blackwashing whatever is gratifying in their lives. Often they will provoke rage in those from whom they ostensibly seek love and care. They thus unconsciously reproduce the interaction with the "bad" mother, who dealt the first and unforgivable blow to the childhood fantasy of omnipotence, but with a new twist: now the *patient* controls the deprivation. He may not be in control of how much he gets, but at the very least, he can determine how much he does *not* get. Furthermore, he can repeatedly reassure himself that the "bad" is located outside of himself. In his adult life he will find the "bad mother" in his choice of friends, lovers, and spouse. She may even appear on the job, in the stock market, or at the airline reservation counter.

In treatment, this mechanism of preoedipal character pathology will appear in certain highly tenacious aspects of the transference resistance. Most frequently, the oral masochistic patient will repetitively transform the therapist into the "bad object," specifically the bad breast or "witch-mother" of the preoedipal period. The patient will compulsively and unconsciously attempt to defeat the therapy to prove that the therapist is a depriving parent. For example, the patient may attempt to sabotage the treatment by not coming, by not talking, by not paying for sessions. He may even be more overtly provocative or abusive in order to induce the therapist into countertransferential acting out. Whatever means he chooses, the intent of such behavior is to maintain an unconscious bond to the "bad mother." By depriving himself of the benefits of therapy, he can perpetuate the indictment of the bad-mother-therapist who "keeps" him ill and unhappy.

Example 1. Alexander: The Contemptuous, Verbally Assaultive Patient

Alexander could never bear to admit that his behavior might have unconscious determinants, despite his brilliance at detecting it in others (including, of course, the therapist). He was deeply offended whenever his unconscious behavior, however trivial, was pointed out, and equally offended whenever interpretations were offered that he had not already thought of himself. Virtually any intervention by the therapist was received, at least initially, as a narcissistic blow to which he would typically respond with a contemptuous, often vitriolic, attack. To acknowledge the validity of any comments from the therapist would imply that she knew something he did not. Even worse, to admit to things about himself that were out of his awareness stimulated the deepest fears of passivity and vulnerability. It was only with the greatest difficulty that he could acknowledge any of the positive changes that occurred during his treatment. Such an admission would betray the fact that the therapist had something good to give, something that he needed and could not provide entirely by himself: the ultimate blow to his infantile omnipotent belief in his self-sufficiency.

Example 2. Marilyn: The Idealizing, Worshipful Patient

Marilyn constantly ridiculed herself by unfavorable comparisons to the therapist. She was *only* a housewife, *only* a mother. Her Master's degree was "meaningless," boring and unrewarding. If only she could be more like the therapist, perhaps then she would be worthwhile. But her crowning failure was that she could not even be a good patient. She didn't speak well, couldn't think straight; everything she discussed was "bullshit." How could the therapist be so indulgent and listen to her hour after hour? Any effort to contradict this negative judgment was further evidence of the magnitude of the therapist's generosity in listening to her at all. Interpretations were quickly incorporated into an assault on herself. If she were any good, she would no longer be doing x, y, or z. After all, didn't we just talk about that last week?

TREATMENT CONSIDERATIONS

For patients with predominantly preoedipal character pathology, the process of analysis is readily experienced as intrusive, a characteristic often ascribed to the "bad mother." If the process should be even slightly successful, it becomes still more dangerous to the patient because it threatens to expose the unacceptable aspects of himself against which, in part, these defenses have been mobilized. Thus, the patient strenuously attempts to prevent the therapist from interpreting, and possibly neutralizing, the projections, a fundamental requirement if the "bad" parts of the self are to be reintegrated. Moreover, the failure of infantile omnipotence becomes more obvious if, through some chink in the patient's armor, any growth should occur. Therapeutic success in this context becomes a direct slap at the patient's remaining fantasies of omnipotence; after all, no one but the patient himself should have the power to cure! Furthermore, having someone to blame is a neurotic treasure that is not lightly relinquished. We all know how many patients never get past blaming, and leave treatment with their ex-therapist at the top of the guilty list. After all, it is a part of the resistance crusade to find the therapist guilty of bad mothering.

Faced with such resistance, it is easy to understand how therapists experience these characterological mountains as virtually immovable. Under such circumstances, therapists will often capitulate to the more attractive role of the "good mother," trying to meet the patient's needs instead of analyzing the unconscious sources of his continued self-deprivation. It is all too tempting to stop at the interpretation of the oral strivings of such patients, their heartfelt conscious wishes for love and fulfillment. But these, too, are often both a disguise for self-pity and an unconscious, rage-filled indictment of the depriving mother–therapist (i.e., one who could provide for all these needs if he so chose).

A major challenge to the therapist is to deal successfully with his own countertransference in the face of the patient's best efforts to defeat him. Being perceived as the "good mother" is neither sufficient nor ultimately effective. Positive transference is often unconsciously encouraged and all too often welcomed by the brow-beaten, tired therapist. However, it must be remembered that as good as it feels, positive transference is itself a defense—a seductive defense—against negative transference. Negative transference must be invited, recognized, and welcomed even in its most subtle disguised forms, and even in the face of the threat of volcanic rage which may lie at its core. To offer oneself as the object of intense, primitive rage is exhausting at best and debilitating at worst. To have the courage to join the patient in an exploration of his most primitive fantasies requires that the therapist face and master his own. A condition must be established which both sufficiently resolves the patient's resistance and at the same time controls the therapist's own countertransference. Such a condition makes it possible to explore and analyze the patient's "bad mother" fantasy, to get beneath the intensely provocative or self-pitying behavior and reveal the "dark sides" of the self against which the defenses have been so powerfully mobilized.

It is at this critical juncture that the therapist is caught between a rock and a hard place. He is faced with the most entrenched resistance coming from the patient (as Anna Freud warned) as well as constraints upon his own functioning which stem from the requirement of analytic objectivity and the often intense countertransferential withdrawal that primitive rage in patients so easily provokes. At this point in treatment, the job of the therapist is extremely complex and may be impossible or detrimental to attempt on his own. It is precisely at this precarious point in treatment that group therapy can be a most welcome "white knight."

The Role of the Group

There are several ways in which group therapy can add to the work of dyadic treatment and, more importantly, compensate for its deficiencies, whether they be a function of constraints on the therapist or limitations inherent in the dyad itself. Group members can behave in ways that the therapist cannot: they can do things which are beyond the limits of appropriate analytic behavior but may be precisely what the situation requires. In addition, there are certain features of the group qua group which can make it pivotal to the resolution of the behavioral problems presented by character pathology.

The first step in dealing with character resistance must be to expose, and ultimately transform, highly syntonic but pathological behavior into dystonic discomfort for the patient. Syntonic behavior patterns or character traits at not likely to be reported to the therapist as problematic in the ordinary course of dyadic treatment. By definition, that which is comfortable is least deemed to be a problem and may only be brought into the treatment if, for example, a parent, spouse, or other significant person in the patient's life demands it, or if the therapist sees it himself.

It is, of course, a function of group therapy that actual behavior —rather than the second-hand reporting of behavior—is an important source of material for treatment. Patient behavior which can be observed by therapist and patient alike is increased and enriched by the mere fact that the patient is face-to-face and interacting with other people whose responses he cannot control and often cannot anticipate. When patients first enter a group, therapists are often surprised, sometimes shocked, at how differently patients behave than when in individual treatment. And, while those behavioral differences may reveal the healthy parts of the patient's personality, they are just as likely to reveal the patient's characterological pathology in action.

That which is characterological by definition feels "natural" and comfortable. Most of these traits or response patterns have a long history in the patient's repertoire, having once served a useful purpose which has long since become vestigial. To find that others are responding in an unfamiliar, even negative way to behavior that one feels to be characteristic of one's "normal" way of being is unnerving at best and may feel critical or attacking at worst. Therapists, operating under constraints of neutrality, are largely prohibited from responding to character pathology in an effective way. But group members can and do respond naively and directly to comembers' cherished pathological behavior patterns. They know it to be part of their contract, in a well-functioning group, to say what they feel or think with a frankness that the observing therapist can rightly envy. In doing so, they will often focus the patient's attention on aspects of himself that he had always accepted as entirely "normal."

By challenging, questioning, or otherwise reacting to the patient, group members provide a new audience for an old act; as audience ratings go down, anxiety goes up and this is the essence of making syntonic behavior dystonic. Thus the actual interaction of group members with the character pathology of any one member can be a powerful force in making that pathology accessible to exploration.

Another important function group members provide is the opportunity to observe pathological behavior similar to one's own from a safe vantage point. It is easier—far easier—to recognize inappropriate, patterned responses in someone else than in oneself. Group members quickly see someone else's behavior as peculiar, misguided, or self-destructive, and it is not long before they understand that that same behavior, or some variant of it, is characteristic of themselves as well. Patients learn in group therapy that they typically respond most strongly to behavior in others which replicates that against which they most strenuously defend in themselves. Since the group continually provides opportunities for this process to occur, the strength of any one member's denial is subjected to a constant wearing away.

Another way in which the actual behavior of group members contributes to the process of analyzing character resistance is by the example they set for one another. Frequently, the resistant patient unconsciously fears exposing highly defended affects or fantasies because of the imagined consequences of such exposure. Other members in the group, for whom any particular set of behaviors, responses, or fantasies is *not* experienced as threatening, will often display or openly discuss them in the group. As a function of the latitude afforded to group *members*, the highly defended patient may have his first opportunity to discover that despite the lethal nature of his fantasy, the actuality is benign. He will find that it is possible to feel the unfeelable, to say the unspeakable, even to imagine doing the forbidden without facing mortal consequences. This is an experience which is available in some form or another, to some member or other, during virtually every group session.

THE THERAPIST AS THE OBJECT OF INTENSE NEGATIVE TRANSFERENCE

The technical challenge to the therapist is only scratched when the characterological defense package is budged. Almost immediately the next and equally serious problem arises, namely, dealing with the intense negative transference and especially the primitive, usually rage-filled fantasies that so frequently emerge as part of the newly exposed material. Thus, the therapist must first be able to withstand the assault, which can be staggering; and second, the therapist must simultaneously be the object of the transference and the interpreter of it, a dilemma which Racker (1968) points to as one of the most difficult of technical tasks (p. 105). Withstanding assaults of primitive rage is difficult under the best of circumstances, and when the therapist cannot "fight back," the situation is fertile for the most primitive countertransferential responses. Similarly, the therapist often cannot function as interpreter when the characterological volcano is active. Under such circumstances, convincing the patient that his transference reaction is in fact *transferential* can be practically impossible.

The Role of the Group

In instances such as these just described, the group can be uniquely helpful to the therapist and to the patient. Since the capacity to withstand primitive rage varies tremendously both between therapists and within any one therapist over time, the group can be a most valuable aid. It can assist the beleaguered therapist because it can "take on" or deflect problematic patients—leaving the therapist room to breathe—and also because it can accomplish many of the technical tasks that the therapist may be unable to perform for whatever reason.

The therapist, as the object of negative transference, cannot be a persuasive voice against the implications of that transference. Since the therapist is perceived as a dreaded authority in the transference, his words of empathy are scarcely comforting. Attempts to dispel projection or displacement with interpretation (or by explanation under pressure) pale by comparison with the defenses mobilized when the negative transference is operating at full tilt. A patient involved in intense negative transference, in other words, often cannot hear, and more often *will not believe*, the therapist's interpretation.

Group members who are not sharing in the negative transference themselves have more options open to them to intervene and help a fellow group member. Unlike the therapist, who may be in no position to challenge the transference of which he is the object, the group can contradict another patient's distortions outright (e.g., "Do you really think she wants to hurt you?" or "That isn't how I remember what happened. Perhaps you felt hurt or anxious and that is why you saw it that way"). Unlike the therapist, who *is* at that moment the "bad parent" of early childhood, another group member can associate with and even begin to interpret the transference process for the resistant patient. For example, members *remember* each other's histories and experiences and can remember *for* each other at a time when anxiety, hurt, or rage might prevent such associations. They will often say to one another, for example, "You have said the exact same thing about your mother that you just said about Dr. X. Maybe you have them mixed up."

And finally, unlike the therapist, group members are encouraged from their entrance into the group to associate to what other members say and do. Group members will frequently say "I can relate to that feeling. I used to feel that myself." Often as they associate, the group member who is in an intense negative transference state can begin to see the distortion of his own perceptions and will consider the possibility of exploring these distortions. As this takes place, the patient can also save face knowing that he is not the only one who engages in distortion. Having another group member speak of shared feelings can be, at times, the *only* way in which a particularly vulnerable, anxious, or intransigent patient can begin to work on his transference resistance.

THE GROUP AS "GOOD MOTHER"

One of the premises of this paper is that characterological resistance is most intense when its origins are most primitive. In other words, intense resistance is mobilized against the most unacceptable parts of the self and the most feared, persecutory fantasies about the external world which have survived from the preoedipal period. This carefully guarded material is far more likely to emerge in a setting which the patient experiences as a "good environment," one which can support the patient (and therapist!) through a sometimes painful and frightening process. A well-functioning therapy group is, in fact, just such an environment, a benign reality which repeatedly demonstrates that the "forbidden" may be exposed in a safe, contained atmosphere without the anticipated catastrophic results (Ezriel, 1973). In this sense, the group becomes an "alkaline base" in that it helps to neutralize persecutory fantasies simply by *being* neutral and accepting.

There is, unquestionably, "safety in numbers" and the group, by its structure alone, offers at least the illusion—if not the reality—of protection. Because of the other people present, the member feels protected against his own destructive fantasies as well as retaliation by the group leader. In addition to sheer numbers, group members can offer outright support and encouragement to say nothing of a degree of sympathy that the analyst is better advised to forego. Lastly, by sharing similar material from their own experience, the group goes a long way not just to reduce anxiety but to soften the narcissistic blow that patients must sometimes face in confronting well-guarded pathology or in hearing an unwelcome interpretation regardless of how diplomatically it may be phrased (Glatzer, 1969).

Thus the group can often begin to be perceived, in the patient's transference, as the good object, the nurturing breast or the developmentally more advanced "good mother." Scheidlinger (1974) hypothesizes that the group becomes positive or "benign" to the members, especially early on, as a function of "a covert wish to restore an earlier state of unconflicted well-being inherent in the infant's exclusive union with the mother . . ." (p. 420). He also notes that the group therapist tends to be the recipient of hostile feelings and therefore is the transferentially feared object. Certainly this notion would fit in well with the fact that splitting, a primitive defense which is usually obvious in the early and even in the later phases of group development (Bion, 1959), often results in the group being perceived as the "good mother" and the therapist as the "bad" or malevolent figure. Indeed, it may be precisely because of this splitting phenomenon that the group member can feel safe enough, protected by this early fantasy of the symbiotic union with the good mother, to express the terrifying fantasies and feelings that can be projected onto and contained by the therapist. Because it allows for more than one transferential object, the group is able to neutralize the most toxic aspects of the preoedipal fantasies. In a sense it even encourages, in its role as the good object, the expulsion of the "bad parts" of the self onto the therapist.

While it should be noted that the group itself can be experienced as malevolent, clinically this happens quite rarely. It is usually much easier to deal with members' monolithic negative perceptions of the group as they are rarely as impenetrable as the heavily defended fantasies attached to the therapist. An individual member almost always has at least one other group member toward whom he feels a special bond, special enough to help jog even a powerful distortion about the group as a whole. Again, the reality testing of the group as a whole is always better than that of any one individual in conflict. The benign pressure of the group to "look again" and listen "to those who care about you" can be very hard for even the most intransigent member to withstand. Scheidlinger (1987) suggests this when he says:

Consensual validation by peers may help a resister of an interpretation to accept it. The supportive group atmosphere also is likely to reduce the anxiety and perceived threat so frequently entailed in receiving an interpretation [p. 349].

THE GROUP AS AN INDEPENDENT STIMULANT OF PREOEDIPAL MATERIAL

Group therapists are well acquainted with the fact that patients will often spontaneously expose more preoedipal material, especially in their transferential reactions, in the group setting than in the dyadic one. Although this can happen with patients all along the diagnostic continuum, it is most dramatic in the better integrated patient who tends to be more out of touch with primitive material. Therapy groups seem uniquely suited to facilitate the emergence of the precise material against which character pathology defends, often making it available for analytic scrutiny for the first time.

It is more than a matter of idle curiosity to wonder what it is about the group that lends itself to the exposure and the exploration of the more archaic sources of psychopathology. Some American group analysts have long been aware of the typically preoedipal, maternal stimulus potential that the group seems to have. For example, going back several decades, we have the contributions of Glatzer (1959) expanding the notion of the negative maternal image or "witch-mother" that so frequently becomes the projective fate of the group therapist and less frequently, the group as a whole.

Durkin (1967) argued quite compellingly in "The Group in Depth" that the strangeness of the gestalt of the therapy group itself is related to the early experience of the omnipotent mother of the nursery. It is this "strangeness," she hypothesized, that stimulates preoedipal transference:

[T]he group is a totality of strange others, the full extent of whose powers and intentions in relation to himself (the patient) he cannot assess. He imagines they will be critical and demanding and render him helpless. It is no wonder that the adult ego which finds itself invaded by anxiety and helpless anger stemming from the past projects its destructive anger to the group and tends to yield with apparent meekness to the group will, in order to avoid imagined injury [pp. 88–89].

Scheidlinger, as noted previously, explored the phenomenon of the group as the nurturing mother of early childhood, "Mother Earth" as he later referred to it (1980, p. 218).

Another more concrete way in which the therapy group may contribute to the production of preoedipal material is in its relative changeability as compared, for example, with the usually consistent dyadic modality. In the dyad, terminations are expected, typically occurring at times agreed upon by both parties. In the group, all members do not always appear for all sessions; absences are frequent. Members do not stay forever; membership changes. Thus, termination is a frequent experience in group therapy and not always predictable. In the group, members face "symbolic" termination each time one or more members are absent, and they typically experience abrupt as well as mutually agreed upon terminations by other members long before their own. Groups are also exposed, on rare occasions, to the prolonged illness or death of a group member and more frequently to such events occurring in each other's lives.

These symbolic and real terminations are built into the warp and woof of group treatment. Furthermore, the response to all the varieties of termination, anticipated or actual, positive or precipitous, even profoundly tragic, are surprisingly similar. Anxiety-laden themes of helplessness, passivity, abandonment, rejection, narcissistic affront, and rage eventually emerge regardless of who is leaving, for how long or for what reason. Thus, continued membership in a group will inevitably lead to repeated experiences which stimulate feelings and fantasies that have clear preoedipal origins which in turn will allow for their exploration in the treatment (Kauff, 1977).

CONCLUSION

Preoedipal character pathology is believed to be at the core of much of the serious, often outright destructive resistance against which an analyst may have no readily effective remedy. Patients who manifest such resistance often find their way into group treatment, an occurrence which turns out to be the right solution though often entered into for the wrong reasons. Groups can be uniquely helpful to such patients.

While preoedipal character resistance varies in strength and degree from patient to patient (depending in part upon the depth of pathology and the resilience of the individual ego), it is nonetheless ubiquitous. No one passes through the preoedipal period of development without some pathological residua. This is critical to keep in mind since it is perfectly clear that intense and often primitive negative transference resistance is simply not limited to our sickest or most dysfunctional patients. It is present in everyone, including therapists, which explains in part why the temptation of the therapist to collude with the patient's evasion of the "dark side" of his inner life is so seductive. And it is all too understandable when the therapist falls prey to a need to avoid the voluminous rage of the less well-integrated patient.

Analytic group therapy can offer an alternative to the many treatment problems and failures that preoedipal character pathology can yield. That the group can simultaneously stimulate preoedipal material while providing both a salutary setting and an effective tool to handle the resistance against it may be its most valuable but least well-recognized contribution to analytic treatment. Certainly for those of us who practice group therapy the technical latitude which the group offers is a compelling reason to include it in treatment planning for all of our patients. In doing so we afford ourselves a chance to breach the barrier that proved a stumbling block even to Anna Freud.

REFERENCES

Bion, W. R. (1959), *Experiences in Groups*. New York: Basic Books.

Durkin, H. (1951), The analysis of character traits in group therapy. *Internat. J. Group Psychother.*, 1:133–143.

———— (1967), *The Group in Depth*. New York: International Universities Press.

Ezriel, H. (1973), Psychoanalytic group therapy. In: *Group Therapy*, ed. L. R. Wolberg & E. K. Schwartz. New York: International Medical Book Corp., pp. 183–210.

Freud, A. (1936), *The Ego and the Mechanisms of Defense*. New York: International Universities Press, 1966.

Glatzer, H. T. (1959), Notes on the preoedipal fantasy. *Amer. J. Orthopsychiat.*, 29:383–390.

———— (1969), Working through in analytic group therapy. *Internat. J. Group Psychother.*, 19:292–306.

———— (1985), Early mother-child relationships: Notes on the pre-oedipal fantasy. *Dynamic Psychother.*, 3:27–37.

Kauff, P. F. (1977), The termination process: Its relationship to the separation-individuation phase of development. *Internat. J. Group Psychother.*, 27:3–18.

———— (1979), Diversity in analytic group psychotherapy: The relationship between theoretical concepts and technique. *Internat. J. Group Psychother.*, 29:51–65.

Kernberg, O. (1975), *Borderline Conditions and Pathological Narcissism*. New York: Jason Aronson.

Klein, M. (1957), *Envy and Gratitude*. London: Tavistock Press, 1979.

Racker, H. (1968), *Transference and Countertransference*. New York: International Universities Press.

Scheidlinger, S. (1974), On the concept of the "mother group." *Internat. J. Group Psychother.*, 24:417–428.

———— (1980), Identification, the sense of belonging and of identity in small groups. In: *Psychoanalytical Group Dynamics*, ed. S. Scheidlinger. New York: International Universities Press, pp. 213–231.

———— (1987), On interpretation in group psychotherapy. *Internat. J. Group Psychother.*, 37:339–351.

Winnicott, D. W. (1965), *The Maturational Process and the Facilitating Environment*. New York: International Universities Press.

Part V

Group Treatment of Children and Adolescents

INTRODUCTION

Scheidlinger's initial work in group psychotherapy began with his experiences with children. Ever since, he has remained involved in issues dealing with young people and the use of the group in providing help for them. His ongoing interest in training and supervision of therapists in this field continues and is referred to by several authors in this section. In chapter 11, Paulina Kernberg and Jo Rosenberg explore the value of group therapy for elementary schoolchildren with conduct problems. These include youngsters who are oppositional and defiant, and those who manifest childhood antisocial behavior. Such disorders of latency clearly interfere with social relationships and often result in academic failure and other school problems. The paper describes the stages in group process and the factors involved in successful treatment.

Whereas most of the chapters in this section deal with the problems therapists encounter in conducting group psychotherapy with emotionally disturbed and intellectually limited children and adolescents, Albert Riester (chapter 12) deals with providing supervision and support for group leaders and therapists who work with this population. Effective leadership is possible only if such leaders are adequately trained and supported by an administrative structure which provides needed technical guidance and reinforcement. This support is essential given the strains and pressure in working with these difficult-to-treat youngsters.

Max Sugar (in chapter 13) explores "Symbiotic Pairing in an Adolescent Inpatient Group Psychotherapy." He describes his criteria for selecting treatment groups of disturbed adolescents. This involves the author's efforts to pair compatible individuals who will participate in the group. He explores the special difficulties concerning "pairing" of borderline adolescents on an inpatient unit.

Gerald Schamess (in chapter 14) offers an original, sensitive application of a specially devised group psychotherapy "design" to encourage unmarried teenage mothers to participate as a group, each bringing her infant or toddler into the initial sessions. He skillfully arranges, in the course of ongoing group sessions, for the children to meet separately as a nearby "satellite" group (when appropriate in terms of phase specificity and therapeutic objectives). In this manner, Schamess encourages the working through of individuation by means of transitional experiences in the group for both the young mothers and their offspring. Not only is the paper valuable from a clinical vantage point. It also demonstrates the rich potential of applying group methods in an innovative manner.

Chapter 11

Play Group Therapy for Children with Socialized Conduct Disorders

PAULINA F. KERNBERG, M.D., and JO ROSENBERG, A.C.S.W.

BACKGROUND AND DESCRIPTION OF THE CHILDREN

Background

The group of children with socialized conduct disorders includes a spectrum ranging from oppositional behavior to socialized conduct disorders, aggressive and nonaggressive, and represents a significant proportion of diagnosis in outpatient clinics requiring professional intervention.

Because prevalent studies of behavior disorders in childhood use different methods of assessment and categorization, the charting of nondelinquent conduct disorders is incomplete. However, Rutter, Cox, Tupling, Berger, and Yule (1975) estimated that conduct disorders occur in 4 percent of a general population among children between the ages of ten and eleven years.

The follow-up data on these children raises serious concern about the risk for later personality disorder (Conger and Miller, 1966; Robins, 1970) and points to evidence that nondelinquent conduct dis-

Acknowledgment and thanks to Fern Cramer-Azima, Ph.D., Howard Kibel, M.D., and Saul Scheidlinger, Ph.D., for their comments and to Rene Azima-Heller for her assistance.

This study was supported by a grant from the Saul Z. and Amy Cohen Scheuer Foundation, Inc.

orders during the early and middle school years may often lead to delinquency at adolescence, especially when there is also school failure.

Description of the Children

We are including elementary school children ages seven through eleven, with the diagnosis of oppositional disorder, conduct disorder, *socialized* aggressive and nonaggressive types (DSM-III) for the group treatment model that we describe. Children from all socioeconomic strata will be eligible for play group therapy, as long as they fit clinically into our criteria for treatment. Since conduct disorders are frequently associated with Attention Deficit Disorders (ADD), children meeting criteria for both diagnoses can be suitable candidates for group treatment as long as the ADD is not the primary diagnosis. The children with conduct problems that would be suitable for group therapy are included in the following categories of *Diagnostic and Statistical Manual of Mental Disorders* (DSM-III-R): Oppositional Defiant Disorder (313.81), Conduct Disorder, group types (312.20), Conduct Disorder, undifferentiated type (312.90), Adjustment Disorder with Disturbance of Conduct (309.30), and Childhood Antisocial Behavior (V71.02), as differentiated from Antisocial Personality Disorder (301.70) in adults.

According to Rapoport and Ismond (1983), oppositional disorder entails persistent opposition to authority figures for a period of six months or more, characterized by disobedience, and negativistic and provocative behaviors, particularly toward parents and teachers. Continually confrontive behavior is exhibited, even when it is destructive to the best interests or well-being of the patient. Such an individual rarely views the problem as originating within himself, and his passive resistance to external authority often causes more discomfort for those around him than for himself. The disorder interferes with social relationships and often results in academic failure and other school problems. Typically arising in late childhood or early adolescence, onset usually coincides with increased difficulties in relations with the family and use of illegal substances. The course is described as chronic, lasting for several years.

Children with conduct disorders have repeatedly violated the basic rights of others or major age-appropriate societal norms or rules for a period of at least six months. Stealing, lying, temper outbursts, running away, truancy, fire-setting, and physical aggression are frequently present. The pattern of behavior can occur at home, school, with peers, and in other facets of the child's environment. While this diagnosis entails many of the traits seen as oppositional disorders, the conduct problems are more serious here. Although aggressive behavior may be present, for conduct disordered children who are socialized, a peer group relationship and the capacity to show concern for a friend is present. It is this capacity to have a caring relationship with a peer, however problematic it may be, that makes group therapy a suitable modality for these children.

The DSM-III-R utilizes the qualifiers of mild, moderate, and severe which provides a dimensional perspective of severity in addition to a categorical perspective. We would include children from all three of these levels of severity, provided that these children have been evaluated to demonstrate a capacity to experience concern, guilt, remorse, and repentence toward peers and friends.

In groups these children have great difficulty interacting with each other. They tend to misjudge the social cues of others, and are unable to detect nuances of feeling. Aggressive outbursts can occur from the onset and the children are frequently unable to respond to verbal limit-setting during such incidents. Sometimes these children flee from the group therapy room before the therapists can intervene. An out-of-control child can cause an entire group of children to become behaviorally aggressive. The other children tend to quickly join in to break or destroy play materials or to try to damage the group therapy room itself. An atmosphere of destructive contagion is very difficult to control once it has occurred. Sometimes time-out periods are not enough and the session must be stopped to prevent the escalation of such dangerous behaviors. Even during quieter periods in the group, these children have great difficulty sharing play materials or taking turns in group activity.

Therapeutic groups provide a forum for interpersonal learning and an opportunity to experiment with new behaviors. As maladaptive social behaviors are revealed in the group, feedback from other members and the therapist as well as self-observation help to correct behaviors which are troublesome. Feedback is especially important for these children as many of them have cognitive deficits. They are prone to have intense affective reactions in which memory becomes blurred so that they lose awareness of their own role in the difficulties they experience with peers and others. In addition, many lack parental feedback or receive it inconsistently. Outside of the therapeutic group, peers cannot be counted on to provide helpful observations either, as these children are attracted to others like themselves who tend: to distort things, to be impulsive, and to take flight.

As new behaviors and attitudes are practiced within the group, members are offered a new chance to achieve consensual validation. The therapeutic group setting offers an opportunity to "rehearse" ways of relating that carry over to life outside. It provides the children with opportunities to improve their self-esteem by way of increased success in interpersonal relationships. Thus the goals and overall treatment aims of play group therapy for these children are as follows: (1) to diminish conduct disordered behavior (e.g., disobedience, aggressive outbursts, and defiance of rules); (2) to improve social adaptation with peers in and out of school; and (3) to improve self-esteem through the acquisition of new skills in making friends, keeping friends, and developing a sense of mastery in solving interpersonal conflicts.

THEORETICAL FRAMEWORK AND OVERVIEW OF TREATMENT APPROACHES

Group theorists have various views as to how best to work within a group; these include intrapsychic, interpersonal, and systems theory approaches, or some combination of these.

Saul Scheidlinger's (1982) position utilizes ego and developmental psychology to explain group processes which are pertinent when thinking about children's groups. In the initial phases of unstructured therapy groups, individual and group-as-a-whole stresses result in a controlled regression to earlier need-satisfying modes as well as to primitive identifications. This includes the search for a nonconflictual, need-gratifying relationship with the mother. Scheidlinger views the group itself as unconsciously representing the mother-group, which is conceptualized as a positive, benign image. Other members and the group therapist(s) become the recipients of ambivalent and hostile attitudes. By displacing the initial negative feelings largely onto the leader the group's supportive character can be maintained. This promotes group cohesion, an important curative factor, so that intragroup conflicts and personal problems can be worked through without anxiety that is unduly threatening. By displacing hostility outward, the supportive climate of the "group as mother" remains benevolent and conflicts of both a positive and negative nature among group members are allowed to unfold. By way of identification with the mother-group, a corrective emotional experience can occur to repair a range of damaged ego functions such as the capacity to delay, to tolerate frustration, and to attend to the task at hand. For the conduct disordered child this may have resulted in disobedience, impulsivity, temper tantrums, fighting, distractability, and low self-esteem. It is implicit in this view that the task of the therapist is to help the children belong to the group, while maintaining their individual identity.

Complementing Scheidlinger's (1982) conceptualizations of unconscious forces operating in the group are those of Irwin Yalom (1970), whose interpersonal here-and-now approach has practical ramifications for the group treatment of children. He views some of the major curative factors of group psychotherapy as imparting of information, interpersonal learning, catharsis, group cohesiveness, insight, universality (sharing common problems), instillation of hope, altruism, corrective recapitulation of the primary family group, imitative behavior, and development of socializing techniques. Although Yalom writes about adult therapy groups, his curative functions are applicable to children's groups as well.

Children referred for group therapy have behavior problems that may have resulted in the development of the sense that they are "bad" children. The group therapy experience can create a new beginning out of which the child can regain a sense of optimism that his own behavior can change. Children need to "belong" to a peer group. It can be helpful for them to see within the group that others have had problems similar to their own. Children can teach each other, and the therapists can also show them other ways of behaving that can be more appropriately gratifying than what they had previously known. The mutual giving and receiving that occurs within the group helps these children feel that they have something to offer which can add to their sense of competence.

The recapitualization of the primary family group described by Yalom is created transferentially within the group as the therapist assumes parental roles, with both positive and negative connotations, and the children become "siblings" to one another. Maladaptive ways of relating within the family can undergo a "corrective emotional experience" through group interactions.

The socializing techniques afforded by play group therapy enable children with conduct problems to learn new skills such as putting feelings into words, sharing, taking turns, delaying gratification, and making, keeping, and being a friend. Through the interpersonal here-and-now encounter in the group, children can improve their observational skills about feelings and behavior which, in turn, helps them to deepen their self-understanding and their relationships to other children.

Group cohesiveness, or the unifying forces within the group, has always been critical to the functioning of a therapeutic group. Children with socialized conduct disorders already have a problem in common, by virtue of their symptom picture and level of ego functioning. Since all of the children know that they are working on behavioral problems that are similar in nature, they can be more accepting of the group goals and more open about working toward change.

Catharsis occurs as the children are permitted to discharge affect. However, limit-setting is utilized as needed to help the children channel their aggressive behavior into more socially acceptable ways of behaving. This goal can be approached by the use of symbolic play materials such as puppets or dolls to help a child express anger toward a peer or the adult leader. Verbalization is encouraged to replace action.

Children learn that life can be painful, despite the rewards that improved behavior can bring them. They also come to see that they must take responsibility for their own actions, and that passing blame onto others does not ultimately free them of their own accountability for their behavior (Kolvin, Garside, MacMillan, Wolstenholme, and Leitch, 1981).

Bion's theory (1959) provides an understanding of the choreography of the transferences that emerge in the group. When "dependency" is the ascending formation, the therapist(s) is seen as an omnipotent, idealized presence who is there to take care of all of the group members. Fight–flight represents members' unconscious wish to become leaders in their own right through aggressive attacks against each other, with flight as a defense against this fighting. In children's groups, an initial form of group cohesion takes place in this combining against the therapist. The basic assumption of "pairing" is the shared group fantasy of members coming together to produce a new member (Bion conceived of a "Messiah") who could "save" the group. "Pairing" also gives birth to a sense of belonging, and being cared for. Sometimes shared secrets in the group may be an example of pairing which promotes commonality in the group, and can help establish a sense of cohesion.

Tension inevitably increases, however, when the basic assumption does not lead to the fantasied result. The three assumptions are not sequential but arise depending upon whichever assumption is dominant at a given point in time.

THE GROUP PROCESS

Strategy and Selection

School-age children of the same sex, who are diagnosed with the disruptive behavior disorders described earlier, will be eligible. Chil-

dren with learning disabilities as a secondary diagnosis and/or attention deficit disorders will be acceptable as long as these are not their
overriding diagnosis. The intellectual functioning of the children who
are acceptable must be 71 I.Q. or higher. Since these children are by
definition action oriented, verbal abilities will not be considered as
part of the inclusionary criteria.

Children's groups have been frequently described as needing the
proper "balance" or mix of children to reflect no one overriding
behavior (Slavson and Schiffer, 1975). Whenever feasible children are
included who have a variety of diagnoses within the spectrum that has
been described. Furthermore, group members have a range of severity which is manageable.

A cotherapy arrangement is useful with this population. Each therapist can help maintain the boundaries of the group, can support the
other's interventions, and together they can model appropriate interactions. Cotherapists also help the group remain a safe place for
all members. It allows for one therapist to work with an individual in
need of one-to-one attention while the other therapist focuses on the
remaining members.

Having children of the same sex in each group is in keeping with
the general tendency in the literature to support group membership
of the same sex in elementary school-age groups, as is common among
normal peer groups at this age. The variation for each group should
be within a three-year age span so that the members will generally be
within similar levels of development. No less than three children
should constitute each group. Given the tendency of these children
to be volatile, the groups should be limited to no more than six children. Sessions should be once a week for one-and-one-quarter hours.

Use of Play in the Group Setting

Play is encouraged in group psychotherapy for children as a facilitator
of communication between the children and therapists and because
of its value in helping children practice new behaviors. The environment of the group contains materials which are at the appropriate
developmental level for the child's emotional needs.

Play in groups allows for the release of anxieties and fears through
abreaction and reenactment. It also helps to serve as a channel for
primitive impulses. Identification is promoted as the child takes on
qualities of some of the other children or the therapists and "practices"
roles that can be put to later use.

Play within the group also helps in the development of problem solving and social skills. Problem solving becomes easier if children can explore the task first through play. Reality testing is aided as children receive validation or the lack of it from the sharing of their fantasies with other members of the group. Through play, children learn to value peers and take an interest in being understood. By way of cooperative play, the social cognitive ability of the latency age child can be improved by including consideration of another point of view as well as by an interest in the way others view him. The group setting can enable the child to begin to deal with peer group pressures as well as the protection of his own individuality in the light of group demands (Grunebaum and Solomon, 1982). Social cognitive skills can be heightened through play within the group by helping the children learn to read cues from others. This helps the children to take into account the motivation of other group members, and it enhances their capacity for empathy for one another.

Techniques of the Therapist

The role of the therapist is to establish a facilitating environment in which the group members can begin to feel safe and where interpersonal interactions can become the therapeutic focus. To this end, the therapists must convey their authority to set limits and establish the norms of the group, and yet remain flexible enough to adapt the norms to the specific group of children with whom they are working.

The children will test and retest the therapists throughout the formative stages of the group. Contrary to the experiences of many therapists who have not previously worked in group with conduct disordered children, the group therapists must from the beginning through the middle phases remain very active in terms of structuring the group sessions. This is necessary to help the children augment the controls which they have not yet internalized sufficiently.

Frequently it is necessary to divide the session into a playtime followed by discussion/snacktime. The therapists set the tone in those initial sessions by choosing the activity, directing the children, and determining the length of time allowed for the playtime versus discussion/snacktime (e.g., half the session for each).

The use of play materials and or choice of games should reflect this highly structured approach at first, as these children have difficulty modulating their regression and thus need activities that will help them contain their impulses which are frequently destructive. Initially, the therapist can encourage individual projects that do not require a high degree of interaction among the members. A sufficient accomplishment in those initial sessions will be for the group members to be able to remain in the room together with the therapists.

A range of materials that could be used over the year are designed to match the maturational phases of the group.

1. Beginning Phase—Therapists Select the Activity. Supplies should be carefully chosen so as not to overstimulate the children. One activity per session may be all that the children can handle initially, and thus the other materials should be added only after the children give evidence that they can master them. Examples of the types of materials that would be used are simple craft projects designed to be completed by each individual within the session, board games such as checkers or Connect-Four; playing cards; construction sets; bean bag games; puzzles; or drawing paper and crayons.

2. Middle through Final Phases—Group Members Select the Activity. Additional supplies are added to enable the children to have choices. The selection should include less structured games and toys. Examples are Nerf balls and Nerf basketball loop; Knock hockey; Lego blocks; craft projects and games requiring cooperative team efforts; art supplies; family puppets, puppet theater; play food and cooking utensils; masks.

Limit-setting by the therapists is an important therapeutic tool. The therapists may need to call for time-out periods for children who have difficulty tolerating the intimacy of the group setting. Another limit-setting measure that may be needed is to shorten the length of the session during the initial phases of the group. Snacks should never be withheld, however, as the nurturing functions of the group therapists help the children to feel accepted despite their behavioral difficulties.

The therapist needs to pay attention to the group process as it unfolds, utilizing a primarily here-and-now approach to work with the group. Varying techniques are employed depending upon the needs of the group members at specific phases of group life. These techniques are as follows:

Facilitation of Interactive Play. The therapist encourages children in the group to interact with each other through play. Play has a cathartic effect in and of itself, and helps the children achieve mastery (e.g., "Adam and Steven, I see you're both playing with Lego . . . if you pooled your resources you'd have more blocks to play with and the possibility of making even a bigger house").

Facilitation of Empathy with Other Children. The conduct disordered child is typically very slow in understanding the nature of peer group interactions and his impact upon others. A specific technique which can be used in the group with this type of children is the interchanging of roles to have the members learn how their peers feel and how they react (e.g., "today we are going to pretend to be someone else in the group; David, you're going to pretend to be Andrew, Andrew you're going to pretend to be Chris. Let's see what happens"). For instance, if a fight occurs during the group, the therapist could try and stop the fighting by having the members who are involved switch roles. In this way they can experience more directly how the other members are feeling and why they are reacting in a certain way. Role-play can enhance the children's development of empathy, and their capacity for an observing ego.

Support. Through the benign regression that occurs within the group, old conflicts and needs reemerge. The group therapist utilizes support by teaching the children new ways of coping so that their previous level of ego functioning becomes broadened. This educational role can also include suggestions, encouragement, and reassurance so that the children are helped to try new solutions for existing problems. In this way the children come to see that they have more behavioral choices in stressful situations than they have known previously. As their coping mechanisms increase they can go on to meet new challenges at higher levels of functioning (e.g., "You boys all want to play with the racing car now. Yet by grabbing for it at the same time, you get into a fight and then no one has the chance to use it. Another way might be to take turns; we could give each person who wants to use it a time-limit so that everyone who wants to play could get a chance. How long a period should we allow for each person?").

Clarification. The therapist's role is to help the play activity unfold and to comment when appropriate in regard to the emerging themes of the play as it relates to the group. The therapist must translate the impact of the individual's play and verbalizations upon the group-as-a-whole, as well as the influence that the group has had upon individual members. For the purpose of clarification, the therapist might request more factual information from the members or use a "tell us more" statement to help the children expand on their thoughts, behavior, or ideas. In addition, the therapist might employ statements directing the children's or child's attention to specific affects or patterns of behavior in the present or previous sessions. Nonverbal and verbal communications are examined in the process of clarification, with attention paid not only to what is said, but what is omitted (e.g., "you are all speaking at the same time, want to play with the same toy, and want to sit next to me—have you noticed that?")

Confrontation. Group therapy provides an opportunity for children to be confronted with feedback about patterns of thoughts, feelings, and behaviors which have been shared in the group. Confrontations are observations or responses to patterns of interactions but do not involve interpretations of deep unconscious motivations. Through the use of confrontation, the therapist can point out to a group member that a problem exists, which can then be validated by the other children in the group. By assisting a child to recognize that such a problem exists, he or she can begin to work it out within the group setting. In an enabling atmosphere, confrontation can be an extremely useful way for members to give and receive important information about themselves. The therapist's sense of timing, empathy, and working alliance with the child and group-as-a-whole help to make confrontations more effective (e.g., "whenever we start making the model of the ship, David, you, start teasing and make it hard for the rest of the group to work. It happened last time too, when we were painting the mural. David, what do you make of that? Can the rest of you kids help David understand this?").

Interpretation. Interpretation is designed to help the child develop an understanding of the hidden motivations and conflicts behind his behavior. The current life of the group allows the therapist to have an in vivo demonstration of interpersonal behavior, without having to rely for data on outside information or only upon the relationship between therapist and child. Interpretations should usually be made in the here-and-now and can be directed at the individual member or the group-as-a-whole. Group norms considered antitherapeutic can also be interpreted in this way. Interpersonal interventions can address anxiety-laden issues which are threatening to the group.

The therapist should attempt to view the play as a metaphor for significant themes, fears, and anxieties in the current life of the group (e.g., "you are all angry at me for having been away last week; rather than telling me straight, Louis and Carl are fighting with each other, Rick is pretending I don't exist by turning his back to me, and Daniel is shooting darts all over the place. A couple even hit my legs").

Another aspect of interpretation is sifting out themes dealing with past life and refocusing them to the here and now. By working with defenses, distortions, wishes, and fears, unconscious material can be explored to help the group become cohesive and to promote understanding of group members in the current interaction. This can lead to the development of insight which clarifies to the child whether his behaviors are adaptive or maladaptive for a particular situation in the group.

An issue critical to the existence or functioning of the entire group always takes precedence over a narrower interpersonal issue. In this way, the working group will be preserved and members will be assisted to take part in the interpersonal learning that goes on in the group (Yalom, 1970) (e.g., "Alan feels unsure that the group will invite him to join in, and he resents that everybody except him is paired together. He tries to split up the group so he won't be the only one alone").

Length of Sessions. The group is held at an after-school hour and each session lasts for a maximum of one hour and a quarter. During the beginning of the year the sessions are often shortened as the members cannot tolerate longer sessions. The group runs from the start of the school year to the summer break, following the school academic calendar. This is because some of the children and their parents tend to lose their motivation for the group, or not to be available for treatment in the summer. A group with less than half the membership present is not viable.

Preparation of Child for Group. Preparation of the children is felt to be essential prior to the first group meeting. In a one-to-one meeting with the therapist, the purpose of the group is reviewed with the child in language appropriate for his or her level of development. This initial meeting provides the child with an opportunity to deal with initial anxiety about joining the group and helps the therapist to receive input about issues felt essential to be worked on from the child's perspective. The importance of regular attendance, the need for confidentiality, and the parameters about parent contacts should also be addressed at this time. The child should be told that the therapists will not share the contents of the talk or play in sessions with parents.

Parent Contacts. The child's parents are contacted before the child is seen, to explain the purpose of the group; that is, to improve the child's ability to form relationships with peers and adults at home and in school, to increase socially appropriate behavior, and to improve self-esteem through mastery of tasks. The importance of attendance on a regular basis and the need for confidentiality are explained to parents. Communication is important, and one way of working with parents would be to have a parents' group held once per week at the same time as the children's group. This group should be led by another therapist and is designed to serve a supportive parent guidance function. There should be regular meetings between child and parent group therapists for the purpose of communication of relevant issues. In addition, the children's group therapists should hold group meetings with parents at least twice during the year so that communication can be maximized. In this way, questions about the group can be answered and parents can receive assessments about how their child is doing in the group. Parents should also be told that the group therapists can be contacted in the event of an emergency.

Parents contacts are important for the following reasons:

1. to help parents understand their child's pathology and the therapeutic purpose of the group;
2. to provide them with support;
3. to provide them with suggestions for the management of different behaviors, such as temper tantrums, disobedience, distractability;
4. to teach them how to structure the treatment (e.g., directing their child to bring back to the group concerns they may have raised at home);
5. to discuss with them the importance of the therapist's communication with the school, to obtain specific information about the child's difficulty with peers;
6. to discuss possible medication issues, if needed.

School Contact. Initial communication with the child's school during the diagnostic assessment prior to the first group meeting is useful, in order to gain a more detailed picture of the child's functioning with peers. If this is not possible we suggest to parents that they show us their child's report cards. Further contacts will occur depending upon clinical needs.

Special Problems

Fighting. Fighting among children can be understood in terms of group dynamics and individual psychopathology. The group therapists should tell the children that no fighting is allowed. Separating fighting children is a tactical approach which may be needed. Having a time-out period for the aggressive children or for the group as a whole can be utilized to stop the action until the children are calm enough to discuss what has occurred. The therapists should also try to actively engage the other children in a discussion about the aggressive behavior that has taken place, and its ramifications for the group, and the individuals concerned. The therapists need to focus the group on ways to control the fighting and to prevent its recurrence, because the children will fear for their own safety unless the therapists immediately step in. Sometimes group contagion may necessitate a curtailment of the length of the session for that day if the members continue to escalate hostilities, despite efforts of the therapists to verbalize what has occurred and to control the group.

A temporary suspension from the group will be used if necessary. If this step is needed it should also include involvement of the parents. In these measures the individuals and the group are told of the therapists aim to reestablish control (not punishment). If none of the above measures is sufficient for any one child, our choice of play group therapy will need to be reevaluated. Sometimes the addition of individual psychotherapy is indicated. In other instances, referrals elsewhere are instituted such as for day treatment or residential placement.

Scapegoating. The therapist should "stop the action" and clarify the process as a group defensive maneuver. Rather than exploring why a particular child is singled out as the group victim it is best to understand how the scapegoated child serves the needs of the group at this moment in time. The emphasis should first be upon the development of a productive group climate without having the group fall deeper into the role of blaming the victim. Furthermore the scapegoat frequently lacks the capacity for self-observation while being ostracized. He may only be able to reflect back on why he was scapegoated once the group is no longer acting out (e.g., George was put down and excluded from all games and subgroupings. He encouraged that by never looking other children in the eye, doing only "his thing" [video games] rather than following other children's suggestions. The therapist began by exploring how relieved each member is to have someone else as the scapegoat and how each child can feel insecure. The therapist then added at a later time that George found pleasure in being special—if not the most popular, the most unpopular).

Refusal to Attend. The absence of a child should be noticed by the therapists. Possible reasons for the absence should be discussed by the group if frequent absences occur, and telephone calls and a letter should be sent if the child misses repeatedly. Concomitantly, the therapists should have a special meeting with the parents to review if they may be colluding with the child to protect him from this "bad" group. As a punishment, some parents may prevent the child (who enjoys the group) from attending. The group should be made aware that the absent member has missed out on new information that may be discussed. He has also lost his "time" to speak and be spoken to by the other group members. On the other hand, his absence should not be a time to talk about him behind his back. The children should be encouraged to express their feelings directly to the absent member, if and when he returns.

TERMINATION

Groups are associated with the school academic year, thus termination will fall naturally in the late spring or early summer. In the termination phase the therapist should try to facilitate a recapitulation of the history of the group and the progress that the various members have made. Regression to the original symptom picture for each child may emerge for brief periods, which is a frequent occurrence during the termination phase. Children alternately may wish that the group could go on forever and the regression can be interpreted with this in mind. As the therapist conveys to the children a sense of optimism about the progress they have made, as well as the finality of the group, a mourning phase occurs and the members begin to accept that the group will come to an end.

Separation anxieties should be addressed, as well as the specific way each child reacts to the end of this group (e.g., two girls are joining together to play house, while two boys are shooting darts outside the window as if the meeting room is a fortress; another child engages the group therapist in a dialogue by pairing with him). The group therapist comments on what the group is saying by their actions and how they feel about the group coming to an end (e.g., "Anne and Jane feel they are losing a safe place of their own; John and Richard are anticipating dangers to come; and Jimmy hopes that he will now have the therapist all to himself").

The therapist needs to assess all the children individually at this time. Those children with a significant decrease of symptoms, more adaptive behavior at home and school, significant increase in social skills, and the ability to sustain friendships, will finish their group treatment at this time. Other children who still need group treatment will be able to continue in a different group in the fall.

Parents will also have feelings of loss, relief, and disappointment which will need to be shared in the parents' group.

REFERENCES

American Psychiatric Association (1980), *Diagnostic and Statistical Manual of Mental Disorders*, 3rd ed. (DSM-III). Washington, DC: American Psychiatric Press.
——— (1987), *Diagnostic and Statistical Manual of Mental Disorders*, 3rd ed., rev. (DSM-III-R). Washington, DC.: American Psychiatric Press.
Bion, W. R. (1959), *Experiences in Group*. New York: Basic Books.
Conger, J. J., & Miller, W. C. (1966), *Personality, Social Class, and Delinquency*. New York: John Wiley.

Grunebaum, H., & Solomon, L. (1982), Toward a theory of peer relationships. *Internat. J. Group Psychother.*, 32:283–307.

Kolvin, I., Garside, R. F., MacMillan, A., Wolstenholme, E., & Leitch, I. M. (1981), *Help Starts Here: The Maladjusted Child in the Ordinary School.* London: Tavistock Publications, pp. 218–221.

Rapoport, J. L., & Ismond, D. R. (1983), *DSM-III Training Guide for Childhood Disorders.* New York: Brunner/Mazel.

Robins, L. N. (1970), Follow-up studies investigating childhood disorders. In: *Psychiatric Epidemiology,* ed. E. H. Hare, & J. K. Wing. London: Oxford University Press.

Rutter, M., Cox, A., Tupling, C., Berger, M., & Yule, W. (1975), Attainment and adjustment in two geographical areas. I. The prevalence of psychiatric disorder. *Brit. J. Psychiat.*, 126:493–509.

Scheidlinger, A. (1982), *Focus on Group Psychotherapy: Clinical Essays.* New York: International Universities Press.

Slavson, S. R., & Schiffer, M. (1975), *Group Psychotherapies for Children. A Textbook.* New York: International Universities Press.

Yalom, I. (1970), *The Theory and Practice of Group Psychotherapy.* New York: Basic Books.

Chapter 12

Supervision and Support Structures for Group Leaders and Therapists Working with Children and Adolescents

ALBERT ERIC RIESTER, Ed.D.

ORGANIZATIONAL CONTEXT

Support for Group Leaders

The leaders of psychotherapy groups for severely emotionally disturbed latency age children attempt to provide opportunities for these patients to develop age-appropriate skills in communication, conflict resolution, and impulse regulation. This is a challenging problem and group leaders continually seek more effective methods and strategies which might create a therapeutic group climate conducive for interpersonal learning, corrective emotional experiences, and socialization.

Group therapists assigned to developmentally delayed children are pressed to draw on a variety of theories with the hope of facilitating therapeutic group experiences. The historical debates about which theoretical orientation is the most valuable may obstruct the therapist's ongoing search for creative and effective group methods for children who have severe cognitive, emotional, language, and motor deficits. Unfortunately, most publications focus on the advantages of one theoretical orientation and describe the intervention methods that are related to that paradigm.

There is an assumption that the group therapist can, on the one hand, assimilate and integrate theory and knowledge, and then on the other hand practice according to the parameters of a defined orientation. Somehow, the group leader is expected to select and orchestrate verbal and nonverbal activities to create therapeutic group experiences. The list of methods, strategies, and models for the ego-deprived child is encyclopedic in scope and may be one of the reasons why clinicians often avoid this population.

Those agencies which have been successful in offering group psychotherapy and therapeutic groups for severely disturbed children need to be studied to learn why they were effective. From such examples, we can identify the essential program elements, assumptions, and methods that have enabled group leaders to succeed with this difficult population. It is important for clinicians to master the group techniques, methods, and strategies so therapeutic experiences consistently occur for severely disturbed children. Therefore, this chapter focuses on what a treatment facility needs to provide for group leaders working with these children so that effective groups can be conducted for this patient population.

The two programs that will be discussed are based at the Southwest Neuropsychiatric Institute (SWNPI) and have been in operation for over three years and are for group psychotherapists and therapeutic group leaders. This organization is nationally recognized as an innovative, responsive, and efficiently managed child and adolescent inpatient and outpatient psychiatric facility. Founded in 1886, the facility is approved by the Joint Commission of Accreditation of Healthcare Organizations (JCAHO) and is an affiliate of the University of Texas Health Science Center at San Antonio. It offers a broad range of inpatient, outpatient, and day hospital services for children and adolescents (ages 3–21), and their families. Operating at four locations in San Antonio, treatment modalities include individual, group, and family psychotherapy, diagnostic assessments, special education, activity and recreation therapies, psychopharmacological intervention, and behavior management. The availability of 120 beds and experienced mental health clinicians and staff enables this facility to offer a variety of inpatient services such as diagnostic workups, residential care, and psychiatric hospitalization for a range of diagnostic categories.

Mental health and special education programs in school districts must be prepared to offer support and supervision for group leaders, teachers, and therapists who provide services for severely emotionally disturbed youth. The availability of a variety of group guidance and counseling experiences in the "mainstream" by churches, agencies, and schools may reduce the need for groups to serve children with mild to moderate emotional and developmental problems. Therefore, clinicians may be required to modify the treatment modalities that historically have not been recommended for ego impaired children who are aggressive, explosive, and impulsive. To implement and maintain services for this clinical population, new support and supervision experiences for group leaders will become a necessity.

The author was responsible for the development and implementation of (1) a supervision group model, and (2) a school-based day hospital managment service. The following list was derived from the two successful program examples that are described in this chapter.

ORGANIZATIONAL REQUIREMENTS AND ASSUMPTIONS TO SUPPORT THE GROUP LEADERS

1. The psychiatric organization must support the therapist or group leaders with ongoing supervision and consultation by qualified senior group psychotherapists.

2. Staffings and supervisory group meetings provide a structure which enhances the group leaders' knowledge and skills necessary to work with severely emotionally disturbed youth. The members of the supervision group as well as the senior supervisor share in the task of finding measures which can help resolve the ongoing problems that emerge in the course of treating this population.

3. It is important to recognize that the psychiatric services for severely ego deprived children require a multispecialty approach plus the ongoing support programs for the therapist and group leader.

4. Group psychotherapists and group leaders who work with the population cannot assimilate and integrate all the knowledge needed to create therapeutic group experiences. Therefore, ongoing supervision groups and scheduled staffings are needed by the leader to successfully employ the group treatment modality.

5. Organizational partnerships are necessary in order for the programs to be cost effective in delivering multispecialty services.

6. The Caplan mental health consultation model (Caplan, 1963) is not sufficient to support the therapeutic group or psychotherapy group leaders who are assigned to the severely emotionally disturbed youth. According to Caplan, the professional responsibility for the patient remains with the consultee. The consultee is free to accept or reject all or part of the input from the consultant. Action for the benefit of the patient that emerges from the consultation event is the responsibility of the consultee. A pyramid approach to treating patients has evolved in which more senior mental health professionals at the apex of the pyramid provide indirect treatment to the patient

by consultation with the caregivers who have the greatest access to persons under stress (Gallessich, 1986). The Caplan model carries the presumption that through consultation a relatively small number of mental health clinicians can extend their impact to the larger base of society.

7. The therapist's personal child and adolescent group experiences become central in understanding which methods and theories can be assimilated and utilized in their clinical practice.

8. The complex countertransference issues related to serving this severely impaired population require ongoing supervision to maintain the group modality as a viable component of the treatment program.

9. Experiential learning in the course of the supervision group gives group leaders the opportunity to assimilate and incorporate new information in the context of their own personality dynamics and training background.

10. The diverse child patient population requires the selection of group models and corresponding methods that are congruent with diagnosis and developmental levels (Schamess, 1986).

PROGRAM EXAMPLES

Day Hospital Management Service

This program involves a therapeutic community or day hospital for twenty-two severely emotionally disturbed latency age children. In operation for three years, this program is unique in that a school district contracts with a psychiatric hospital to provide a full-time clinically trained "manager" or program director to operate their school based special education services for severely emotionally disturbed students. Under this contract, the psychiatric facility also provides trained child care workers, and biweekly child psychiatric consultation for the staff. Group, individual, and family counseling, and traditional case work are available as needed for the twenty-two latency age students. The school district hires and assigns the special education teachers, secretary, and classroom aides to this program who are then accountable to the psychiatric facility's manager for the operation of the day hospital program. The district is responsible for providing the facilities and all maintenance and operational costs. In brief, this creative partnership has established a cost effective program for severely emotionally disturbed latency age children by drawing from what each organization is most qualified to provide. The management model and partnership with two community organizations has given the "on campus" support for group leaders (teachers and clinicians) who work with these children in groups.

The ongoing support is offered by the program manager, child care workers, and consulting psychiatrist by means of staffings, crisis intervention, casework, and close family communication. The staff assigned from the psychiatric facility are trained in behavior management and developmental programming. They are sensitive to psychodynamic concepts (such as projective identification, countertransference, and parataxic distortions). The program manager helps teachers and staff understand the impact of this severe student population on their own personality dynamics. With the support systems provided, the group leaders have become creative and effective in their practice, and this day hospital facility is now the preferred special education teaching assignment in the school district.

The program manager provides the overall direction and coordination of the program according to the hospital and school district policies and procedures. This new management model replaces the Caplan (1963) mental health consultation model that was previously utilized by the district for special education teachers and administrators. In a drastic departure from this consultation practice, the psychiatric facility assumes full management responsibility for the operation of a day hospital program for twenty-two students identified (by the school district's assessment procedures) as being the most impulsive, explosive, and disturbed students in their special education population. This structure permits teachers to practice their specialty (special education) and the mental health specialists to deliver direct services such as group and individual counseling, casework, and behavior management.

The majority (13) of the children (12 boys and 1 girl) had a history of psychiatric hospitalizations. Their cognitive and psychological developmental problems occurred at an early age. The majority of the children have a dual diagnosis of psychiatric and neurological problems requiring individualized educational programming and an ongoing monitoring of their psychotropic medications by the psychiatric consultants and staff.

The students initially seemed so developmentally diverse that subgrouping plans for classroom and group counseling placement seemed impossible. By drawing on models developed by Schamess (1976) and Scheidlinger (1965) to serve children with severe psychopathology, the following subgroup structure was designed and successfully implemented in this new program.

Developmental Groupings

Students were assigned to one of three groups (each coded by color) based upon their assessed level of functioning along several developmental dimensions.

Red Group students experienced significant neurological and neuropsychological impairments with severe behavioral manifestations including severe impulsivity, explosive temperament, very limited capacity for self organization and regulation of behavior, and severe developmental delays (most notable in the areas of language and social skills). Because of the nature of severity of their various impairments, students in Red Group most frequently required a high degree of one-to-one supervision.

Blue Group students tended to evidence less significant impairments of cognitive, social, and language functions. Psychological factors were most frequently the primary etiological components of problems manifested by deficient capacity to tolerate frustration and regulate aggressive impulses and to form stable relationships with others. These students tended toward more aggressive "blow-ups" with potential for assaultive and destructive behavior. However, when not stressed, they demonstrated a relatively greater ability to focus attention and organize their behavior around a task. For this reason, a staff-to-student ratio of one to two was generally adequate.

Students in the Green Group demonstrated deficits and dysfunctions similar to those students assigned to the Blue Group, although to a less severe extent. These students had improved in their ability to function with less intense supervision. They could function cooperatively as members of a small group. They were approaching readiness to return to a special education classroom in a mainstream campus. A staff-to-student ratio of one to two was sufficient in working with these youngsters.

The application of child group psychotherapy models which resulted in subgrouping the children and assigning the necessary staff to provide the needed level of structure is regarded as central in the success of the day hospital program. The manager's mental health background further provided the support system for the teachers, aides, and child care workers who interact intensely with these severely emotionally disturbed children. Without the scheduled staffings, supervision, and ongoing support from a clinically trained manager, the staff would experience "burnout" and lose the flexibility and creativity necessary to establish a positive learning and therapeutic experience for the students.

SUPERVISION GROUP

The second SWNPI Center program example is a supervision group for the therapists assigned to conduct inpatient groups for severely emotionally disturbed children and adolescents. The author developed the supervision group based on Edward Soo's model (Soo, 1986) and it has been in operation for three years. Prior to the implementation of this learning experience for clinicians, group psychotherapy at the SWNPI was not consistently offered as a treatment modality. At present, two supervision groups meet weekly for one hour for approximately twelve senior clinicians and residents. Six to seven patient groups now meet twice a week for both the inpatient and residential programs for patients, ages five to eighteen. With careful attention to developmental programming concepts for assigning group members, group psychotherapy has emerged as a primary treatment modality at the SWNPI. The supervision group of therapists has also differentiated group psychotherapy from other inpatient therapeutic group experiences such as community meetings, activities groups, and special education guidance groups.

The supervision group for therapists offers ongoing opportunities for the group psychotherapist to select verbal and nonverbal activities that will provide therapeutic experiences in group psychotherapy. Initially, supervisee resistances occurred around the use of nonverbal activities and the therapeutic benefit of games, field trips, refreshments, and sports. As the cotherapists discussed their own child and adolescent group histories, insight was gained into how they unconsciously press the patients to engage in events that were part of their own childhood group experiences.

The intense countertransferences that inevitably arise in conducting patient groups were discussed openly in the supervision group after initial trust was established (Gaoni and Neumann, 1974). Cotherapy conflicts and variations in leadership styles were reviewed during the supervision group sessions. The use of denial by the clinician in dealing with patients' termination from group and the "emergency" excuse for not attending a scheduled patient or supervision group meetings were frequently issues for the supervision group. This group became a safe setting to learn new techniques and gain insight into how the therapists' personality dynamics impacted their practice with this child and adolescent population.

Although the supervisors for the two supervision groups are senior clinicians and regarded as experts in this treatment modality, participants began to recognize that "the" model does not exist to practice with this severely disturbed population. The supervision group gave the leaders the opportunity to evaluate the methods and strategies that they used, and the supervisors identified the therapeutic benefits of these interventions. The supervision group session was a time to plan developmentally appropriate activities, behavior management strategies, and required levels of structure for the patients so as to have a therapeutic experience in a group. Verbal and physical acting out was now understood in the context of the individuation process which is most visible during the middle stage of group development (Fried, 1970). A patient who refused to share or cooperate in group was now perceived as egocentric or narcissistic rather than manipulative or oppositional. As the supervision group became established in the psychiatric facility, group leaders learned new ways to provide the level of structure necessary for severely emotionally disturbed patients so as to facilitate therapeutic group experiences. The learning and integration necessary to interact positively with this population requires an ongoing supervision group which can work at identifying the leadership style that fits the personality and group experiences of the therapist (Grotjahn, 1955).

After permission was obtained by the facility and supervisors, an outside evaluator conducted a study of the supervision groups. A questionnaire was designed to obtain data from the participants regarding their perception of what factors are important to their learning in the supervision group (Nelson, 1978). The questionnaire focused on group structure, group process, and dynamics and the role of the supervisor. This evaluation process is recommended to give the supervisor and group information concerning how to strengthen the program. Furthermore, it provides useful information concerning why supervision groups are useful in an inpatient or outpatient setting.

Cohesiveness, trust, and supervision group size were regarded as the most important factors in influencing communication in these groups. The respondents indicated that they favored didactic materials along with the experiential learning that was provided by the group. The study concluded that the supervisor is perceived as important to the group members. The supervisor becomes a model for the therapists who make up the group. However, the opportunity to model the supervisor's leadership styles was not consciously sought when the supervisory group began. Clearly stated goals and expectations are also important for group effectiveness for the supervisees responding to the questionnaire in this small sample.

SUMMARY

Organizational support and supervision is necessary for the staff who treat and teach severely emotionally disturbed children and adolescents. Unless supervision is available, the staff will be unable to deliver the services and programs required for this population. Group leaders at all experience and training levels need ongoing supervision to effectively practice with these patients and special education students. As our severely disturbed child and adolescent clinical population grows, organizations have to design support and management structures that focus on the affective and cognitive needs of group leaders. By offering these opportunities, effective therapeutic experiences and psychotherapy groups can be conducted by prepared and qualified leaders. The psychodynamic–developmental viewpoint in supervision group and ongoing support activities gives group leaders didactic and experiential opportunities to learn and to implement appropriate group interventions for severely emotionally disturbed youth.

REFERENCES

Caplan, G. (1963), Types of mental health consultation. *Amer. J. Orthopsychiat.*, 33:470–481.

——— (1984), *Principals of Preventive Psychiatry*. New York: Basic Books.

Fried, E. (1970), Individuation through psychotherapy. *Internat. J. Group Psychother.*, 20:450–459.

Gallessich, J. (1986), *The Profession and Practice of Consultation*. San Francisco: Jossey-Bass.

Gaoni, B., & Neumann, M. (1974), Supervision from the point of view of the supervisee. *Amer. J. Psychother.*, 28:108–114.

Grotjahn, M. (1955), Problems and techniques of supervision. *Psychiatry*, 18:9–15.

Nelson, G. (1978), Psychotherapy supervision from the trainee's point of view: A survey of preferences. *Prof. Psychol.*, 9:539–549.

Schamess, G. (1976), Group treatment modalities for latency-age children. *Internat. J. Group Psychother.*, 26:455–474.

——— (1986), Differential diagnosis and group structure in the outpatient treatment of latency age children. In: *Child Group Psychotherapy: Future Tense*, ed. A. E. Riester & I. A. Kraft. Madison, CT: International Universities Press, pp. 29–68.

Scheidlinger, S. (1965), Three group approaches with socially deprived latency-aged children. *Internat. J. Group Psychother.*, 15:434–445.

Soo, E. (1986), Training and supervision in child and adolescent group psychotherapy. In: *Child Group Psychotherapy: Future Tense*, ed. A. E. Riester & I. A. Kraft. Madison, CT: International Universities Press, pp. 157–171.

Chapter 13

Symbiotic Pairing in Adolescent Inpatient Group Psychotherapy

MAX SUGAR, M.D.

Groups are known to have positive or negative forces, based on how they pair with the leader. There are descriptions of positive and negative valences in the group, of pairing in terms of bad and good, mother and father, and other paired transferences.

With borderline and narcissistic patients pairing is routinely seen in their clinging to the symbiotic object. In a psychotherapy group their pairing is an expectable event, since they quickly find someone with whom to fashion a repetition of the earlier clinging and fused relationship. In this chapter an effort is made to illuminate some features of symbiotic pairing that occur with adolescent borderline and narcissistic disorders and some conduct disorders in inpatient group therapy. This has not been noted previously in the literature.

ON ADMISSION

Unlike others with an acute hospitalization who have a memory of healthy functioning and anticipate that treatment will lead to a restoration of health, adolescents who are admitted for psychiatric care (especially those in intermediate or long term treatment) usually have little, if any, healthy recollections and cannot imagine a different pattern since their pathological one has been dominant and long-standing. These adolescents perceive the psychiatric hospital or residential treatment center as a threat to their life-style and immediately

221

begin planning for escape, while at the same time demonstrating a pretense of good behavior; or they actually run away.

Admission to a hospital or residential treatment center involves a separation for borderline adolescents from their primary symbiotic object. With this there is an immediate sense of abandonment (Masterson and Rinsley, 1975) and there follows a search for a substitute object or some way to restitute and resume the tie with the original symbiotic object. Along with the latter are numerous testing, provocative, and manipulative efforts by the patient to appear healthier than he is and not in need of hospitalization, in order to obtain an early discharge and reunion with the symbiotic object. Simultaneously, the patient is arranging for substitute symbiotic partners and soon finds someone with whom to continue the type of relationship that had been in the forefront of his object relations prior to hospitalization.

Soon he becomes involved with someone who is on the same unit, or on another unit, who may or may not be in the same therapy group with him. This person then becomes formidably important, just as the former or the original symbiotic object had been to him. When he moves away from this object he experiences marked anxiety or terror and efforts at reunion follow. With this object there are mutual protective and rescue operations, with loose boundaries, each speaking for the other, joint scheming against the unit structure and therapy, even to the point of causing riots or wreaking havoc as they did at home.

Concomitantly, if one of the pair should become friendly or even courteous at times to another patient, get involved in therapy, or have a positive attitude toward the therapist, the other member of the pair feels abandoned, or threatened with abandonment. Then he becomes readily angered and promotes sabotage to undermine the partner. The partnerships may change as the process continues in a similar fashion with others even after a therapeutic alliance is forged which begins to deal with this. At times it may be necessary to separate the pairs administratively by limiting contacts or having the patients on separate units.

Initially these patients test, check, and apply their usual pathological efforts to maneuver an early discharge. Sometimes these are successful. In such cases the patient may seem very involved as a working paired member of the therapy group, while undermining in the activity group or school or simply going through the motions of participation in individual therapy. Efforts to avoid this require all therapeutic modalities to be constantly in contact with one another to correlate data and work cooperatively, and with the family.

ON AN INPATIENT UNIT

On an inpatient unit all aspects of pairing are furthered by the daily involvement that follows from living closely together, which may lead to separateness and boundaries becoming easily blurred, squelched, or artificially made to appear as if actually attained. This is aided by the patient using other borderline or narcissistic patients on the unit for reality testing, consensual validation, identification, and incorporation.

The borderline has difficulty in giving up the symbiosis with the mother and his fear of emptiness leads him to fusion with others by clinging reactions and intrusive needs for instant acceptance in toto. Therefore, he interprets a limited relationship or any hint of criticism as rejection. When any of these features seems to be present, such a patient feels impelled to find another symbiotic partner immediately. The possibilities for the occurrence of such pairing are immense on an inpatient adolescent unit, since most of the patients are not psychotic and there are many varieties and degrees of symbiotic relatedness occurring among those with narcissistic and borderline personality disorders.

In an outpatient group there may be a borderline or a narcissistic patient for another with the same diagnosis to identify with and form an early pairing. However, an outpatient adolescent group is not usually arranged to have only borderlines, since an all-borderline group would be easily overwhelmed with one another's needs and would have a premature termination.

An adolescent inpatient psychotherapy group may go on for a lengthy period since these patients require intensive long-term hospital treatment. Since there are many severe character disorder patients in the hospital setting, a group that is largely made up of borderlines is not very difficult to arrange. Further, it is not difficult for them to be maintained in the group in spite of their pairing since the controls in the hospital setting do not allow the acting out that would destroy the group if it were an outpatient one.

IN THE EARLY PHASE

We aid the development of early pairing in the composition and selection process by trying to arrange the therapy group to avoid isolates and scapegoating. This is done by having someone for each person who is in some way like themselves, with whom they can identify, compare notes, and share. This provides a vehicle for reduction of the patient's anxiety in the early group sessions.

We espouse further pairing during the early phase of the therapy group to help the members become a therapeutically cohesive group. Narcissistic ties, ego-ideal ties, cleavages, and complementary group transactions (Anthony, 1965) may all contribute to the early pairings in group therapy.

Ross (1958) writes that the phenomenon of pairing in adults between the group therapist and the adult assistant or auxiliary leader may be useful in the initial phase to promote therapy. He goes on to say that pairing along with other phenomena can "prolong the initial phase and retard the use of transference, countertransference, leadership, auxiliary leadership and identifications, towards the psychotherapeutic working of the middle phase" (p. 47).

Wolf and Schwartz (1962) echo this feeling in more detail, especially in regard to the alternate session and in analyzing the need for pairing mostly as resistance, again with adults. It may not be possible to distinguish early phase pairing from symbiotic pairing.

IN THE MIDDLE PHASE

After six to ten sessions the group should be in the middle phase and then the features of symbiotic pairing should be more readily discernible.

Since the inpatient groups are open-ended, members of the group may learn soon after admission of the effort in group therapy to deal with symbiotic pairing. Although some may then learn about the current metaphor used to describe it, the path takes many lengthy detours and much time to turn toward therapeutic success.

The metaphor of the day may change over time but it soon becomes an easily recalled phrase for the concept of pairing. At times I have called it "being under the same skin," "sharing the same skin," "breathing for one another," or "being in the saddle together." Eventually this diffuses from the individual and group sessions to the family sessions.

Dependency ties, contagion of affects, leader–follower ties, or similar life-style ties (Sugar, 1986) and role suction (Redl, 1942) may be stimuli for continued pairing in the middle phase but should not be confused with symbiotic pairing.

The transference dilution offered by the group is at once a safety valve for borderlines with their intense, almost psychotic transferences and the potential for acting out. It also offers other targets for their positive and negative feelings, which can then be viewed by the group patients in the course of therapy and ultimately, possibly, be understood and dealt with in a more suitable form than previously.

Each such patient may have multiple symbiotic pairings simultaneously in and out of the group, but more likely one is waning and one is waxing while other pairings are going on with other peers on the unit. The patient seems to feel empty unless he is with someone all the time. Since they have such low self-esteem, their feeling of abandonment and worthlessness is confirmed if they are alone even for an hour.

Further, it is to be understood that more than one pair is operating in the adolescent inpatient unit in which most of the patients have borderline or narcissistic disorders. There may be three or four pairs operating simultaneously and antagonistically to each other in and out of the group. At times the pairing may change but the pairing does not necessarily reflect the total group climate, since, if this were the case, the group would come to a standstill with a massive and interminable resistance.

The symbiotic pairing is so intense that there is no room for outsiders at times and the twosome is very hard to reach. At the same time another twosome may be involved in something similar, but they are not operating in conjunction with the other symbiotic pairs. This allows a window of therapeutic opportunity for the other patients who are not thus involved to see the symbiotic nature of the pairing and confront them. It also allows the therapist the opportunity to help the patients by focusing on this and to see the defensive need that is currently leading to clinging or rescue operations as part of the symbiotic pairing.

The reality testing provided in the group by the peers is a most significant part of the total therapy.

A combined supportive–interpretive approach by the therapist with interpretation of the omnipresent rage, grandiosity, narcissistic injury, rivalry, fears of abandonment, despair, projection, splitting, revengefulness, denial, and sadistic acting out has been found to be useful.

Limit-setting and confrontation along with supportive efforts are most significant among the therapeutic approaches. The use of videotaping as part of this should be kept in mind, since it offers all of the above, but especially the ability to view their defenses immediately in operation in the here-and-now. Frequently, the playback helps the patients to perceive their denial, splitting, projection, manipulation, prevarication, clinging, or other features of their functioning. Interpretive efforts focused on the immediate situation or phenomena in the group, as well as about linkages to the past, are integral to the therapy.

By observing the pairing in the group, discussing and bringing it into focus, the patients become clearer about it with continued effort. Progress in this awareness is enhanced by a concomitant individual and family therapy focus on this topic.

Eventually, the patients may be able to see their current symbiotic pairing as a replica of the interaction with the original symbiotic partner and the repetitiveness of their relationship patterns.

Pairing in the middle phase in group therapy is addressed as resistance since it often continues after the initial phase (although there may be some shifts) with subgroups. Generally, this does not pose an insurmountable difficulty for the therapist. In essence then, pairs come and go in a therapy group. If they do not go, then they are treated as resistance to further development and growth, which needs very close therapeutic effort.

When appropriate, the therapist needs to bring to the attention of the individuals in a pair, as well as to the group, the healthy aspects of their pairing in terms of positives such as compassion, empathy, differentiation, autonomy, and changes in their interests and defenses.

The following illustrate some typical, symbiotic paired situations that occur in the middle phase of group therapy with inpatient adolescent borderline and narcissistic disorders.

ILLUSTRATION 1

Patients C1 and C2 are females in middle adolescence with practically the same symptoms and diagnosis. They formed a coalition after they became acquainted with each other shortly after their first group session. One spoke for the other, or spoke for both of them, or their body language indicated similar reactions to material coming forth from the other one or from other patients in the group. Both patients went after the same boy, then relinquished their target, then went after another boy simultaneously in a rivalrous fashion. They seemed to have a mother–daughter, sibling, or mother–infant transference to each other, or a symbiosis, and at times all of these. Since they felt the original symbiotic object had failed them, they replaced it with a new one. When one of them felt abandoned or threatened with abandonment by positive therapeutic changes they found another symbiotic partner.

Thus, when C1 began to improve, C2 felt abandoned since they no longer had the same resonance or relationship. Then C2 became angry, vituperative, and went after C1's "boyfriend" in a rivalrous, vindictive fashion. It seemed on the surface that she was going after the boy, but she really was out for revenge against C1 for rejecting her by making progress, leaving her behind, and by finding a boy instead of maintaining the tie to C2. Now, C2 no longer had her treasured symbiotic partner. Thus, there were multiple occasions of blurred boundaries, rescue operations, interchanging, and speaking for one another. At times they even seemed to be breathing for each other or clinging like Siamese twins, only more so.

The following is an example of the tie between them.

Pt C1 (to therapist): You're saying we're in the saddle just because I did this with C2, when it has nothing to do with her. If it had been anyone else I would have done the same thing. I just didn't think about it, before I did it. You don't need to analyze anything there. If I had thought about it before doing it I wouldn't have done it. I don't want to get into trouble.

(A few minutes later, shouting)

Pt C1 You want us to be in isolation from each other, but it doesn't work. If I sit next to her in group I can tell her things, jokes, etc., that only she and I know and just with a few words. If we sit across from each other we can tell each other things with our eyes, because we know each other so well and we both know the stories so well.

The patient was provocative, arguing and shouting down the therapist's efforts to interpret her retaliatory wish to be removed from group therapy for confronting their symbiotic pairing and acting out.

ILLUSTRATION 2

Patient B. complained about the group and said, "I don't plan to talk in here. I only talk in individual therapy. Nothing gets done in the group."

She had brought this up in her individual therapy, and expressed anger at her therapist for not giving her his undivided and concentrated attention in the group. She then complained almost routinely about the group or refused to talk in the group. She made numerous efforts to avoid group therapy, or tried to have the therapist all to herself. She was resentful, sullen, negative, or openly hostile, but mostly nonverbal in group therapy.

When her remarks were mostly splitting efforts based on sibling rivalry and sadism, they were discussed using the analogy of Aesop's fable of the fox and sour grapes, or in terms of her wish to continue to use a rusty old vehicle when she has a new one available.

The patient's effort to have the therapist entirely to herself, after being discussed in individual therapy, was seen as based on a maternal transference and wish to reconstitute her maternal symbiosis with the therapist. Hostility to the group was open and repetitious. The therapist asked her if there was "something going on between us?" When the patient did not respond, the therapist alluded to something they had discussed in individual therapy. The patient recalled it, but said, "I don't want to talk about it." On other occasions she did discuss the issue at hand.

If the patient refused to elaborate, then the group knew the patient ws avoiding, and the group members then pursued the patient to discuss it. Here the patient was suffering mortification and anger over rejection by her transference symbiotic partner. By making it a group issue she had the support of the whole group and was brought back into the group with verbalizing and relating to the members along with having the therapist's efforts focused on her to deal with her transference wish.

ILLUSTRATION 3

Patient E. is a sadistic, tortured, and torturing boy who tormented his younger male sibling for years. When placed with his noncustodial parent at his own request, he tormented a female stepsibling who was the same age as his brother. When confronted about such behavior he invariably played dumb, denied, and dissembled.

Patient F., who is somewhat older than patient E., had been having a guilty rivalry with her younger female sibling whom she tormented.

Both patients had an intense symbiosis with their mothers, who were easily swayed to indulge their child when the youngster played dumb, helpless, or manipulated with temper tantrums or threats.

The patients recognized each other as emotionally similar and alternated maternal–child roles with each other as their mothers had done with them.

Th. (to Pt. E.):	What are your feelings about Patient D.?
Pt. E.:	What do you mean? You mean what I like about her or about her running away?
Pt. F.:	About her and what you feel about her.
Th. (to Pt. F.):	You feel you have to speak for me?
Pt. F.:	'Cause he doesn't understand.
Th. (to Pt. F.):	You rescued him very well. Are you trying to get into the saddle with him?

Scheidlinger and Pyrke (1961), as well as Scheidlinger and Holden (1966), treated a group of adult female outpatients with severe character disorders, some of whom appear to have been borderline. This was a well-managed group, which was given "feeding" and a great deal of support. Although pairing was not the focus in these papers, it is of marked interest that the group managed to continue as long as it did with benefit to patients with such severe pathology, considering the amount of pairing that was going on.

Many authors have written of acting out in various ways in groups, but the acting out has been viewed as a transference or negative transference to the therapist or other significant figure (Berkovitz and Sugar, 1976), and not as symbiotic pairing.

Although the pairing assumption of Bion (1959) addresses the issue of pairing as a resistance to the work of the group, it is viewed as involving the dyad and the whole group in a shared fantasy of producing a new leader from their sexual union and to deal with psychotic anxiety. This reference is to adult groups and again not to symbiotic pairing.

Wong (1979) mentions a twinship reaction by one narcissistic adult patient to another, whereby the first patient then felt a loss of identity and unanchored. This refers to Kohut's (1971, p. 115) substitute phrase for alter ego transference which is a variant of the grandiose self and the opposite of symbiotic pairing.

Roth (1980) described his countertransferences with a group of identity-impaired adult outpatients over five years during which there was continued pairing in twos or threes and acting out by the pairs. He viewed pairing as a major resistance based on the frustration of their wish for an exclusive link with him. Further, he felt that pairing also:

[R]epresents some further differentiation of self and superego functioning in that it organizes a defense against recognizing the separateness between the therapist and the group. In pairing there is a group reaction to the therapist's real external failure and a turning toward parts of the group to have needs met [p. 417].

But he is not describing symbiotic pairing.

From their research on pairing in a schizophrenic outpatient group, Johnson, Geller, Gordon, and Wexler (1986) observed that it occurred when the group begins, rebels, faces a loss, and ends. However, they did not note symbiotic pairing.

From my experience I would add that when borderline adolescent group members face a loss, or threat of a loss, pairing becomes more intense, but their pairing is going on almost constantly.

Johnson et al. (1986) recommend encouraging the discussion of pairing and attending to both the functional and dysfunctional aspects of any given pairing in the group. I can only agree emphatically with this prescription.

Symbiotic pairing in adolescent group therapy needs to be differentiated from transferences and other phenomena which resemble transferences but which are not (Sugar, 1986). Roth's (1980) group had a persistent reluctance to explore their transferences to him. The fact that a number of these phenomena may be occurring simultaneously requires the therapist's utmost attentiveness to differentiate which is operating at a particular time, which patients are involved in it, the nature of their involvement, the defensive need for it, and which part of it is dysfunctional or forward moving for them.

OBSERVATIONS ABOUT PROGRESS

If therapy develops suitably, the patient eventually has decreased acting out with improved behavior and clearly, though unconsciously, recognizes others like himself. But he defends against the pain and conscious awareness of this by proclaiming loudly about others' patterns, and readily sees their displacement, splitting, projection, and denial. By then the patient also has the beginning of a more reasonable superego, with less punitive, sadistic revengefulness to self and, thereby, less projective identification. His ego is able to tolerate emerging awareness of the projections and resonances with the symbiotic partner. Then the patient is able to think more of responsibilities and considerateness to other people, friends, and even family members.

With this there is a decrease in feelings of entitlement, more anxiety about recognizing one's own former patterns in others, fear of regression, some ability to tolerate tension, somewhat decreased impulsivity, and more follow-through on interpretations.

IN THE TERMINATION PHASE

When they are ready for discharge from the hospital, which may require from six to twenty-four months, the prevarication, projection, denial, and splitting have decreased markedly. The patient is readily made aware of, and is able to even note, such efforts himself sometimes before, or immediately after, the impulse surfaces into action. This does not mean therapy ends, since the patient needs to continue in group, family, and individual therapy for some time after hospital discharge.

In the separation process the patient is able to say, "I hate you 'cause you are pushing me out 'cause you don't like me." The "you" may apply to the therapist, group members, nurses, peers, or past symbiotic partners. Following that, he may say, "But I know I'm ready and glad to leave. But I hate you." This is in contrast to the stance at the beginning of therapy, when patients hate and reject anyone who does not comply with their wishes, and then busily arranges to scapegoat another person to justify and prove this. *

At this juncture further acting out or acting in is not unusual. The sense of loss of the therapist, group, and the protective, dependency-gratifying milieu can be profound and is a major stimulus for acting out. At this time the therapist has to be more alert to these feelings and needs of the patient, as well as the group, each of whom are faced with intense feelings about separation from each other.

The departing patient above all is faced with the loss of the familiar therapeutic support system he has come to rely on during hospitalization. This type of patient is constantly at risk for resumption of such pairing and the accompanying pattern of behavior, until he has worked through this area of difficulty and moved forward to another level of psychosexual and object relations development. This is usually not attainable in the hospital, which makes continuing intensive outpatient individual therapy with concomitant group and family therapy the necessary or requisite means to obtain that end.

CONCOMITANT FAMILY THERAPY

Family therapy is indicated along with individual and group therapy for such a patient. Without dealing with the other member of the original symbiotic pair, the patient has a most difficult time individuating and then integrating into the family at a different level of object relations with different defenses. When the specific parent or parent-surrogate who has been involved in a symbiosis with the patient can accept and work on this issue the patient has a greater likelihood of being able to deal with it more successfully.

When the family members make changes in their object relations and defenses the patient again undergoes a threat of loss or a feeling of abandonment since the previous patterns are no longer, or not as easily, operative as they once were. At such times the patient feels more threatened with annihilation and may then make many more clinging efforts toward the substitute partners found on the unit in or out of group therapy. Some families do not allow themselves to be involved in family therapy, which creates a therapeutic difficulty for the patient since the original objects are still available and attainable for the continuation of the prior symbiosis.

AFTER HOSPITALIZATION

At discharge patients should have the rudiments of an observing ego, which is fragile and may be easily overwhelmed by impulses. But their overall impulsivity may be moderately or markedly decreased, although not absent. During discharge, and for a while after, the patient may have intense episodes of despair, which require immediate supportive–interpretive efforts. Therefore, additional phone time and extra appointments may be needed after hospital discharge.

Further acting out with the family and efforts to reunite with the symbiotic object or a substitute may recur due to the anxiety on separation from the hospital, personnel, and other patients. The period of transition to living with the family and in the community is one of great stress for the youngster. During this time many manage to move on suitably, while others regress. Their essential support system involves the family with continuing family and individual therapy. A suitable outpatient therapy group, especially of a group of recently hospitalized similar patients, may be a source of further major support and development for the youngster.

After discharge from the hospital the borderline adolescent has marked ambivalence and feels abandoned, though pleased to have improved sufficiently to be out of the hospital. The intensity of these feelings frequently propels him/her into symbiotic relationships and acting out due to the unconscious wish for hospital readmission and the fantasized symbiotic reunion with the institution, certain peers, the group, or the therapist.

COUNTERTRANSFERENCE

Countertransference reactions are especially important in such a group and need close monitoring. Roth (1980) described his reactions with an adult group of borderlines. Halperin, Lauro, Miscione, Rebhan, Schwabolk, and Schachter (1981), Marshall (1983), Giovacchini (1985), Feinsilver (1985), Sanders (1985), and Gartner (1986) have described countertransference with individual adolescents but not in group therapy. In an adolescent therapy group composed mostly of borderline or narcissistic disorders the therapist may experience many of the countertransference responses noted by Roth (1980). Feelings of desertion, powerlessness, ineptness, despair, guilt, betrayal, and anger are quite common from my experience. However, by constant checking and investigating the stimulus and source, the therapist may be able to avoid problems. With symbiotic pairs these feelings seem more intense, guilt-provoking, and inappropriate. By considering that these feelings emanate from the patients, the therapist may be able to connect these feelings he is experiencing with the patients' productions, behavior, and transferences. Then the therapist is in a better position to make appropriate interventions.

The countertransference provides information to the therapist about the group-as-a-whole and about specific pairs. Countertransference appears to be the royal road to the unconscious with youngsters, more so than dreams, since it is a constant in therapy, while dreams may or may not be brought in (and less often with adolescents and children than adults), particularly in group therapy.

SUMMARY

This chapter focuses on the omnipresent symbiotic pairing that occurs in inpatient adolescent groups with the borderline or narcissistic disorders. The observations deal with the initial, middle, and termination phases for such pairs in such a group, as well as with the behavior and reactions of the patient. Particular aspects that promote the pairing as well as differentiating it from transferences and other phenomena are noted. Critical aspects related to changes, losses, progress, discharge, and postdischarge states are given particular attention.

Despite the intensity and the difficulty of their resistances and pathology these patients may be helped with group therapy. It is possible to help them achieve a better awareness of the nature of the symbiotic pairing, as well as its genetic roots, and to deal with it in the transference, when they attempt to have a symbiotic pairing with the therapist or peers.

The countertransference features are especially significant in working with this type of pairing in a group. However, it is also possible to deal with symbiotic pairing therapeutically and help the patient in the inpatient therapy group with this.

REFERENCES

Anthony, E. J. (1965), Age and syndrome in group psychotherapy. *Topical Problems in Psychotherapy*, 5:80–99. Basel & New York: Karger.

Berkovitz, I. H., & Sugar, M. (1976), An experience in teaching adolescent group psychotherapy: Observers become participants. *Internat. J. Group Psychother.*, 26:441–453.

Bion, W. R. (1959), *Experiences in Groups*. London: Basic Books, 1961.

Feinsilver, D. L. (1985), The family meeting as a darkroom: Countertransference issues with severely disturbed adolescents. *Adol. Psychiat.*, 12:509–523.

Gartner, A. F. (1986), Countertransference issues in the psychotherapy of adolescents. *J. Child & Adol. Psychother.*, 3:187–196.

Giovacchini, P. L. (1985), Countertransference and the severely disturbed adolescent. *Adol. Psychiat.*, 12:449–467.

Halperin, D., Lauro, G., Miscione, F., Rebhan, J., Schwabolk, J., & Schachter, B. (1981), Countertransference issues in a transitional residential treatment program for troubled adolescents. *Adol. Psychiat.*, 9:559–577.

Johnson, D., Geller, J., Gordon, J., & Wexler, B. E. (1986), Group psychotherapy with schizophrenic patients: The pairing group. *Internat. J. Group Psychother.*, 36:75–96.

Kohut, H. (1971), *Analysis of the Self*. New York: International Universities Press.

Marshall, R. J. (1983), Countertransference with children and adolescents. In: *Countertransference*, ed. L. Epstein & A. H. Feiner. New York: Jason Aronson.

Masterson, J. F., & Rinsley, D. B. (1975), The borderline syndrome: The role of the mother in the genesis and psychic structure of the borderline personality. *Internat. J. Psycho-Anal.*, 56:163–177.

Redl, F. (1942), Group emotions and leadership. *Psychiatry*, 5:573–596.

Ross, D. W. (1958), The initial phase in group psychotherapy. In: *The Development of Group Psychotherapy Programs in Various Existing Settings*. Proceedings of the Second Annual Institute of the American Group Psychotherapy Association. New York, January 22–23, pp. 45–47.

Roth, B. E. (1980), Understanding the development of a homogeneous, identity-impaired group through countertransference phenomena. *Internat. J. Group Psychother.*, 30:405–426.

Sanders, J. (1985), Principles of residential treatment: Staff growth and therapeutic interaction. *Adol. Psychiat.*, 12:361–370.

Scheidlinger, S., & Holden, M. A. (1966), Group therapy of women with severe character disorders: The middle and final phases. *Internat. J. Group Psychother.*, 16:174–189.

——— Pyrke, M. (1961), Group therapy of women with severe dependency problems. *Amer. J. Orthopsychiat.*, 31:776–785.

Sugar, M. (1986), Transference in adolescent group therapy. In: *The Adolescent in Group and Family Therapy*, 2nd ed., ed. M. Sugar. Chicago: University of Chicago Press.

Wolf, A., & Schwartz, E. K. (1962), *Psychoanalysis in Groups*. New York: Grune and Stratton.

Wong, N. (1979), Clinical considerations in group treatment of narcissistic disorders. *Internat. J. Group Psychother.*, 30:389–404.

Chapter 14

The Group as Transitional Object: Reflections on the Treatment Process in a Long-Term Psychotherapy Group for Unmarried Teenage Mothers and Their Infants or Toddlers

GERALD S. SCHAMESS, M.S.S.

Although group therapy is the treatment of choice for many adolescents and young adults, there is very little literature describing expressively oriented explorative groups for unmarried teenage women who have chosen to keep and raise their children as single parents. In the United States the number of single teenage mothers has increased by 350 percent over the last twenty years and currently constitutes a large and growing population of "at risk" children and parents. This paper describes an experimental group treatment program for teenage mothers, their infants, and toddlers. Over the past eight years the program has proven unusually successful in limiting many of the identified negative consequences of single teen motherhood (failure to complete high school; multiple, closely spaced births; high rates of child abuse and neglect, etc.) and in promoting normative developmental processes in both mothers and children.

The long-term group treatment program for unmarried teenage mothers, their infants, and toddlers began with one group for mother–infant dyads and subsequently divided into two separate but interconnected groups as the children entered the practicing subphase of separation–individuation. By modifying traditional structures and therapeutic roles we enhanced the group's potential to serve the function of a transitional object, linking fantasy and reality, "me" and "not me" experiences (Winnicott, 1951). This approach has been unusually successful in helping the group members: (1) reexperience and partially satisfy dependency needs that originated in a less than "good enough" primary relationship; (2) develop a more secure and individuated sense of self; (3) address and master the crucial developmental tasks of adolescence. In conjunction with these internal changes, the group members have completed their high-school educations, moved into the work force, and deferred second pregnancies at a rate which is notably better than the national average for single teenage mothers.

LITERATURE REVIEW

In 1960, Scheidlinger described how traditional forms of activity group therapy could be modified to address ego deficits and unmet developmental needs among "severely deprived," atypical, or borderline latency age children. He discussed the changes in therapeutic role and group structure which are necessary to create a manageable "physical and psychological environment" for children with serious deviations in ego organization. "The children are offered a benign, family-like setting, where, in contrast with their homes, there is a maximum of constancy and gratification and a minimum of frustration . . . enhanced by . . . the therapist's role of greater directness, protective restraint and verbal clarification" (Scheidlinger, 1961, p. 148). By combining a facilitating environment with a therapeutic approach which addressed specific areas of ego weakness in an organized manner, Scheidlinger created a group structure that effectively stimulated new and healthier identifications while also enhancing self-esteem and self cohesiveness. In this treatment model, change resulted from ego building interpersonal experiences rather than from attempts to encourage insight.

Subsequently, Scheidlinger (1961) described similar modifications of group structure and technique in the treatment of economically deprived, black and Hispanic women suffering from "severe character disorders." This approach called on the therapist to demonstrate interest and concern for the group members by: (1) writing or telephoning to encourage regular participation; (2) actively stimulating group discussion during periods of silence; and (3) providing coffee and cookies as a form of psychological nourishment. Here again, the modified format encouraged "realistic and symbolic identifications with the therapist, with the group entity and with peers" (Scheidlinger, 1961, p. 213).

In these reports, Scheidlinger emphasizes that for patients with significant deficits in ego organization, the therapist must actively offer protection from verbal abuse and/or physical attack (in children's groups) and must also abandon the expectation that group members will talk spontaneously about themselves in an emotionally meaningful way. Even though neutrality and spontaneous self-revelation are hallmarks of traditional therapeutic technique, their use is antitherapeutic with this population of patients. Scheidlinger emphasizes that economically disadvantaged, ego-damaged patients assume that nondirective therapists don't care about them and are uninterested in what they might have to say. This observation, coupled with the innovations in structure and technique noted above, constitute a fundamental and far-reaching contribution to the theory and practice of group therapy. By establishing these principles, Scheidlinger not only made it possible to use groups effectively in the treatment of children and parents with significant ego deficits, but also made a notable contribution to our understanding of how traditional forms of psychotherapy can best be modified to meet the psychological needs and cultural expectations of patients who are both emotionally disturbed and economically disadvantaged.

In a contemporaneous report, Black and Rosenthal (1970) described their therapeutic work with a different population of "untreatable" patients; delinquent, lower-class, black, adolescent (14–16-year-old) men. Although their ideas differ from Scheidlinger's in regard to the risks and benefits inherent in allowing group members to directly verbalize intensely hostile feelings toward each other and the leader, their work overlaps with Scheidlinger's and affirms a number of crucial underlying principles about the construction of therapy groups for particularly difficult adolescent populations.

Black and Rosenthal modified the traditional structure of adolescent groups by using refreshments as the focal point of group interaction. A sizable amount of food was served. The refreshments for each session were chosen by the group members after a great deal of heated discussion and were provided, within reason, by the therapist. In encouraging the members to focus on food both as a real gratification and as a form of symbolic psychological nourishment, the therapist emphasized the metaphorical construction of the group as symbolic family.

The process of choosing, dividing, and eating the refreshments precipitated intense transferential feelings. For a considerable period of time it seemed as if there could never be enough of the right food for these young men. Nonetheless, the availability of food made the group compelling and gratifying to the members. Typical transference reenactments involved the direct expression and/or projection of greedy, rageful, envious, competitive, punishing, referential, and orally sadistic fantasies. The process highlighted how extraordinarily dangerous it was for these young men to trust or depend on anyone. Until well into the second year of treatment, members would react to any controversy about food or to any other interpersonal disagreement with threats of violence. They were quite explicit in explaining that they felt it necessary to attack their enemies before their enemies attacked them.

While one can reasonably question whether this hostility was amplified (iatrogenically) by the group structure, it is important to remember that these young men had long histories of antisocial acting out. Whether or not one agrees with the techniques proposed in this report, one must acknowledge that the therapeutic issue is not whether the members felt intensely hostile prior to their group experience, but whether a process of guided gratification designed to minimize the open expression of hostility would be more beneficial than a process of guided gratification designed to facilitate its open expression. In either case treatment depends on the therapist's ability to let the group know that he likes the members, finds them interesting, and is willing to learn about how they view the difficulties they are having.

Black and Rosenthal (1970) present a considerable amount of clinical evidence to support their contention that until group members openly verbalize aggressive impulses they do not emotionally understand that it is possible to hate without destroying or being destroyed and that hateful feelings can be resolved in face-to-face discussion. The leader played a crucial role in promoting this understanding by successfully limiting physical expressions of aggression and by insisting that, in the group, all hostile impulses should be expressed verbally. Nonetheless, it was so difficult to achieve even a semblance of group cohesiveness during the first eighteen months of treatment, that the authors warn others who wish to treat this population in groups that they are likely to feel incompetent and professionally devalued for a year or longer, before there is any indication that the members view the group as meaningful or beneficial.

Because of the members' ongoing reliance on projection and projective identification as primary defense mechanisms, it became necessary, after a year of treatment, to make a second major structural modification. During the middle stage of treatment the therapist began to talk about carefully selected personal and professional experiences that had aroused painful feelings in him. He adopted this technique as a way of demonstrating that it is possible to feel "sadness, fear or grief" (Black and Rosenthal, 1970) without being overwhelmed, relinquishing one's masculinity, or abandoning one's sense of security. It was extraordinarily painful and frightening for these young men to acknowledge some of the vulnerability hidden beneath the menacing facade they presented to the world, but they gradually did so in response to the therapist's example. Here again, we see the importance of identification as a primary curative factor in the group process.

While the technical modifications which Black and Rosenthal recommend differ from Scheidlinger's to the degree that they encourage the direct, verbal expression of primitive aggressive feelings as part of the group interaction, both formulations reflect the central importance of: (1) providing children and adolescents who have particular ego deficits with a physical and psychological environment that is both gratifying and manageable, and (2) encouraging corrective identifications with the leader, other group members, and the group as a whole.

Slavson (1979) also recommends an essentially experiential form of treatment for adolescents with ego deficits. He discusses the process of designing group structures for particular patient populations as "the proper matching of the patient and the type of treatment to be employed . . . [involving] a thorough understanding of the patient's personality and his problems, a knowledge of a variety of techniques of psychotherapy and a flexibility to apply them" (Slavson, 1979, p. 715). He goes on to discuss "para-analytic" group psychotherapy as the treatment of choice for adolescents, describing it as the fusion of "analytic group psychotherapy with guidance, counselling, advice and teaching" (Slavson, 1979, p. 723) in whatever proportions are necessary to meet the emotional and developmental needs of the young men and women who are in treatment. In the language of classic psychoanalytic theory, this process would be described as introducing "parameters" into the treatment process (Eissler, 1981, p. 437), while in contemporary object relations theory it would be conceptualized as creating a developmentally appropriate "holding environment."

GROUP PROGRAMS WITH TEENAGE MOTHERS

Although group therapy is the treatment of choice for many adolescents with developmental, characterological, and/or internalized emotional problems, there have been very few reports that describe expressively oriented, relatively unstructured group treatment programs for unmarried teenage mothers and their children. As far as

I can tell, this gap exists not only in the literature but also in the world of practice. It persists in spite of the fact that between 1960 and 1985 there was a 350 percent increase in the rate of out-of-wedlock births to teenage women and a 900 percent increase in the rate at which unmarried teenage women chose to keep and raise their children as single parents. This startling demographic shift has led to an enormous increase in the number of teen pregnancy and parenthood programs operating in public schools and social agencies. While most of these programs emphasize some form of group intervention, almost all of the available reports describe groups which are short-term, highly structured, and educationally focused (Barclay, 1969; Papademetrious, 1971; O'Leary, Shore, and Wilder, 1984). Although some of these educationally oriented programs are not only beautifully constructed, but also eloquent in the personal and family values they present (Kennedy Foundation, 1982), they rely heavily on cognitive forms of influence to alter attitudes, values, feelings, and behavior in a population which contains many individuals with significant developmental problems.

In searching the literature I have found only three reports of long-term, expressively oriented treatment groups for this population. I will summarize them below. Kaufmann and Deutsch (1967) describe a group that functioned for two-and-one-half years, beginning during the last trimester of pregnancy and continuing during the first two years of motherhood. The group ended when the therapist left the agency, although there is reason to think it could have continued longer. In this program, seven of the eight teenage mothers decided to keep their children. These women continued to attend the group regularly after delivery. Although the group was run in the prenatal unit of a general hospital and the members were a "captive population," it was still necessary to do considerable outreach and to serve food during the first four sessions in order to engage the members in treatment. Over time, the group was able to openly discuss and deal with a range of anxieties around conception, bodily changes, the process of delivery, the pain they had experienced during delivery, contraception, ongoing relationships with men, and child care. None of the participants became pregnant again during the life of the group, a notable achievement for any intervention program with teenage mothers.

In a recent report, Pat Convery (1984) briefly discusses groups run and/or sponsored by the Children's Aid Society of Toronto, Canada. While this report provides few clinical details, it clearly states that the Society runs both short- and long-term groups, that the long-term groups are open-ended, that the program provides transportation, advocacy, environmental supports, and other outreach services, and that child care facilities are maintained so that group members can bring their infants with them to be "entertained" while the mothers attend their groups. She notes that adolescents "more readily accept guidance and explore alternatives from peers . . . [and that groups] serve as a special force in altering attitudes and behaviors" among teenage mothers (Convery, 1984, p. 438).

Kolodney and Reilly (1972) describe a group for unmarried teenage mothers that met for fourteen months at a family service agency in the Boston area. The group encouraged open and frank discussion about relations with parents and boyfriends, interest in and concerns about sexuality, feelings of shame, and social stigmatization, and the physical as well as the psychological problems that arise as a consequence of being an unmarried mother receiving Aid for Families with Dependent Children (AFDC). The authors comment that:

> [F]luid group approaches . . . are currently most needed . . . approaches which are in many respects unstructured and which call for workers (therapists) . . . who are able to keep their preconceptions at a minimum. These approaches offer a way of establishing meaningful emotional contact with the unwed mother, offering her support and social insight from her peers and retaining contact with her into that period when problems which arise from her own tendencies toward social isolation . . . are likely to be exacerbated [Kolodney and Reilly, 1972, p. 615].

DEMOGRAPHICS

The mother–infant group described in this paper is sponsored by a family agency located in a small New England city. The group is open-ended and meets in the Agency for one-and-one-half hours, once a week, from September to June of each year. It was originally constituted in 1977 as a follow-up service for teenage mothers who had participated in the Agency's prenatal education and counseling program, and who needed additional help with both emotional and environmental problems. At the group's inception the members ranged in age from fifteen-and-one-half to eighteen-and-one-half years. The group is co-led by a nurse, a clinical social worker, and a developmentally oriented educator. The nurse and social worker had previously established individual relationships with the young mothers when they were attending the prenatal program.

Because of the community's demographic composition, all of the twenty-four young women who attended the group for three or more months between 1979 and 1984 were Caucasian. Two of the participants were of Hispanic origin while the rest were of Polish, Irish, French Canadian, or English–Scottish extraction. Most of the group members came from working-class backgrounds although there were some from poverty families and a small number from middle-class backgrounds. While this demographic distribution is not typical of the national population of teenage mothers, it does reflect the fastest growing segment of that population. The rate of single parenthood decreased by 6.8 percent among black teenagers between 1970 and 1978 but increased by 13.4 percent among white teenagers during the same time period (Guttmacher Institute, 1981, p. 36).

ETIOLOGY AND DYNAMICS

Divorce, single parenthood, foster placement, incest, unemployment, poverty, overt family violence, and psychosis were not present in the families of these teenage mothers at higher rates than in the national population. Neglect and abuse did occur at somewhat higher than average rates, but did not seem to be unusually influential in determining the life choices and adaptive patterns these teenage women preferred. As best we could determine, the major family stressors for the group members were very high rates of: (1) unacknowledged marital conflict between the parents, and (2) alcoholism, especially among the fathers. These young women had conflictual relationships with their mothers based on ambivalent or inconsistent care during childhood, but seemed to have received some meaningful nurturance from mothers or surrogates when they were young. Almost all of them had assumed a "parentified" role in their families of origin as part of an effort to minimize marital conflict and hold the family together. This role involved their covertly caring for a parent or younger sibling(s) during much of their childhood and early adolescence.

The young women who participated in the group were not among the most seriously disturbed teenage mothers who participated in the prenatal program. They were not psychotic, or addicted to heroin, and they were not regularly engaged in life-threatening forms of acting out (such as driving while intoxicated). They were very clear in saying that they did not want to neglect or abuse their children, they had not been abandoned by their families of origin, and they could form meaningful attachments to an adult helper, over time.

Although there was some diagnostic heterogeneity among the group members, the large majority were quite similar in personality organization and had the following characteristics in common. None of them had been identified as unusually problematic in latency. By the time they reached midadolescence, however, they had begun to experience significant disappointments in their academic and social functioning. Although few of them were failing out of school, their academic work was, at best, marginal. For the most part they were bored, humiliated, and defeated in their attempts to master educational tasks and wanted to leave school as soon as possible. While they were of at least average intelligence, distractability, preoccupation with fantasies, family worries, and/or learning disabilities interfered with their ability to learn. Within school peer groups they were drawn to young women and men who acted out against authority, experimented with sex, drank, and took drugs. Although they only acknowledged this after they had been in treatment for several years, by the time they became pregnant they were already experiencing and defending against serious depressive feelings accompanied by a significant loss of self-esteem. Their attempts to preserve a precarious sense of self-cohesion led them into further acting out which only increased their need to flee from or otherwise blot out intense feelings of disappointment in themselves.

As they tried to imagine their future in a community which strongly values feminist ideals of personal independence, close supportive relationships with other women, and a meaningful career, they experienced further frustration. As their educational aspirations evaporated, they found it more and more difficult to imagine a successful career or even the likelihood of living independently, away from their families. For the most part they tried to avoid the intolerable feelings of frustration, sadness, and hopelessness that this dilemma evoked in them by turning to sexual experimentation and other kinds of adventure with their boyfriends. In these relationships their history of disappointing experiences with critical, uninterested, psychologically absent, needy, or alcoholic fathers further undermined their capacity to function effectively and to feel positively about themselves. They could neither choose men who would treat them well nor act in ways that preserved a positive relationship with the men they chose. Some of them, who had in childhood turned to their fathers or older brothers to compensate for disappointments or failures in maternal nurturance, discovered (again) that even the most nurturing teenage male is at best, a "sometimes thing."

DEVELOPMENTAL ISSUES

The normative developmental tasks of adolescence are thought to be:
(1) reexperiencing and reworking the subphases of separation–individuation (Blos, 1962); (2) establishing a secure sense of ego identity
which provides continuity, direction, and purpose over time (Erikson,
1950); (3) substituting new, age-appropriate libidinal objects from
outside the family, for the highly cathected oedipal and preoedipal
objects who had previously occupied the center of the growing child's
libidinal world (A. Freud, 1958).

When we correlated the pattern of maladaptive functioning outlined above with the phase specific tasks of adolescence, it became
apparent that for these young women, progressive development had
come to a halt. When they became pregnant, it did not matter much
whether the pregnancy had occurred as a result of unconscious design,
incorrect information about conception, cognitive immaturity, social
pressure, or some combination of several variables. The pregnancy
forced them to consider their life predicament at both a conscious
and unconscious level of experience and led them to the conclusion
that unmarried motherhood was the best, if not the only, "solution"
to the developmental impasse they were experiencing. At least for a
time, they were certain that unmarried motherhood would cure all
the ills that had plagued them during adolescence. This attitude seems
quite prevalent, not only among the teenagers discussed here, but also
nationwide. In 1985, 90 percent of the single teenagers who carried
their pregnancies to term in the United States made single motherhood their first, irrevocable "career" choice.

In an earlier paper (G. Schamess, 1987), I described this decision
as an "adaptive initiative" in which the pregnant teenager simultaneously attempts to deal with the developmental tasks of adolescence
and with the environmental problems which arise because "under-
educated" teenagers have such limited access to social and economic
opportunity in this society. By choosing motherhood these young
women consciously proclaim that adolescent issues are of no further
concern to them because they have arrived at adulthood, complete
and full blown. A sixteen-year-old unmarried mother says it simply
and clearly: "It isn't as if you're a teenager when you have a baby.
I've got all the responsibility and everything you've got when you're
an adult. I'm getting adulthood early. If I didn't have a baby I'd still
be living under my mother's roof" (Scheller-Gilkey, 1984, p. 103). In
considering this phenomenon, Stephanie Schamess (1985) observes
that:

[F]rom a developmental standpoint, the teenage mother assumes a role which, on the one hand, seriously limits her opportunities to have the . . . experiences she needs for her own continued development, and on the other hand demands of her a level of cognitive, social and emotional functioning which she has not yet achieved. This tension may lead to a kind of pseudo maturity in which the mother takes on the external functions and behaviors of her newly-acquired role, but remains adolescent in her emotional needs [p. 23].

This ongoing tension constitutes the first major dilemma inherent in the decision to embrace single motherhood.

A second dilemma stems from the first. In order even to *play* the role of adult caregiver, most teenage mothers desperately need their own mothers. The new and highly valued representation of self as autonomous adult exists in stark contrast (but without apparent awareness of internal conflict) to the reality that by choosing to raise their infants, unmarried teenage mothers become much more dependent on their families of origin. This was true for *all* the young women who participated in the mother–infant group, and it was also true for the sixteen-year-old woman quoted above by Scheller-Gilkey. National statistics confirm this pattern and also indicate that teen mothers do considerably better when their families provide them with active support and care after the baby is born (Crawford and Furstenberg, 1985). The teenagers in the mother–infant group returned home or lived with a close relation for at least a year after delivery, even when one or both parents actively disapproved of the pregnancy and of the decision to keep the baby. Regardless of whether the adolescent mother was accepted or reviled in her family, the infant provided her with a new opportunity to be taken care of, at least for a time.

TRANSITIONAL ISSUES

When viewed from this perspective, it is evident that teenage motherhood provides a pathway back to an essentially dependent (sometimes symbiotic) relationship with a primary caretaker. This occurs in a manner that allows the teenager to conceal her true needs from herself and others, thus preserving a measure of self-esteem. At best this "solution" creates a situation in which the teenager can gratify some of her early needs for nurturance while reexperiencing and reworking her relationship with a primary caretaker in a more satisfactory way. At worst, the teenager's need for care and protection is again frustrated, with the result that both internalized and real object relations continue to be heavily burdened by aggression. In addition, her most desperate fears about herself and others are not only revived, but also at least partially realized.

It is in this context that the concept of the transitional object becomes particularly useful as a way of understanding the internal experience of at least some teenage mothers. Clinical evidence from the mother–infant group suggests that these mothers, after literally creating their children both in the flesh and in the imagination, then make psychological use of them in much the same way that babies use a transitional object in their normative progression from "infantile" to "mature" dependence (Kosseff, 1975, pp. 222–223). This observation suggests that during the second separation–individuation process (Blos, 1962), transitional issues may temporarily reemerge, at least for those teenagers who had not, previously, been able to separate adequately from a primary caregiver. Given the very small and skewed sample involved in this project, it is difficult to tell whether the observation has any general applicability, but it is intriguing and deserves further study by interested clinicians.

For the group members, transitional needs were played out in the following way. The infants initially led their mothers back to the familiar (if not wholly satisfactory) safety of a dependent relationship with a primary caretaker. In the process they provided their mothers with a respected and respectable "career" (motherhood), thus sheltering them from the academic, social, and vocational demands of the "real" world. The infants also warmed and soothed the mothers, letting them imagine, at least intermittently, that internal and external reality were securely under their control. Over time, however, the changing demands created by the infants' internal developmental timetable, coupled with the mothers' wish to function more adequately and autonomously, motivated the mothers to test out new adaptive initiatives through which they hoped to reestablish their capacity for progressive growth. By activating both regressive and progressive forces in their mothers, the infants served the function of a "multi-directional bridge," alternately sheltering the mothers from and leading them toward the world of external objects, realistic challenges, and autonomous functioning (Greenacre [1971], quoted by Kosseff [1975, p. 235]).

When the mothers were experiencing stress, they often turned to their infants, hoping that the infants' presence would insulate them from the demands and responsibilities of adult life. If the mothers made this demand when the infants were available for contact, they found that they could play with the infants in ways that would comfort them and/or absorb their hostility. On those occasions, the mother–infant interactions had a refreshing effect on the mothers and strengthened them to reenter the adult world. However, if the infants were not available for this kind of play when the mothers most needed it, the mothers became frustrated by the infants' "failure" to respond to their needs. As the infants grew older and began to "differentiate" the "failures" occurred more frequently and the mothers experienced considerable disillusionment with the infants. It was my impression that, in the mother–infant group, their frequent requests for advice and information on how to "discipline" the children reflected this growing disillusionment. Over time, the disillusionment impelled the mothers to transfer their transitional object needs from the infants to the group-as-a-whole. I will discuss this issue further in the concluding section of the paper.

TRANSITIONAL PHENOMENA IN PSYCHOTHERAPY GROUPS

In discussing borderline patients who have reached an impasse in individual treatment, Kosseff (1975) describes how a therapy group can serve the function of a transitional object for patients who are seeking to emancipate themselves from "infantile dependence" on primary objects. He comments that the group becomes a tangible representation of the relationship between patient and therapist. Like the blanket, it has attributes of both patient and therapist, yet is not one or the other, nor simply both of them together. For the patient, the group has the security value of a part of the self which has already experienced a modicum of trust in the object and can therefore begin to imagine the possibility of new kinds of self and object relatedness. Kosseff goes on to say that in providing a "space between" therapist and patient, the group creates an area of freedom for the patient to fill creatively, by spontaneously playing different roles with other group members, moving back and forth between experimentation and security and moving closer to or further from the therapist (Kosseff, 1975, pp. 231–235).

While I do not view the teenagers in the mother–infant group as borderline, I do think their inability to master phase specific tasks produces a transitory internal organization that is similar to borderline organization, particularly in regard to the ways separation–individuation issues are played out. Certainly, Kosseff's description of how his borderline patients use the group-as-a-whole to serve transitional functions coincides remarkably well with our observations of how the teenage mothers use their experience in the mother–infant group.

THE MOTHER–INFANT GROUP

In this section I will briefly describe how we modified the structure of the mother–infant group in our efforts to meet the special needs of these adolescent mothers.[1] I will then present the first three phases of group development in some detail. These phases illustrate how the members used group to address their need for a transitional experience. They are also worth studying because they constitute the most difficult and challenging aspects of the group process; the aspects which determined whether the group would coalesce and serve a therapeutic function for its members. Once the group had passed through these phases it increasingly resembled a traditional young mother's therapy group, meeting concurrently with a parallel but separate children's group. In presenting clinical material I will focus on total group phenomena, particularly as they were expressed in group themes, group resistances, and therapeutic interventions that influenced the functioning and emotional climate of the group-as-a-whole.

When we developed the mother–infant program we were convinced that a flexible model of group therapy would be the treatment of choice for these teenage mothers. Because all of them were attempting to master phase specific developmental tasks by choosing to bear and raise their children as single parents, we assumed they would have enough in common to form a cohesive, interactive group. Based on prior experience with adolescent and young adult groups, we knew we could provide a group structure which would satisfy at least some dependency needs, strengthen overall ego functioning, support strivings toward autonomous functioning, and encourage identifications with other group members and with the leaders. We also knew that the group interaction itself would make it necessary for the members to experience and test out their fantasies about destroying the caregiving object through the expression of hostile feelings.

[1] The following clinical practitioners have been involved in this program. Deborah Roth-Howe, M.S.W., Sally Dean Lake, M.S.W., Paul A. Verson, M.S.W., Andrée Vanpee, R.N., Nancy Webb, R.N., Elizabeth Jarvis, M.S., Claudia Lefko, M.S., and Stephanie Schamess, M.Ed. I am deeply grateful to all of them for their generous and thoughtful participation in developing the theoretical formulations and practice model presented in this paper. As consultant to the program I have been consistently impressed by their clinical skillfulness as well as their creativity, patience, and devotion to the needs of these young women and their children. I am also grateful to the young mothers and children for sharing their life stories with us. Their intelligence, vitality, and capacity to overcome serious emotional and environmental difficulties have earned my deepest respect. All of us have also appreciated their sense of humor even when it was most pointedly directed at us and even when it hit the mark.

STRUCTURAL MODIFICATIONS

We modified a number of structural elements in the mother–infant group from its inception. These modifications were derived from Slavson's (1943) model of activity group therapy, Scheidlinger's (1961) modification of that model, my reflections on the relationship between group structure and clinical diagnosis (G. Schamess, 1986), and Garland and Kolodney's (1965) model of social group work practice. In addition, the therapists periodically changed aspects of the group structure as part of their ongoing effort to understand and address the members' developmental needs. While I will not focus on the implications of various structural changes, I will mention some of these changes in passing and the reader should be aware of them as major factors which influenced the group process. The most important modifications are listed below: (1) The mothers' group was co-led by a registered nurse and a clinical social worker. The infant–toddler group was led by a developmentally oriented educator. We thus provided the members with easy access to three different but interrelated areas of professional expertise. (2) The therapists deliberately refrained from establishing firm boundaries around group membership. Anyone who had ever attended the group could (and many did) return at any time for one or more sessions. This modification emphasized the group's psychological function as a symbolic family which would always welcome past and present members. In addition, the open boundaries provided a concrete acknowledgment of the realistic and emotional factors which made it difficult for these adolescent women to attend group on a regular, ongoing basis. (3) Food was served at every meeting and, over time, the members participated actively in choosing, preparing, and serving refreshments. (4) Mother's Day, Halloween, and Christmas were celebrated as group events every year. Each celebration was designed to recognize the holiday's specific importance in the lives of mothers and children. The celebrations were also designed to facilitate discussion about what the holidays had meant to the group members when they were growing up and how they currently celebrate them with their own children and their extended families.

PHASE I. PROGRESSING FROM ISOLATION TO DEPENDENCE

During the first six months of its existence the therapists had serious concerns about whether the group would coalesce or even survive.

Attendance was sporadic at best and it was difficult to get all the members together in the same room at the same time even though the leaders provided transportation to and from group meetings. Almost all of the group members were quite attached to their infants and liked showing them off when they were feeling good about themselves and the babies were "behaving." When they attended the group they also liked to talk about their experiences in giving birth and taking the infants home from the hospital. In spite of these positive shared experiences, they attended group mainly when they were distressed about some crisis in their lives. At those times individuals tended to monopolize sessions, directing most of their attention to the group leader with whom they had established a close individual relationship during the prenatal program. They were not inclined to examine their own feelings or the effect their behavior was having on others. They asked for information or advice and craved "support" from a therapist. Their search for advice frequently concealed serious complaints about the infants, but nonetheless, they were highly (although intermittently) motivated to become more adequate as parents.

At this stage of the group process, the therapists provided a considerable amount of information about nursing, formulas, eating and sleeping patterns, and other aspects of infant care. They also emphasized that child rearing is a challenging and difficult job which causes *all* mothers significant difficulty, at least some of the time. They tried to encourage group interaction by redirecting questions to other group members who had previously struggled with similar issues or who had some relevant experience with a particular problem. And, they repeatedly encouraged members to talk about how these problems made them feel. Nonetheless, getting the group started was a slow and, at times, discouraging process that required enormous patience, tact, and perseverance.

We (therapists and consultants) were surprised to observe that initially, the group members seemed relatively uninterested in peer interaction. We had assumed they would welcome an opportunity to be with other women who were having similar experiences, especially since they had been somewhat deprived of normative peer group contact during the last trimester of pregnancy. In trying to understand this lack of interest, we initially hypothesized that it was an expression of their narcissistic investment in themselves and their infants. It turned out that we were quite mistaken, at least in terms of the feelings of which they were aware. Much later in treatment they spontaneously revealed how ashamed they had been about, "you know, getting pregnant in high school." They also admitted that they were frightened of coming to group because they expected disapproval both from peers and the leaders. It took most of a year for them to emotionally assimilate the fact that they all really were "in the same boat." In the third year of the group one member talked poignantly and angrily about how, at school, she had acquired the reputation of being a "slut," after her classmates learned about her pregnancy. That reaction had driven her away from her peers and out of school. Other group members listened sympathetically to her story and began to recount how stigmatized their pregnancies had made them feel. Subsequently two of the group members volunteered to be interviewed by the local newspaper for a story about teen pregnancy and parenthood. They stated emphatically that they wanted the community to know how things looked from their perspective because they didn't want to feel ashamed any longer. Since we had assumed that community disapproval of teen pregnancy and parenthood had markedly diminished, we were surprised by how deeply stigmatized the members felt. Even after making considerable allowance for their tendency to project feelings of shame, guilt, and anger, we were still impressed by the degree to which, at least in this mostly Caucasian, New England community, teen sexuality, pregnancy, and unmarried parenthood continue to be viewed as signs of serious moral deficiency. Accepting and dealing with feelings of shame and stigmatization was a fundamental component of the group process from the very beginning, although the members did not directly discuss such feelings until they felt secure with one another and with the leaders. At that point in treatment one member said, with considerable rage, "Do you know, there are still people out there who call our kids 'little bastards'."

The group gradually became more cohesive as the children began to "differentiate" and the mothers began to more openly share feelings of frustration and inadequacy in caring for their infants. This common theme was first articulated in disguised form through questions, a desperate search for "advice," and persistent complaints that they did not understand their children. It was enhanced by the increasingly painful realization that their adolescent years were slipping away and that they were being "cheated" of the good times their friends were having. As the therapists continued to accept and universalize the difficulties they were having as parents, the members began to speak more openly about their anxieties. The following excerpt is from the thirty-fourth session, approximately one year into treatment.

> Louise said she yelled a lot and described Sonya (one year old) as purposefully making mischief. Kathy said she also yelled a lot and was surprised because she used to love baby-sitting. Several other group

members agreed that baby-sitting had been a real pleasure *before* they became mothers. One of the therapists said she thought it was more difficult to be patient with your own child. Kristen agreed. Kathy and Debbie both said they never really knew what was going on with their children. The therapist asked how they handled not knowing. Kathy said that she'd go out to visit friends since she found it easier to manage Judith when she was not alone. Debbie said she found it more difficult to be with other people when the baby was crying. Eva added that she yelled a lot and put Joshua in the playpen to keep him away from her. Debbie said she feared for the future. If things got more difficult she didn't think she could handle it. She felt she didn't really like her baby enough and was very impatient with breast feeding. In a subsequent session Debbie revealed how disappointed she was about having given birth to a daughter rather than to a son. Before Dana's birth Debbie had purchased several blue outfits and in the hospital she felt Dana couldn't be her baby because Dana was so "ugly." "Every time they brought her to me, I'd wish she belonged to someone else."

While these discussions were going on, the infants remained in the treatment room with their mothers. The mothers cared for them with reasonable attentiveness, but with varying degrees of skill. The leaders sometimes pitched in to help as did other group members. While the mothers and infants were reasonably well attached, the therapists quickly observed the mother's impatience with any fussiness and their insecurity in dealing with problems. These difficulties increased as the infants began to actively differentiate and crawl around the room. In subsequent mother–infant groups, we introduced a developmentally oriented educator into the process at this point in treatment. She now plays an active role either in helping the mothers or caring for the babies herself, depending on what the mothers prefer. Because these young women suffer from serious problems in self-esteem and tend to view advice as criticism even when they request it, we have accepted the fact that they learn best by observing. Accordingly, we have arranged the room so they can watch what the educator does with the children, if and when they wish to do so.

During the first six months of treatment, the group showed only limited interest in the coffee, soda, and cookies the leaders provided. However, as the members began to talk about their feelings of inadequacy, they also began to eat enthusiastically and greedily. Acceptance of the food seemed to signal their willingness to be nurtured by the group and this shift ushered in an extended period of dependence during which they increasingly looked to the group and the leaders as a primary source of care and protection. Their need for "sweets" continued into the fourth year of group treatment, at which time they substituted cheese and "veggies" for the soda and cookies. They made the change because they were concerned about their health and their weight. However, it was only at the end of the fifth year that they were able to voluntarily relinquish their yearly pre-Christmas celebration. This was a ritual in which they baked Christmas cookies for "the children" and then proceeded to eat all the cookies themselves, without the slightest suggestion of self-consciousness or remorse.

At the end of the first year's treatment they had become a nearly perfect example of a dependency basic assumption group (Bion, 1959), a development we viewed as a notable therapeutic triumph. Nonetheless, difficulties persisted. While attendance had improved considerably (to 60–70%) and a sense of cohesiveness had been achieved, the members still missed sessions whenever they had revealed too much about themselves, were confronted in a way that made them anxious or angry, or had to deal with some "real" crisis in their lives. Given the patience, perseverance, and capacity to tolerate painful feelings that the leaders had to exercise in order to keep the group going during the first year, it is understandable that most clinicians prefer to work exclusively with educationally oriented groups in programs which provide a "captive population." While the therapists did not experience the level of professional "devaluation" that Black and Rosenthal (1970) report, the group certainly did not provide much professional gratification during the first year of its existence.

During that first year the leaders and consultant constantly struggled with countertransference reactions which made them feel anxious and inadequate. They felt abandoned and rejected when the members did not attend sessions, incompetent when it proved so difficult to promote group interaction, worried that the infants would be neglected or abused, and hopeless about their capacity to "make" the group successful. When we considered these reactions retrospectively, they seemed to accurately reflect how the group members were feeling about themselves and their life circumstances at a time when they still could not articulate such feelings directly. In this context we concluded that the countertransference reactions were, for the most part, normative in trying to work with this population and that they reflected the members' use of projective identification as a primary form of interpersonal communication (Racker, 1968; Spotnitz, 1969; Rosenthal, 1977; Soo, 1980; G. Schamess, 1981; Ogden, 1982).

PHASE II. WILL THE CAREGIVING OBJECTS SURVIVE THE GROUP MEMBERS' DESTRUCTIVE IMPULSES? TESTING (ROSENTHAL, 1971; BERKOVITZ, 1972)

As the group developed, the members began to act more and more like defiant teenagers. They had previously presented themselves as anxious and insecure young mothers whose children occupied the center of their attention. Gradually they began to talk about how their children "deliberately" tormented them. Nancy Webb (personal communication, 1987) conceptualizes this as the fantasy of the "omnipotent child" who is capable of destroying its mother. The mothers described how their eight- to sixteen-month-old children kicked, bit, soiled, and/or hit them and how helpless they were to stop such behavior. They interpreted the behavior as willful disobedience, designed to hurt them and make them feel bad. They asked how to "discipline" or "punish" the children so they would not be so aggressive. One group member, with support and encouragement from her own mother, insisted that her nine-month-old son was already "antisocial" because of the ways in which he "attacked" her. She arranged for extensive neurological testing to determine whether he should be medicated or institutionalized. While some of the group members challenged this view, her concerns struck a responsive chord with other members. They talked about children and adults they knew who had become "incorrigible" at a young age. When the group leaders tried to educate them about the relevant aspects of infant development they were silent, tight-lipped, and impatient. They were somewhat less hostile to an approach which suggested that they had good reason to be concerned about how aggressive their children might eventually become, given how violent some of the fathers and the other men in their lives had been. Nonetheless their projections continued and provided an early indication of the degree to which they saw themselves as incorrigibly hostile and destructive. In addition, we later realized that these projections served to rationalize their own acting out, a subject which soon became the predominant group theme.

Group members began to talk about going out on weekends to have a good time. They explained that caring for the children was exhausting and that they owed themselves a good time on the weekends since their "best years' " were passing quickly. They described how they spent weekends drinking, driving with friends who were drunk, "doing" drugs, and picking up men at bars for casual sexual encounters. They complained about being mistreated by these men and waking up horribly hungover; completely "wiped out" for days. While they expressed some regrets about these incidents they patiently explained to the therapists that they needed to do *something* to get away from the children. They complained about how difficult it was to arrange baby-sitting, even with parents or grandparents, and frequently described situations where it was not entirely clear how the children were being cared for. These reports caused the therapists considerable anxiety as they tried to evaluate whether the children were seriously at risk.

The members sharpened the transference implications of these stories by asking the group leaders what bars they went to. When the leaders didn't respond, the members followed up by inviting the leaders to join them at their bars so "we can all have a really good time." When the leaders politely declined, the members laughed gleefully and said: "you don't have to worry, we'll show you around . . . you're missing some great partying." The group members insisted that they were just enjoying themselves like any other kids their age. However, their transferential anger and defiance of parental expectations were quite explicit. Their attitude clearly conveyed the message: What are you going to do about it? Are you going to join us? Will you try to stop us? What makes you think you *can* stop us?

After deciding that it would not be useful either to join or interpret this particular resistance, the therapists chose to pursue an approach in which they sympathetically commented on how bad the women seemed to feel after the adventures were over. They then pursued the issue by wondering aloud whether other group members thought that the women who were reporting the week's most dangerous and exciting adventure were taking good care of themselves. The therapists conveyed the attitude that they did not want to spoil what "little fun" the members had arranged for themselves, but were concerned about each member's health, safety, and emotional well-being. They didn't want anyone to injure herself or get into serious trouble.

With frequent repetition this approach was thought provoking to the group. Individuals began to comment on how self-destructively other members were behaving. While such confrontations were rarely genteel, they were effective: "That was really dumb. . . . Don't you know he's an asshole like most men. . . . You're going to get yourself killed if you don't watch out. . . ." These confrontations would periodically upset a member sufficiently so that she would miss one or more sessions. However, the offended member usually returned in a much more sober frame of mind, particularly if a group member or a leader contacted her to say she was missed.

Over the course of the second year of treatment this rebellious/acting out/self-destructive behavior peaked and then gradually began to recede. However, it did not disappear entirely until much later in treatment. In looking back at how they had behaved in group, the members commented on how similar it was to their behavior before they became pregnant. They talked about what "hellions" they had been in high school and how they had made fools of their parents and teachers. When they were in high school it was important to have a reputation for being "tough" and "dangerous" but that reputation became a heavy burden even though "we never would have admitted it at the time." The group members went on to say that they only respected teachers who were very strict and that neither the school nor their parents had offered them any protection. One member (whom I am quite certain had not read Scheidlinger) commented that: "Those who didn't help protect us, didn't care." When the therapist asked about their reactions to this comment they began to talk about having been hurt, neglected, and left to fend for themselves by teachers and parents. They later talked about how much it meant to them when the group therapists didn't get angry, but instead expressed concern by encouraging them to take better care of themselves.

Paula Verson (personal communication, 1986) observed that when the group members initially became pregnant, they not only felt hopeless about the future, but were also engaged in serious self-destructive behavior. Choosing to have and raise a baby provided them with an eighteen to twenty-four-month moratorium during which time their self-destructive acting out diminished or stopped entirely. Verson added that in her view, many teenage mothers become pregnant again after eighteen to twenty-four months, hoping that a second, third, or fourth pregnancy would again help them control their self-destructive behavior.

During this second stage of treatment, the mothers emphasized their impatience with the toddlers by trying to force them to stay in the adjacent room where the children's group was now meeting. It was clear that the mothers were engrossed in their tales of adolescent adventure and did not want to be interrupted. Since even those children who were in the practicing subphase of separation–individuation needed to check in with their mothers from time to time, they were quite distressed by this overt rejection. The more their mothers pushed them away, the tighter they clung, and the more they cried. The mothers responded to their demandingness by scolding, yelling, threatening, and, on occasion, hitting ("swatting") the children, all the while attentively scanning the therapists to see how they were reacting. If nothing else worked, they relented briefly, and impatiently held or talked to the distressed child. If that didn't work, they began to yell and threaten again.

When the group leaders tried to explain the children's need for contact and/or initiate a discussion about other "better" ways of calming children, the mothers visibly tried to suppress their irritation and behave in accordance with the therapists' wishes. However, these attempts to propitiate the therapists never lasted very long since the mother's own needs were so intense. When the leaders decided that group members were "swatting" their children too often, they established a "no hitting" rule in the group. They thought the mothers would be relieved by the rule and at an unconscious level, they probably were. However, at the level of manifest content, they responded angrily, complaining that the leaders were making a big deal out of nothing. After making their views known in the group, they revenged themselves with considerable imagination and delight. On leaving a group session (obviously having planned this in advance) they stood in the parking lot, shouting up through the windows for the leaders and everyone else in the Agency to hear: "We're out here in the parking lot beating up our children and there isn't a thing you can do about it."

It quickly became apparent that the incidents which occurred during group were pale reproductions of what happened at home when the children were fussy or interrupted some activity the mothers were invested in. Over time we recognized that the mothers were slowly learning about child care from *observing* how the children's group leader comforted, engaged, or distracted the children. Nonetheless, the mothers' attitudes changed very gradually and then only after some of their own adolescent issues had been addressed and at least partially worked through.

A BRIEF DIGRESSION

Therapists, nurses, educators, and other caregiving adults who are strongly committed to the welfare of dependent children tend to forget that single teenage mothers are adolescents first and mothers second. When caregivers are temporarily able to put aside the moral assumption that parents who choose to raise children should also be prepared to care for them, they begin to recognize that most teenage mothers (and fathers) are only able to provide adequate care for their children when their own emotional needs are recognized and met. If therapists lose sight of this fact they unwittingly collude with the adolescent mother's view that she can do anything an adult can do without having to address and master the crucial tasks of adolescent development. Caregivers who accept the teenage mother's posture of "pseudo-maturity" at face value (S. Schamess, 1985) inadvertently support a kind of "false self" (Winnicott, 1965) and thus confirm the young mother's unconscious conviction that human contact can only be preserved if she ignores (denies and represses) her true wishes and feelings.

PHASE III: FROM CONFRONTATION AND RAGE TOWARD AUTONOMOUS FUNCTIONING

During the third phase of treatment the members began to show signs of improvement, much to the relief of the therapists, the consultant, and the "agency as a whole." Although the group members talked more about feeling depressed during this phase, their acting out decreased markedly, and they gradually became more appropriately self-assertive. Simultaneously, they began to confront and master challenges in the "real" world which previously they had avoided. And they struggled to establish peer relationships in which they would be better treated, thus signaling positive changes in self-esteem. However, these accomplishments did not become apparent until the members had presented the therapists with still another transference test.

Even as the group members gained better control over the more overtly self-destructive aspects of their acting out, several of them began to talk about wanting to have a second child. A member initiated this theme by coming to the yearly Halloween party dressed as a pregnant teenager. The other members were entranced. The wish for another child arose as their children entered the rapprochement subphase of separation–individuation and gained momentum as the group members struggled with the fact that their children were becoming more autonomous whether they liked it or not. One member expressed these feelings for everyone saying; "even though Jeff (20 months old) can be a real little shit, sometimes he's a pretty good kid and I miss having a baby to look after." This and other similar statements aroused a great deal of nostalgia in all of the mothers.

When the group members were asked, they said they did not remember the difficult days and nights they had spent trying to care for their newborn infants, nor did they recall the confusion and inadequacy they had felt during the first months after their children were born. In their view the children were problematic now, but had been easy to care for when they were little. Even though most of the mothers had not established stable relationships with men and were still moving out of, back into, and back out of their parents' homes, they thought that becoming pregnant would be "wonderful." Although a few members were not sure whether they wanted to be pregnant again just at that moment, even they seemed wistfully indulgent toward the other members who longed for a second child.

The therapists decided to see whether they could persuade the members to examine this wish before acting on it. After affirming each member's right to decide for herself, the therapists calmly but persistently (over the course of several months) presented the normative consequences of a second out-of-wedlock pregnancy at a young age. These included: (1) poverty for an extended period of time; (2) financial dependence on AFDC; (3) emotional dependence on parents and other family members; (4) inability to acquire the skills necessary to qualify for an interesting, well-paid job; (5) inability to keep a job of any kind for more than a short period of time because of the complications involved in arranging child care for two or more children of different ages. This sobering confrontation with reality precipitated two contrasting sets of reactions in the group, one transferential and the other adaptive.

On a transferential level the members were furious and quickly challenged the leaders. They argued about whether the statistics were accurate, told about single teenage mothers they knew who were doing "just fine" after having a second child, denied they would experience any negative consequences even if other people did, denied they would care about the negative consequences if they did experience them, and insisted that having a second child was easily the most rewarding thing they could do with their lives. In a more playful and imaginative vein, they systematically explored how the leaders would react to various forms of defiance, both open and covert. They came to group and announced that their periods were late, wondered whether the therapists could arrange pregnancy tests for them, revealed (casually) that they had been drinking and "forgotten" to use contraception, explained in detail how all forms of contraception were "inconvenient and disgusting," and observed in passing that they had forgotten how to use this or that contraceptive device properly. On occasion they elaborated by saying how much they would enjoy getting pregnant just to upset the therapists.

The therapists remained (outwardly) calm in the face of these provocations. They insisted that each member would have to decide for herself, but that they would make better decisions if they considered all the relevant issues. The therapists reiterated that they could not encourage members to have a second child in the near future, given the national statistics, and their ongoing concern for each member's welfare. Although for the most part the group was aligned against the leaders, some members tentatively challenged the majority. As the discussion was joined, group members began to ask factual questions about contraception, pregnancy, and the changes that had occurred in their bodies during their previous pregnancy. In response to these questions, the nurse cotherapist spent a number of sessions presenting factual information about the female reproductive system. She discussed conception, contraception, abortion, and various types of venereal disease, complete with charts and models. She also provided the group with various contraceptive devices to look at, hold, and smell. The questions were particularly interesting since the nurse had presented similar material on a number of previous occasions. The group members made it clear, however, that they found it difficult to learn and remember this kind of information.

In discussing the facts that were presented, various group members admitted how much they disliked having to think about contraception and how "disgusting" they found most contraceptive methods. This led to considerable discussion about their bodies, touching themselves, and putting "things" into themselves. They also talked about some of their sexual practices, emphasizing how difficult it was for them to "control themselves," especially when they had been drinking. Two of the members mentioned that they experienced very little pleasure during intercourse and that they mostly enjoyed having someone in bed with them whom they could hold and feel close to. Other members talked about being afraid of the dark and sleeping with their children to reassure themselves.

These themes led the members to directly express feelings of loneliness, sadness, disillusionment, and disappointment. At this point in treatment their capacity to tolerate and articulate depressive feelings had increased markedly and they were able to talk openly, not only about feeling "gypped" by society, but also about feeling they had "blown" their lives. During a Mother's Day celebration toward the end of the third year of treatment, a group member commented: "Kids get sick, they're aggravating, and they're demanding. What's so great about being a mother?" The other members were silent. The great pregnancy rush had . . . abated, without a single conception. Although the wish for another child frequently reappeared as an issue for individual members, it never again had the same intensity as a total group issue.

At the level of adaptive functioning, the therapist's expectation that the group members would discuss their wish for a second child before acting on it seemed to stimulate considerable movement in the direction of autonomous functioning. As they considered both the implications of becoming pregnant and the alternatives, they began to mobilize themselves to confront issues and tasks they had previously avoided. Some took driving lessons (the sine qua non of independence in this rural community), others investigated programs through which they could earn their high-school diplomas, and all of them investigated day care programs for their children. In addition, several of them applied for AFDC and began to survey the housing market for their own apartments. These group members were able to articulate some of their ambivalence about leaving home. They said that they would miss the help their families had given them, but not the "hassles." They realized they would always be viewed and treated as children as long as they remained in their parents' home.

The therapists not only facilitated these discussions but also actively supported their autonomous strivings. They identified key people in various childcare, education, and housing programs who would welcome an initiative from the group members and prepared the members for the questions and issues that would arise when they requested service. In those instances where there seemed to be a realistic or psychological reason to do so, one of the therapists would accompany a member to her first interview. And, when the group members could reach consensus, the therapists arranged for and accompanied the entire group on visits to programs (day care, etc.) that were of special interest to all the members.

OUTCOME

Throughout the body of this paper, I have made passing reference to changes in ego organization and object relations that took place during the first three phases of treatment. A full list of these changes would include: (1) increased capacity to tolerate depression without acting out; (2) decreased anxiety about the possible destructive consequences of hostile feelings and improved control over the expression of hostile feelings; (3) more positive self and object representations; (4) significant gains in reality testing, judgment, cognitive functioning, and self-esteem; (5) decreased impulsivity; (6) better modulated libidinal attachments to primary objects; (7) progress toward more autonomous and individuated functioning; (8) a more highly developed and secure sense of personal identity.

In addition to the intrapsychic changes listed above, there were a number of specific behavioral indicators that reinforced our positive evaluation of the group's effectiveness. Of the twenty-one mothers who spent three or more months in the group between 1970 and 1984 and who were still available for follow-up in 1986, only two had again become pregnant as of June 1986 (two to eight years after the birth of their first child). Nationally, 50 percent of unmarried adolescent mothers become pregnant within three years of their first delivery (Kirsh, 1984, p. 368). Fifteen (75%) of the mothers treated in the group had completed their high-school diplomas as of June 1986, and five more were studying for equivalency examinations. Only one of the twenty-one mothers (4%) had abandoned her efforts to complete her secondary school education. Nationally, 50 percent of the single teenage mothers who give birth before the age of eighteen never complete their high-school educations (Konner and Shostak, 1986, p. 330). And finally, as of June 1987, none of the twenty-one mothers had been formally cited for child neglect or abuse and none had been referred for problems involving substance abuse.

While no one in the group achieved anything remotely resembling genetic insight, most of the members did eventually acknowledge their frustrations, disappointments, and ambivalent feelings toward particular family members. They became considerably more realistic about how they felt toward significant people in their lives and what they might reasonably expect from relationships with those people. In addition, their capacity to establish and maintain positive peer relationships with other women improved markedly, a direct carry-over from the relationships they had developed in the group. While they were considerably less ambivalent toward their children, they still had difficulty in providing consistent care and attention at times when they were experiencing significant personal or environmental stress. With one exception, they no longer permitted men to exploit them physically or emotionally, but, in general, their relationships with men continued to be conflictual and unsatisfying. The group was still working on this issue well into the fifth year of its existence.

CONCLUSION

The mother–infant group proved to be a fascinating, instructive, and effective therapeutic experiment. Although it had not initially occurred to us that teenage mothers might be seeking (and need) a compensatory transitional experience, our observations of the group gradually convinced us that this was, indeed, the case. Eventually, we recognized that by organizing the group around mother–infant dyads, we had created a psychological environment which did not interfere with the group members' need to view each other and the group-as-a-whole as a merged unit in which everyone was very much alike. The group's homogeneity, especially in regard to shared frustrations with children and other significant objects, encouraged the illusion that the group was a subjective creation of each members' imagination. Although the group was certainly not "inanimate" and individual members could not actually control the process, the membership was homogeneous enough to ensure that during its beginning phases, each member's illusion of control was not (often) threatened. The "illusions" of sameness and control persisted into the third phase of treatment, at which point the members began to differentiate from each other and from the group-as-a-whole.

The group's curative potential was based on its capacity to simulate a transitional object experience, and on the members' complementary willingness to imaginatively accept and use that simulation. The following factors were of central importance. (1) The group functioned as a created "me-not-me" possession which not only protected and soothed the members, but also survived their attacks, and absorbed their hostility. As the members recognized the group's capacity to fulfill this function, they gradually transferred some of their transitional object needs from the infants to the group-as-a-whole. This was particularly important when the members began to express hateful, destructive, and defiant feelings in the transference. As they and the therapists struggled to deal with those feelings the members gradually internalized an understanding that their hatred would not destroy them or the group and that the therapists would not reject or otherwise retaliate against them. (2) The group provided the members with an intermediate area of experience between the (mostly) unconscious fantasies that had motivated them to keep and raise their children, and the difficult realities of their day-to-day existence as teenage mothers. By becoming a secure "space between" illusion and reality, the group made it possible for the members to playfully experiment with new modes of feeling, behavior, and interpersonal functioning that gradually helped them deal more adaptively with the demands and responsibilities of the new reality they had chosen for themselves. The group's playful experimentation with new ways of challenging adult authority was particularly evident when the members called up from the parking lot to announce that they "were beating up" their children, and when the members arrived at group proclaiming that they were pregnant. (3) The group also encouraged new, more adaptive identifications with the leaders, other members, and the group-as-a-whole. These identifications tended to support reality testing, verbalization of feelings, delay of gratification, and cognitive control over impulses. In addition, as the members discovered that they were accepted in spite of their hostile feelings, their self-esteem improved and they became less vulnerable to internal attacks from punitive superego precursors.

The mother–infant group is a complex and creative form of intervention which should be replicated with other "at risk" populations of mothers and young children. Its unique contribution lies in its use of real and symbolic family interactions to create an environment in which patients can safely move backward and forward in psychological time. Group members experiment with merger and separateness, with the security of familiar forms of behavior, and the excitement of exploring what is still unknown, with old and new patterns of identification, and with well-established and innovative ways of relating to peers. In the process, they continually create new and more adaptive boundaries between fantasy and reality. With proper leadership, the format generates a unique balance of regressive and progressive forces in the service of helping its members reestablish their capacity to address and master the phase specific developmental tasks of adolescence, young adulthood, and parenthood.[2]

REFERENCES

Azima, F. J. C. (1986), Countertransference: In and beyond child group psychotherapy. In: *Child Group Psychotherapy: Future Tense*, ed. A. E. Riester & I. A. Kraft. Madison, CT: International Universities Press, pp. 139–156.

Barclay, L. E. (1969), A group approach to young unwed mothers. *Soc. Casework*, 50:379–384.

Berkovitz, I. H. (1972), On growing a group: Some thoughts on structure, process and setting. In: *Adolescents Grow in Groups*, ed. I. H. Berkovitz. New York: Brunner/Mazel, pp. 6–30.

Bion, W. R. (1959), *Experiences in Group*. New York: Basic Books, 1961.

Bittner, R. (1984), Therapeutic mother-child groups: A developmental approach. *Soc. Casework*, 65:154–161.

[2] In honoring Saul Scheidlinger one is tempted to emphasize his encyclopedic knowledge of the psychoanalytic and group process literature, his ability to organize and apply those theories to clinical practice, and his contributions to the development of a "metatheory" for the field. However, this chapter is written in appreciation of another important aspect of his work, his ongoing efforts to develop treatment models and procedures that are relevant for children and parents who not only have significant deficits in ego organization, but who are also socially and economically disadvantaged. This area of theory and practice has been much neglected, particularly in the more sophisticated group therapy literature, so it is a great pleasure to formally recognize Saul's unique contribution to the emotional health of people who are usually ignored or labeled as "untreatable" by the mental health community at large.

Black, M., & Rosenthal, L. (1970), Modifications in therapeutic technique in the group treatment of delinquent boys. In: *New Approaches in Child Guidance*, ed. H. S. Strean. Metuchen, NJ: Scarecrow Press.

Blos, P. (1962), *On Adolescence*. Glencoe, IL: Free Press.

Carrothers, M. L. (1963), Sexual themes in an adolescent girls group. *Internat. J. Group Psychother.*, 13:43–51.

Convery, P. (1984), Group work with unmarried parents. In: *Child Welfare: A Source Book of Knowledge and Practice*, ed. F. Maidman. New York: Child Welfare League of America, pp. 437–441.

Crawford, A. G., & Furstenberg, F. F. (1985), Teenage sexuality, pregnancy and child-bearing. In: *A Handbook of Child Welfare*, ed. A. Hartman & J. Laird. New York: Free Press.

Eissler, K. R. (1981), The effect of the structure of the ego on psychoanalytic technique. In: *Classics in Psychoanalytic Technique*, ed. R. Langs. New York: Jason Aronson, pp. 437–454.

Erikson, E. H. (1950), *Childhood and Society*. New York: W. W. Norton.

Freud, A. (1956), Adolescence as a developmental disturbance. In: *The Writings of Anna Freud*, 7:39–47. New York: International Universities Press.

——— (1958), Adolescence. *The Psychoanalytic Study of the Child*, 13:255–278. New York: International Universities Press.

Fried, E. (1956), Ego emancipation of adolescents through group psychotherapy. *Internat. J. Group Psychother.*, 6:358–373.

Garland, J., & Kolodney, R. (1965), A model for stages of development in social work groups. In: *Exploration in Group Work: Essays in Theory and Practice*, ed. S. Bernstein. Boston: Boston University School of Social Work.

Guttmacher Institute (1981), *Factbook of Teenage Pregnancy*. New York: Guttmacher Institute.

Hoffman, T. E., & Bryne, K. M. (1981), Simultaneous semipermeable groups for mothers and their early latency-aged boys. *Internat. J. Group Psychother.*, 31:83–98.

Holman, S. L. (1979), An early intervention program for developmentally-at-risk toddlers and their mothers. *Clin. Soc. Work J.*, 7/3:167–181.

Kaufmann, P. N., & Deutsch, A. L. (1967), Group therapy for pregnant unwed adolescents in the prenatal clinic of a general hospital. *Internat. J. Group Psychother.*, 17:309–320.

Kennedy Foundation (1982), *A Community of Caring*. Joseph P. Kennedy, Jr., Foundation.

Kirsch, S. (1984), Working with unmarried parents. In: *Child Welfare: A Sourcebook of Knowledge and Practice*, ed. F. Maidman. New York: Child Welfare League of America.

Kolodney, R. L., & Reilly, W. V. (1972), Group work with today's unmarried mother. *Soc. Casework*, 53:613–622.

Konner, M., & Shostak, M. (1986), Adolescent pregnancy and childbearing: An anthropological perspective. In: *School Age Pregnancy and Parenthood*, ed. Lancaster & Hamburg. New York: Aldine DeGruyter.

Kosseff, J. W. (1975), The leader using object-relations theory. In: *The Leader in the Group*, ed. A. Liff. New York: Jason Aronson, pp. 212–242.

MacLennan, B. W., & Felsenfeld, N. (1968), *Group Counselling and Psychotherapy with Adolescents*. New York: Columbia University Press.

Maidman, F. (1984), Group work with unmarried parents. In: *Child Welfare: A Sourcebook of Knowledge and Practice*, ed. F. Maidman. New York: Child Welfare League of America, pp. 437–441.

National Center for Health Statistics (1980), *Final Natality Statistics 1980; Monthly Vital Statistics Report*, Vol. 2, No. 2. Washington, DC: National Center for Health Statistics, U.S. Department of Health and Human Services.

Ogden, T. H. (1982), *Projective Identification and Psychotherapeutic Technique*. New York: Jason Aronson.

O'Leary, K. M., Shore, M. F., & Wilder, S. (1984), Contacting pregnant adolescents: Are we missing cues? *Soc. Casework*, 65:297–305.

Papademetrious, M. (1971), Use of a group technique with unwed mothers and their families. *Soc. Casework*, 52:85–90.

Pfeiffer, D. (1979), Current fads and modes in adolescent group treatment: Perspectives on distinctions, common elements and the question of therapeutic relevance. *Group*, 3:195–202.

Rachman, A. W., & Raubolt, R. P. (1984), The pioneers of adolescent group psychotherapy. *Internat. J. Group Psychother.*, 34:387–414.

Racker, H. (1968), *Transference and Countertransference*. New York: International Universities Press.

Rosenthal, L. (1971), Some dynamics of resistance and therapeutic management in adolescent group therapy. *Psychoanal. Rev.*, 58:353–366.

——— (1977), Qualifications and tasks of the group therapist with children. *Clin. Soc. Work J.*, 5:191–199.

——— (1987), *Resolving Resistance in Group Psychotherapy*. New York: Jason Aronson.

Schamess, G. (1981), Boundary issues in countertransference. *Clin. Soc. Work J.*, 9:244–259.

——— (1986), Differential diagnosis and group structure in the outpatient treatment of latency age children. In: *Child Group Psychotherapy: Future Tense*, ed. A. E. Riester & I. A. Kraft. Madison, CT: International Universities Press, pp. 29–70.

——— (1987), Parallel mother/infant/toddler groups: A developmentally oriented intervention programme for unmarried teenage mothers. *J. Soc. Work Pract.*, (London, U.K.), 2:29–48.

Schamess, S. (1985), *The Relationship Between Maternal Developmental Stage and Mother/Child Interaction in Adolescent Mothers and Their Toddler Age Children*. Unpublished Doctoral Proposal. University of Massachusetts, Amherst, Massachusetts.

Scheidlinger, S. (1960), Experiential group treatment of severely deprived latency-age children. In: *Focus on Group Psychotherapy: Clinical Essays*, ed. S. Scheidlinger. New York: International Universities Press, pp. 133–150, 1960.

——— (1961), Group therapy of women with severe character disorders in a family service agency. In: *Focus on Group Psychotherapy: Clinical Essays*, ed. S. Scheidlinger. New York: International Universities Press, pp. 191–214, 1966.

——— (1974), On the concept of the "mother group." In: *Focus on Group Psychotherapy: Clinical Essays*, ed. S. Scheidlinger. New York: International Universities Press, pp. 75–88.

Scheller-Gilkey, G. (1984), *Case Studies of Unmarried Adolescent Mothers from a Develop-*

mental Perspective. Unpublished Doctoral Dissertation. Smith College School for Social Work, Northampton, Massachusetts.

Slavson, S. R. (1943), *An Introduction to Group Therapy*. New York: International Universities Press.

——— (1979), Para-analytic group psychotherapy for adolescents. In: *Dynamics of Group Psychotherapy*, ed. M. Schiffer. New York: Jason Aronson, pp. 715–724.

Soo, E. S. (1980), The impact of transference and countertransference in activity group therapy. *Group*, 1:222–234.

——— (1986), Training and supervision in child and adolescent group psychotherapy. In: *Child Group Psychotherapy: Future Tense*, ed. A. E. Reister & I. A. Kraft. Madison, CT: International Universities Press, pp. 157–172.

Spotnitz, H. (1969), *Modern Psychoanalysis of the Schizophrenic Patient*. New York: Grune & Stratton.

Strean, H. (1968), Reconsiderations in casework treatment of the unmarried mother. *Soc. Casework*, 49:91–100.

Tuttman, S. (1986), Theoretical and technical elements which characterize the American approaches to psychoanalytic group psychotherapy. *Internat. J. Group Psychother.*, 36:499–516.

Vinouskis, S. (1981), An epidemic of teenage pregnancy? Some historic considerations. *J. Fam. Hist.*, 6:205–230.

Winnicott, D. W. (1951), Transitional objects and transitional phenomena. In: *Through Pediatrics to Psycho-Analysis*. New York: Basic Books, 1958, pp. 229–242.

——— (1965), Ego distortion in terms of true and false self. In: *The Maturational Processes and the Facilitating Environment*. New York: International Universities Press, pp. 140–152.

PART VI

The Evolution of Psychoanalytic Group Theory

INTRODUCTION

Over the years, there has been a gradual evolution in the theory and practice of psychoanalytic group psychotherapy. A study of the history and development of group techniques can enhance the perspective of theorists and practitioners.

Horwitz (in chapter 15) raises the question as to whether the group therapy process functions more effectively when the focus is on group-as-a-whole dynamics or when the focus is on individual dynamics within each group member. He looks back at the history of group psychotherapy acknowledging that American group therapists have stressed individual dynamics whereas the British have focused on the dynamics of the group-as-a-whole. In recent years, the group-as-a-whole approach has carried more weight than previously in the United States, since a modification has been employed in which the group leader focuses initially on the needs of the individual group members. Once this occurs, the communality of the group is established via a group-centered approach which can then be further employed without inflicting narcissistic injury on individuals in the group. Such developments, Horwitz contends, enhance the therapeutic exploitation of the group for meaningful growth of the members.

Chapters 16 and 17 deal with the history and evolution of psychoanalytic group theory and treatment. Relevant to both essays is the influence of Freud's personality and relationships (Tuttman, 1981, 1986) as well as the climate in Vienna at the time (Schorske, 1961). In chapter 16, Roth examines Kanzer's contention that the Vienna circle of colleagues which met with Freud weekly may be considered the first psychotherapy group (even though the field of group therapy had not yet been formally defined or organized and the alleged function was that of a study group led by Freud). Utilizing the *Minutes of the Vienna Psychoanalytic Society* (Nunberg and Federn, 1962–1975) and the data of biographers and historians, Roth explores the possible influence of Freud's "group" experience as well as the effect of his personality problems upon his views on group psychology expressed in the famous monograph (Freud, 1921). Although many of Roth's contentions are hypothetical, given limited access to primary sources, it is important for experienced, contemporary group therapists to reexamine Freud's views on group psychology in the light of current theory and clinical experience.

Bacal begins his paper (chapter 17) by also referring to Freud's Vienna circle as the first therapy group! He then utilizes this historical example as a means to illustrate an insight which self psychologists and others utilize to enhance the potential effectiveness of contemporary psychoanalytic group treatment; namely, that the group experience can be an opportunity to learn to perceive empathically our own needs, as well as those of other group members when group conditions enhance therapeutic possibilities. Although this optimal therapeutic application need not be limited to practitioners of one particular theoretical school; self psychologists (along with those who apply the insights of Ferenczi, Balint, Mahler, Scheidlinger, Winnicott, and others) are able to maximize the therapeutic potential in groups.

REFERENCES

Freud, S. (1921), Group psychology and the analysis of the ego. *Standard Edition*, 18:69–143. London: Hogarth Press, 1955.
Nunberg, H., & Federn, P. eds. (1962–1975), *Minutes of the Vienna Psychoanalytic Society*, 2 vols. New York: International Universities Press.
Schorske, C. (1961), *Fin-De-Siecle Vienna*. New York: Vintage Books, 1981.
Tuttman, S. (1981), A historical survey of the development of object relations concepts in psychoanalytic theory. In: *Object and Self: A Developmental Approach*, eds. S. Tuttman, C. Kaye, and M. Zimmerman. New York: International Universities Press, pp. 3–51.
——— (1986), The impact of trauma on Freud's life and work. *Issues in Ego Psychology*, 9:5–12.

Chapter 15

The Evolution of a Group-Centered Approach

LEONARD HORWITZ, Ph.D.

Ever since psychotherapists began treating patients in groups, they have had to face the issue of understanding the dynamic forces that are set in motion, as well as the more challenging problem of how to use those forces to therapeutic advantage. The controversy in this field has not been whether group dynamics exist in psychotherapy groups but rather to what extent they can be exploited therapeutically. Attitudes have varied from Bion's (1959) contention that the group therapist's major task is to attend to the group's basic assumptions, to Slavson's (1957) opposing view that any effort to work with the dynamics of the group-as-a-whole will lead to a variety of antitherapeutic effects. This debate was waged rather heatedly in the late 1950s and early 1960s, and Parloff (1968), in his comprehensive review of the various approaches to analytic group psychotherapy—individualistic, interpersonal, and integralist, observed that the integralist or group-centered approach was the least-used method during the mid-1960s but showed the greatest promise for integrating individual and group dynamics in a psychotherapy group. In my view, his prediction that the field would move toward a group-centered approach had indeed been confirmed, and the debate has now shifted to how best to integrate the dynamics of the group with strategies of individual intervention.

This chapter was presented in abbreviated form on August 26, 1986, to the Ninth International Congress of Group Psychotherapy held in Zagreb, Yugoslavia.

THE AMERICAN SCENE

During the fifty-year history of group psychotherapy, there have been two major loci of activity, the United States and Great Britain. The indisputably dominant American figure for the first twenty-five years (1935–1960) was S. R. Slavson. The mentor of many who later became leaders on the American scene, he was quite forceful, if not dogmatic, in asserting an individualistic point of view about the proper model of group psychotherapy. He addressed the issue in a 1957 article entitled "Are There 'Group Dynamics' in Therapy Groups?" and answered this question with a resounding "no!" He differentiated therapy groups from a wide variety of task-oriented groups, contending that the former do not have "a common group goal." Groups other than therapy groups show a "synergy" in which individuals give up a portion of their ego to encourage a group ego, while therapy groups avoid doing this. Although there may be a groupwide reaction or a contagion effect in a group, the therapist is always focused on individual differences in these reactions, the individual character patterns, the quantity and kind of affect, as well as the source of the reaction.

Thus, even though Slavson acknowledges a number of dynamic forces in all groups, including mutual induction, intensification, and identification, he believes that the pivotal difference between psychotherapy groups and ordinary groups is that the former seek to uncover intrapsychic determinants within each individual; hence any emphasis on the similarities among members based on group dynamic considerations is antitherapeutic. In fact, says Slavson, group dynamics should be nipped in the bud, analyzed, and explored before a group pattern or group effect begins to set in. He equates these dynamics with homogenization, artificial uniformity, and submersion of individual differences, with the result that individual problems cannot be thoroughly communicated and worked through. Slavson (1964) decried any evidence of the group acting as a unit: "The therapist has to deal here with a mass reaction, rather than with an individual, a situation fraught with difficulties and even danger. . . . The therapist must always be on the alert against unanimity of any sort in the therapy group, for unanimity in groups is derived from hostility against the therapist" (p. 386).

Equally vehement in their attack on group dynamics were Schwartz and Wolf (1960), Wolf and Schwartz (1962), who crusaded forcefully to eliminate the heresy of thinking about the group as a unified entity. Because much of the work at that time on the study of group dynamics was being conducted by social psychologists under the leadership of Kurt Lewin, Schwartz and Wolf were concerned about the wholesale transfer to psychotherapy groups of concepts derived from the study of nonclinical groups, thus engendering superficial thinking and a neglect of unconscious motivations. Like Slavson, they were afraid that conceptualizing the group as operating in a unitary fashion would lead to a neglect of individual differences, to a demand for conformity on the part of the members, and to an expectation that the patients would become submissive to the leader's wish for homogeneity. In general, Schwartz and Wolf established a dichotomy between treating the group and treating the individual, and believed that the two modes of thinking were incompatible.

These anti-group-centered points of view were extremely influential on the American scene in the 1950s and 1960s, but they were by no means representative of all American group psychotherapists. In fact, several leading writers of that period expressed views considerably different from those of Slavson and his followers. Thus Redl (1942) emphasized the phenomena of group contagion and role suction, and Semrad and Arsenian (1951) proposed the similar concept of billet. They believed that an individual's behavior in a group setting cannot be understood fully by reference only to individual dynamics, and that the emotional currents within a group often pressed patients into relatively atypical roles. Durkin (1957) joined this debate and displayed an unusual degree of openness to group dynamic concepts, in particular the view that the cohesiveness or the attractiveness of a group to its members should be an essential part of every group therapist's thinking. Whitaker and Lieberman (1964) produced the first systematic theory in the United States which recognized the unitary functioning of the group in what they termed the "group focal conflict" or the commonly held wish or motive countered by various defensive operations.

Saul Scheidlinger (1952) attempted to steer a middle course between the antigroup dynamicists and those writers, such as Bion (1959), whom he believes were exclusively preoccupied with group phenomena at the expense of individual personality factors. Scheidlinger has consistently been interested in various group dynamic elements, such as group climate, structure, and norms, but he has equally been opposed to any characterization of the group that smacks of "group mind." Thus he (1968) stated that:

> Group members can maintain shared or common fantasies; they can even act in unison in response to group occurrences, such as the entry of a new member or the absence of the leader. And yet, this need not mean that the group *as a group* now has a certain fantasy or acts in a certain manner. . . . Shared fantasies are far from being the same in

each individual. . . . A group can possess observable characteristics, can be perceived and related to as a whole, but this makes it a social and psychological reality, not a physical reality; it does not indicate a "group mind" [p. 8].

Although most writers would agree that *shared* fantasies are not the same as *identical* fantasies, Scheidlinger appears to believe that Bion's "group mentality" implies this kind of identity. The issue he raises is how to define the observed commonalities as well as the individual differences and how they should be used.

THE BRITISH SCENE

Compared to the American emphasis on an intra-individual approach, the British from the very beginning have emphasized a groupwide or group-centered approach. Although the major early contributors, Bion, Ezriel, and Foulkes, had different theoretical perspectives, they were all definitely in a group-centered camp which emphasized the importance of group dynamic properties and, to a greater or lesser extent, used the concept of unitary functioning. Depending on one's perspective, these British writers were either misguided or, as I prefer to believe, were influential in facilitating a significant shift toward integrating individual and group dynamics. In my view, American group psychotherapy has gradually begun to incorporate some of the significant contributions of our British colleagues as we have moved from an intra-individual emphasis to a group dynamic or group-centered approach. How and why the British adopted a group-centered stance so much earlier than the Americans deserves further study. The fact that many leading British psychiatrists and psychoanalysts were assembled during World War II at the Northfield Hospital (Trist, 1985) where they collaborated on applying group methods to the treatment of psychiatric casualties of the war may have contributed significantly to their advanced thinking in group approaches.

Unquestionably, the leading British theoretician, and one whose influence has been felt universally by all group psychotherapists, is Wilfred R. Bion. Social psychologists associated with Kurt Lewin's Survey Research Center studied Bion's writings for insights into the more regressed levels of group functioning. To a greater or lesser extent, the work of the Tavistock Institute of Human Relations, the group relations conferences sponsored by the A. K. Rice Institute, and the sensitivity training programs sponsored by the National Training Laboratories used Bion's views regarding the basic assumption—life in groups and the way these forces obstruct the primary task of a work group. Although Bion interrupted his work with groups prematurely and did not write extensively about the application of his ideas to psychotherapy groups, many of his theoretical notions were adopted by the group psychotherapists at the Tavistock Clinic where his ideas were translated into a specific model of group psychotherapy.

Following World War II, Bion was invited by the Tavistock Clinic to begin "taking groups," and he pursued an intensive study of his work with patient groups as well as study groups of professionals for the next few years. His series of articles on his experiences and formulations were published first in the journal *Human Relations* between 1949 and 1951 and subsequently in a book, *Experiences in Groups* (1959).

According to Bion, groups operate at two levels of functioning, the work group and the basic assumption group. The former consists mainly of conscious, rational, goal-directed activities dictated by the task of the group, while the latter consists of less conscious, more regressed emotional currents that express a more primitive "group mentality" and often tend to interfere with the primary task. Bion described the mechanism by which the group becomes caught up in one of the three basic assumptions (dependency, fight–flight, pairing) as the Kleinian concept of projective identification in which members attempt to put parts of themselves into each of the other members and attempt to influence and manipulate the others into certain desired roles. The therapist's main tool for perceiving and understanding the group mentality is an inner feeling of being manipulated by the group into certain behavioral responses. This description is not unlike the phenomenon of countertransference reactions within the analyst that illuminate the patient's conscious or unconscious attitudes. Bion's important contribution, however, was his detailed description of the unitary functioning of groups with some suggestions about how to turn these understandings into therapeutic benefit.

Using Bion's notions of the group mentality, Ezriel (1952) proposed that the group therapist's interpretive task is to ferret out the underlying common group tension, a conflicted fantasy shared by all group members. The conflict consists of a commonly held wish that cannot be openly expressed because it would create excessive anxiety. Ezriel described this conflicted situation as a three-tiered relationship; a wished-for or "desired" relationship, defended against by a "required" relationship, lest a "catastrophic" situation ensue. The therapist's role is to diagnose both the common group tension as well as the three-tiered relations manifested by each member (a somewhat formidable task!). The general structure of the interpretation offered by the therapist to the group is essentially an explanation of the prevailing common group tension and how each individual is responding to this conflicted situation in his or her own unique, idiosyncratic way. Here we have the first effort to integrate the commonly shared dynamic force within the group with each individual's characteristic patterns of dealing with this conflict.

This first serious effort to integrate individual and group dynamics, however, has not fared well over the years under the critical scrutiny of researchers and clinicians alike. In a survey of patients who had undergone group psychotherapy at the Tavistock Clinic using the Ezriel method, Malan, Balfour, Hood, and Shooter (1976) found a universal complaint that there was excessive emphasis on the group-as-a-whole to the exclusion of individuals, and that the therapist seemed more concerned with the commonality of the group than with the conflicts of individual members. Both Day (1981) and Horwitz (1977) are proponents of some form of the Tavistock model, and have implicitly concurred in Malan's criticism insofar as we have observed in our clinical work that the Ezriel method rigidly imposes a constraining influence on the therapist and prevents a timely response to the individual needs of patients.

Foulkes (1964) also subscribed to the view that there is a unitary quality to the functioning of a therapeutic group. This idea is embodied in his concept of a matrix, which he described as "the common ground of operational relationships, comprising all the interactions of individual group members" (p. 110). He believes that all individual reactions must be understood as a "figure" in relationship to the "ground" of the group-as-a-whole. He also uses the metaphor of the individual as a single neuron embedded in the total nervous system which is analogous to the total network of communication within the group. His view of the group functioning holistically is concretized by his recommendation that the group's productions should be regarded as equivalent to the free associations of a single individual, and that the latent meaning of the communication within a group can best be ascertained by means of this free associative approach.

All three British writers share a common perspective on the functioning of the group-as-a-whole. Bion's group mentality, Ezriel's common group tension, and Foulkes's mental matrix may differ in detail and specificity, but they share the notion of an all-important group emotion—whether it be a commonly shared fantasy, conflict, or tension—that produces a significant effect on the behavior of each member. These writers also agree that, to intervene accurately and usefully, the group therapist must at some point define and integrate the influence of the group upon the individual.

THE CURRENT SCENE

Slowly and imperceptibly the theory and practice of group psychotherapy have increasingly emphasized a group-centered method. Using Parloff's terminology, the method appears to have moved sharply away from the individualistic and the interpersonal approach toward the "integralist" or group-centered approach. Evidence of such a transition may be seen in the work of Kibel and Stein (1981), the book by Rutan and Stone (1984), and the report of the Task Force on General Systems Theory chaired by Helen Durkin (1982), as well as the writings of Boriello (1976) and Agazarian (1981). The present writer has also been an active proponent of the group-centered approach (Horwitz, 1971, 1977).

Group-centered thinking is represented by a broad spectrum of theoretical approaches ranging from a circumscribed application to specific developments in a group to a view that group dynamic forces are omnipresent and need to be uncovered by the group therapist. I shall delineate three main points on this spectrum.

The most limited view about groupwide phenomena and their interpretation is that espoused by Yalom (1980). Although recognizing that a group has important system properties, he is opposed in general to what he describes as "mass interpretations." The pejorative connotation of his term seems to convey his attitude that such interventions unduly emphasize patient–therapist relationships as opposed to peer interactions, and, furthermore, that one may fall into the error of artificially squeezing into the mass interpretation individuals who may not belong there. Therefore, Yalom would restrict his groupwide interpretations to situations wherein the therapist finds it necessary to remove obstacles to the progress of the entire group; for example, when the entire group is under the influence of some anxiety-laden issue that members are unable to address, or when an antitherapeutic group norm is beginning to develop, such as the collusion among members to begin taking turns.

A second, more expanded view of groupwide functioning is one in which individual and group issues alternate. According to Whitaker and Lieberman (1964), the group focal conflict consists essentially of a shared wish countered by a commonly held fear, and only through interpretation can the group begin to resolve the conflict and find an "enabling solution," thus progressing in its task of dealing with personal conflicts of its individual members. This perspective contrasts sharply with the Ezriel notion that personal issues become integrated with group issues, and that it is possible to work on the two simultaneously rather than discretely.

Day (1981) gradually became disillusioned with the Tavistock method of emphasizing the common group tension and organizing individual interventions around groupwide themes. His observation from his own clinical experience was that if the therapist continues to address primarily the group, the patients will eventually leave and find their satisfactions elsewhere. He currently uses groupwide interventions only when certain events clearly affect the entire group (such as the therapist's absence, a member's success or failure, an entry or departure of a member), particularly events that alter the group "envelope." On the other hand, when the group is working cohesively and there are no groupwide disturbances in the alliance, individual transferences become prominent. Day agrees that there are times when individual transferences may have some similarities and may be explored in parallel. His point of view regarding the alternation between group and individual issues seems close to that of Whitaker and Lieberman.

Scheidlinger's views on this issue are not readily categorized, mainly because he does not believe that our field has yet achieved a good theoretical or practical integration of group and individual elements. As mentioned earlier, even though he recognizes the presence of certain shared or common fantasies in a group in reaction to group occurrences, he asserts that phenomena such as regressions, identifications, and fantasizing operate in individuals only. Furthermore, he believes that individual personalities in a group, with their genetic and dynamic properties, are involved in a complex interaction with group dynamic elements, such as climate, goals, and structure, and that this dual interaction is embedded in two main levels of group functioning: (1) the dynamic contemporaneous level that is more readily observed and includes the expression of conscious needs and adaptive patterns, and (2) the genetic regressive level which primarily consists of unconscious and preconscious motivations, defenses, and conflicts.

Although Scheidlinger believes that we are not ready to formulate a method of integrating these varied and complex forces, one gains the impression that he is leaning toward Whitaker and Lieberman's alternation hypothesis. In referring to group conflict theory he wrote (1980): "Conflictual phases were found to be interspersed with periods of group interaction which were devoid of conflict. This last observation, together with a greater allowance for individual group member differences and varying degrees of repression, is more consistent with current notions of ego psychology than the concepts of Bion and Ezriel" (pp. 277–278).

The third and broadest conceptualization of the group-centered approach views the common group tension as a constant presence in the group, although it is perhaps not always readily observable. Rutan and Stone (1984) adhere to this point of view and state that at times group-as-a-whole factors are quite significant, while at other times these processes may fade into the background, but never disappear. According to Rutan and Stone, groupwide phenomena become most significant when boundaries are changed, such as when a new member enters the group, because the change affects the entire group. Although they lean heavily in the direction of the constant presence idea, they believe that at times group transactions "represent a specific pathological configuration that emerges in the group" (p. 66) and offer as an example the group's reaction to a monopolizer. It is not entirely clear why this kind of group event would not have repercussions for the entire group.

Kibel and Stein (1981) have also moved close to a constant presence point of view, with some reservations. Their major thesis is that the transference to the therapist is a basic "major dynamic force" (p. 421) behind all group interactions and that, at any given moment, it determines the direction and nature of the group process. But they caution against interpreting such transference before dealing with and interpreting the peer interaction. They believe that *peer* transference is comparable to transference resistance, while the *therapist* transference is the major transference content, and they argue that resistance should be addressed before content. An evaluation of the merits of this argument is beyond the scope of this paper, but the main idea that the transference to the therapist is an underlying and constant motivating force indicates a significant adherence to group-centered thinking. On the other hand, Kibel and Stein back away from the position that group themes are always dominant and always express core elements of group phenomena. They believe that such a position constitutes an unwarranted analogy to individual psychology because an individual's synthetically functioning ego creates a unity in the individual's psyche that is not present in the group.

Like Kibel and Stein, Scheidlinger explicitly addresses the dilemma of recognizing that there is a certain unity in a group's functioning (e.g., groupwide themes, reactions, and resistances) but that the group also manifests diversity based on differences among individual members. In my view, there is no inherent contradiction between the idea of a shared group conflict and individual differences among members. To use the most often cited stimulus to a groupwide reaction—the

arrival of a new member—all the patients will share a variety of reactions and conflicts concerning the arrival. In this sense, there is a
common group tension about assimilating the new person. At the
same time, each individual will experience a unique reaction to this
shared dilemma; therefore the common group tension does not force
us into the untenable position of a "group mind" that carries with it
the connotation of identical reactions among members.

The system of group psychotherapy that I (Horwitz, 1977) have
proposed clearly embraces the idea of a common group tension as a
constant presence and shares the Bion and Ezriel theoretical base that
associates the unity of the group with projective identification (Horwitz, 1983). But I believe this system modifies the Tavistock approach
sufficiently to overcome some of its weaknesses. In the early 1960s,
John D. Sutherland, Medical Director of the Tavistock Clinic and a
collaborator with Ezriel, became a consultant to the newly formed
Menninger Foundation Group Psychotherapy Service and we, at Men-
ningers, were persuaded to adopt the Tavistock model. Gradually,
however, we found that the method exerted undue constraints on the
role of the therapist insofar as individual work with patients could be
done only after the group theme or group conflict had been uncovered and interpreted. As noted earlier, the weakness of this deductive
method was also described in the research report by Malan et al.
(1976). The modification I proposed was to use an inductive rather
than deductive method in which the individual work with several
patients precedes the interpretation of the group theme; that is,
groupwide phenomena are gradually defined from the common
thread running through the associative content of each individual
member.

I (Horwitz, 1986) have recently elaborated and illustrated this
method, so I will not describe it in detail here. But I would note that
the inductive method is a model or paradigm, not a rigid system, and
it needs to be adapted to particular circumstances. In some instances,
a groupwide theme may extend over several sessions, and the therapist
may wish to move back and forth between individual and group interventions. Also, the method represents a way of thinking rather
than a specific technique and superficially may appear quite similar
to a more individualistic approach. The difference from other approaches, however, lies in the therapist's special perspective toward
the material, and in his or her way of listening to it, thinking about
it, and occasionally bringing these observations to the attention of the
group. The therapist engages in a process of "listening with a fourth
ear": The third ear listens for the unconscious communication of each
individual member, while the fourth ear attends to the common theme

among all these contributions. A group-centered approach has the following advantages:

1. It enhances group cohesiveness by emphasizing shared anxieties, defenses, and conflicts.
2. It contributes to a deepening of the material insofar as one usually uncovers a more regressed level associated with shared here-and-now transference reactions.
3. It leads to discerning such defenses as the spokesperson phenomenon, scapegoating, or role suction—all indications of a shared conflict.

Using an inductive method, one can accrue these advantages while not suffering from the disadvantage of submerging individual needs.

SUMMARY

American and British group psychotherapy developed from widely divergent beginnings, but they now are showing a greater degree of convergence. The American approach, mainly under the dominance of Slavson, emphasized the uncovering of each individual group member's conflicts and defenses and regarded group dynamics as antitherapeutic and homogenizing. Conversely, the British contributors, such as Bion, Ezriel, and Foulkes, held that a common group tension was omnipresent and required interpretation to fully elucidate the uniqueness of individual reactions. American group psychotherapy seems to have moved steadily toward some adaptation of the British theoretical base, although many variations in its application exist. One of these variations is a so-called inductive group-centered approach that modifies the Tavistock model by placing greater emphasis on the needs of individual members.

REFERENCES

Agazarian, Y. (1981), *The Visible and Invisible Group; Two Perspectives on Group Psychotherapy and Group Process by Co-Therapists*. London: Routledge & Kegan Paul.

Bion, W. R. (1959), *Experiences in Groups*. New York: Basic Books, 1961.

Boriello, J. (1976), Leadership in the therapist centered group-as-a-whole psychotherapy approach. *Internat. J. Group Psychother.*, 26:149–162.

Day, M. (1981), Process in classical psychodynamic groups. *Internat. J. Group Psychother.*, 31:153–174.

Durkin, H. E. (1957), Toward a common basis for group dynamics. *Internat. J. Group Psychother.*, 7:115–130.

—— (1982), Change in group psychotherapy: Therapist and practice: A systems perspective. *Internat. J. Group Psychother.*, 32:431–439.

Ezriel, H. (1952), Notes on psychoanalytic group therapy: II. Interpretation and research. *Psychiatry*, 15:119–126.

Foulkes, S. H. (1964), *Therapeutic Group Analysis.* New York: International Universities Press.

Horwitz, L. (1971), Group-centered interventions in therapy groups. *Comprehen. Group Stud.*, 2:311–331.

—— (1977), A group-centered approach to group psychotherapy. *Internat. J. Group Psychother.*, 27:423–439.

—— (1983), Projective identification in dyads and groups. *Internat. J. Group Psychother.*, 33:259–279.

—— (1986), An integrated, group-centered approach. In: *Psychotherapist's Casebook*, ed. I. L. Kutash & A. Wolf. San Francisco: Jossey-Bass, pp. 353–363.

Kibel, H. D., & Stein, A. (1981), The group as a whole approach: An appraisal. *Internat. J. Group Psychother.*, 31:409–427.

Malan, D. H., Balfour, F. H. G., Hood, V. G., & Shooter, A. (1976), Group psychotherapy: A long-term follow-up study. *Arch. Gen. Psychiat.*, 33:1303–1315.

Parloff, M. B. (1968), Analytic group psychotherapy. In: *Modern Psychoanalysis*, ed. J. Marmor. New York: Basic Books, pp. 492–531.

Redl, F. (1942), Group emotion and leadership. *Psychiatry*, 5:573–596.

Rutan, J. S., & Stone, W. (1984), *Psychodynamic Group Psychotherapy.* Lexington, MA: Collamore Press.

Scheidlinger, S. (1952), *Psychoanalysis and Group Behavior: A Study of Freudian Group Psychology.* New York: W. W. Norton.

—— (1968), The concept of regression in group psychotherapy. *Internat. J. Group Psychother.*, 18:3–20.

—— (1980), Discussion. In: *Psychoanalytic Group Dynamics: Basic Readings*, ed. S. Scheidlinger. New York: International Universities Press, pp. 277–282.

Schwartz, E. K., & Wolf, A. (1960), Psychoanalysis in groups: The mystique of group dynamics. In: *Topical Problems in Psychotherapy*, Vol. 2. New York: Karger, pp. 119–154.

Semrad, E. V., & Arsenian, J. (1951), The use of group processes in teaching group dynamics. *Amer. J. Psychother.*, 108:358–363.

Slavson, S. R. (1957), Are there "group dynamics" in therapy groups? *Internat. J. Group Psychother.*, 7:131–154.

—— (1964), *Textbook of Analytic Group Psychotherapy.* New York: International Universities Press.

Trist, E. (1985), Working with Bion in the 1940's: The group decade. In: *Bion and Group Psychotherapy*, ed. M. Pines. London: Routledge & Kegan Paul, pp. 1–46.

Whitaker, D. S., & Lieberman, M. D. (1964), *Psychotherapy Through the Group Process.* New York: Atherton Press.

Wolf, A., & Schwartz, E. K. (1962), *Psychoanalysis in Groups.* New York: Grune & Stratton.

Yalom, I. D. (1980), *Existential Psychotherapy.* New York: Basic Books.

Chapter 16

Some of the Origins of Freud's Paper on Group Psychology: A Psychohistorical Exploration

BENNETT E. ROTH, Ph.D.

If there is one paper that analytic group psychotherapy claims as its birthright, it is Freud's "Group Psychology and the Analysis of the Ego" (1921). Scheidlinger's "Psychoanalytic Group Dynamics" (1956) begins with an assessment of Freud's paper. His first book (Scheidlinger, 1952) leaves no doubt that Freud's "Group Psychology" is paradoxically both a flawed cornerstone and an enabling event. While it allows analytic group psychotherapists to claim for themselves the rich emerging conceptualizations of psychoanalytic principles, it is a paper with distinct limitations.

The current sociohistorical climate allows a healthy inquisitive attitude permitting a different historical reconstruction of Freud as a man and as a theoretician. Psychoanalytic biography is now regarded as a legitimate albeit speculative domain. To study origins and history is certainly part of the archaeological attitude of psychoanalysis. Thus consideration of the sources of this important and incomplete theoretical paper, "Group Psychology," is a legitimate area of applied analytic investigation.

The historical Freud, his papers, and his seminal ideas have been subjected to reevaluation, clarification, and criticism both from within the field and from members of other intellectual disciplines. In this chapter a psychohistorical account is offered that will examine some possible sources of "the Group Papers" and clarify some of the psychohistorical processes involved in their creation. Freud's personality qualities, described by many, will be acknowledged, as will reports of his "group" experiences with "The Vienna Circle." It is not my intent to create another "pathography" but to examine some of the sources of his ideas about groups and group leadership.

FREUD, THE MAN AND THE GROUP LEADER

Sigmund Freud was a psychologically complex man, and we currently have only a partial grasp of his complexity. To some extent, the air of personal mystery about Freud was self-encouraged. In addition, it was part of the collective group transference toward him, and was partially insured by his keeping his full correspondence and notes from public scrutiny. Despite recent autobiographical studies and Freud's use of his own dreams for interpretation, much remains private and unknown. This is particularly relevant when considering the sources of his ideas, many of which germinated for long periods of time before publication.

The revolutionary ideas that emerged from his middle-class home and office in Vienna were to change the course of intellectual history, the practice of medicine and psychology, and ultimately our views of what make us human. More important than the sociohistorical factors, and standing central to his theories, is Freud the man struggling with his own ideas and their conflictual origin while conducting his exacting lifelong self-analysis.

Gedo (1986) recently proposed that Freud exclusively used intro-spective insights to advance and validate his clinical work with neurotic patients. Such an interpretation, while appealing, is not sufficiently explanatory. It does not consider Freud's extraordinary gift for hy-pothetical construction that transmuted his insights into an enduring metapsychology (Holt, 1973). Had he not creatively transmuted both his introspection and his clinical guesswork, it is more than likely his psychoanalytic psychology would have been a failed experiment.

Instead of a failed experiment Freud ascended to the role of leader of an intellectual movement; a group leader surrounded by men of lesser abilities than himself, with different character structures and conflicts, who as yet have not been held to the same critical biograph-ical standards. Freud embarked on what was to be a solitary journey with dual aspects. First, to make clearer what were the essential human dramas of the dynamic unconscious life of his patients, and, second, to reveal about us all the essential developmental human struggle.

Much has been written about the autobiographical nature and conflictual origins of his theories (Gedo, 1986). Much has been written about Freud's preoccupations with Moses and Joseph, and his attraction to myths and antiquity (Kanzer and Glenn, 1983), but little attention has been given to his role as a group leader. For example, Freud's autobiographically influenced paper on Moses (1939) is his first about a historically significant group leader. His insights in this late-in-the-life essay may be applied in many different analytic directions; about leaders, about Freud as a group leader, and about his conflicted feelings about being Jewish (Schur, 1972; Schorske, 1961; Shengold, 1983a; Gay, 1988, pp. 645–648). Here, however, the focus will be exclusively on his group relations and group papers.

The 1930s, when his Moses paper was written, were a moving and creative time in psychoanalytic theorizing; prompted by Freud's (1923) conceptualization of the ego, the emergence of his structural theory, and by the changing political and economic climate in Europe. Freud, then in his late sixties and seventies, was preoccupied with two major works, the man and myth of Moses, and "Analysis Terminable and Interminable" (1937). At this juncture Freud himself had suffered many personal problems: the progressive cancer of the palette that had been discovered in 1923 and required many painful surgical procedures; his adopted city and all of Europe was again on the brink of political upheaval; and he had been reduced, in his own eyes, to a figurehead in the analytic movement (Schur, 1972). He had faced and mourned the defections of Rank, Adler, and Jung, and the death of a daughter Sophie and grandson, as well as the early death of the "loyal Prussian" Karl Abraham. The veiled pessimism that is under the surface of his two last major works was undoubtedly of a man who had long been preoccupied with his own death (Schur, 1972) and had come to view himself as the "discarded patriarch" of an important intellectual movement (Kanzer, 1972; Shengold, 1983b) and a prophet in the dessert (Schur, 1972).

There were earlier roots to Freud's feeling of being discarded, a theme which often appears in his personal correspondence. Analysis of his earlier work on "The Moses of Michelangelo" (1914b) had demonstrated Freud's own inner struggle between the man who seeks respite after having struck out in anger and the man with great capacity for remorse and introspection. These themes probably had their psychic origins in Freud's own struggles with the internal representations of his father, his creative struggles particularly with his oedipal theory, and his struggles to lead and perpetuate the radical (analytic) intellectual movement (Schorske, 1981; Krüll, 1986). Freud possessed a dual inner bond of identification: with the rebel against the patriarchal father, and conversely with the father against the dis-

heartening desertions and characterological failures of his real and
fantasied sons. This conflictual identificatory process found expression throughout most of his life, in his theoretical papers regarding
the identifcatory patterns in men and his patterns of leadership of
the analytic movement.

However conflicted, the analytic resolve of the man who called
himself a conquistador by temperament while searching for the peace
of the "Promised Land" should not be ignored. Nor, on the other
hand, should we ignore the connection between his lifelong struggle
with his conflicting feelings about his father, his own Jewishness, and
his superego conflicts. One interpretation of "Moses and Monotheism" (1939) contends that Freud attempted to repudiate through his
identification with Moses his own Jewishness and his own internal tie
with his father. At the same time he struggled to accept his own
mortality as well as his status as the aging patriarch within his own
family and the intellectual movement he founded. The strength of
his inner paternal identification, which strengthened as he aged,
found constant expression in the univocal emphasis on the role of the
father in all of his psychoanalytic theory. This overemphasis would
be balanced in group theory by others who came to appreciate the
importance of maternal role and influence.

THE VIENNA CIRCLE: THE FIRST ANALYTIC STUDY GROUP

Much of the data in this section is derived from secondary sources:
"On the History of the Analytic Movement" (Freud, 1914a); Kanzer's
paper "Freud: The First Analytic Group Leader" (1972) which contains his somewhat idealized interpretations of the Minutes of the
Vienna Psychoanalytic Society (Nunberg and Federn, 1962–1975);
and the Jones (1953–1955) and Gay (1988) biographies. In that context Freud's first organized experience with a working group in which
he was the leader can be examined in the light of his own "group"
theory and a contemporary theory of group dynamics.

The first analytic study group met in Freud's office. It was first
proposed by William Stekel and contained many people who were
simultaneously or had been previously in treatment with Freud. (If
they were in treatment at all, it was of very short duration—for example, Eitington was analyzed in two weeks [Kanzer, 1972].) Many
who sought out Freud were specifically interested in becoming analysts, and the group was composed of people from many diverse fields

and backgrounds. The fantasies that brought these men to Freud were not the subject of exploration. Kanzer asserts that, for some, the fantasy of engaging in social and professional work with one's own analyst was the group's first gratification. These fantasies (Kanzer, 1972), usually oedipally motivated, often include the wish to eliminate the analyst (group leader) and take his place. Nevertheless the decidedly rebellious personal and inspired intellectual course taken by this group throughout its meetings cannot be fully explained by oedipal dynamics. Kanzer seems to have ignored that many in this group were not analyzed in any formal sense. Current understanding permits us to recognize that many preoedipal issues underlie apparent oedipal conflicts in this group. Both types of conflicts were likely a motivation for seeking Freud out and likely later fueled the ideational and personal breaks with Freud (Greenacre, 1963).

In Freud's early theory, the nature of transference in general was still obscure and it is likely that such factors were not appreciated or understood in the Vienna Group. For example Gay (1988) inadvertantly reveals that many of the papers presented were manifestly autobiographical, and personal investments in topics of papers would be quite complex. By 1906 this group, historically unstable in number, had grown to nineteen men and formal minutes were kept. Many of the members were Jews, middle-class intellectuals like Freud, who were not seeking treatment for themselves. They sought affiliative and transference bonds not only to the man but to some sense of belonging. For example, in regard to the question about analysis for analysts, Nunberg in 1918 proposed that all future analysts be required to undergo an analysis. This proposal was not accepted until 1926 (Roazen, 1969) because it meant, from one vantage, that the group's more informal methods of learning, such as talking with Freud and with each other, would then be considered inadequate preparation. From another perspective only future analysts would face being in the "analytic" position and all that that implied.

While the manifest thrust of this first group appears to be, as Kanzer states, educational, many group therapists would easily discern that the therapeutic aspects of the group stretched beyond some of its individual members' characterological capabilities (see also Gay, 1988, pp. 172–179). Freud was clearly the intellectual giant among younger (filial) recruits making the bond of not only son to father but creating severe horizontal transferences (sibling). To be a group member meant a particular kinship and identity: it meant being a radical thinker, sharing ideas with friends, and being self-revealing. Kinship to Freud also meant receiving financial aid, being part of a cause and a career, receiving patients, being admitted into the sanctum of knowledge (often sexual knowledge) and receiving the blessings of the group's father (Greenacre, 1963).

Meetings were held in Freud's office, symbolically the birthplace of psychoanalysis, and the place where some were later to be treated. Freud always presided, and while all remarks and papers were presented to the group-as-a-whole, they were in reality presented to the leader. An aspect of free association was employed for the purposes of discussion and after a presentation each member was called on in turn and obliged to speak when his name was drawn from a Greek urn. The "imperatives of the urn" would later become a focus of rebellion and open group resistances and deserves separate study. However, at this time, group behavior and individually different reactions to group events were largely ignored; instead Freud preferred to work one-to-one approximating both a dyadic and a teaching model of mentor and pupil.

Kanzer (1972) states that submissive acceptance of the great man's remarks and intellect was overtly common. For example, it was Freud's prerogative to intervene at will or to have the first response. When he himself presented a paper to the group, the lucidity of these presentations (Schur, 1972) and his advanced thinking in comparison to the other members must have been a continuous source of narcissistic awe and injury to the other members (see chapter 7). It is frequently reported that Freud's verbal presentation, without written notes, was publishable without changes (Rose, 1988). From the vantage of current analytic thinking, analytic working through processes (had this been a therapy group), were not possible: under study-group conditions the reported events would set in motion complex resistances and defenses.

Freud characteristically remained somewhat aloof, masterful, and intellectually committed to the furthering of psychoanalysis (Gay, 1988). The perception of Freud as distant was perhaps the result of his aloofness translated through the transference distortions of the followers. Followers were prone to refer to themselves as his pupils and only Stekel had the temerity to address him directly with the more familiar "Herr Professor"; others called him "the Master (Maestro)." Graf compared Freud to a "Moses" presiding over a religious sect, or, according to Tausk's allusion, "a scientific Religion." To Nunberg, Freud was an "impossible ideal" and therefore a source of constant frustration to some of his more ambitious pupils (Jacoby, 1983). In the early stage of the analytic movement Freud was openly more even-handed with divergent opinions and certainly more so than is reported about other group members (Nunberg and Federn, 1962–1975). He initially accepted divergent ideas and the shortcomings of his students because they accepted psychoanalysis, and he wished to build continuous links between his vision of psychoanalysis and to mobilize others to the analytic cause.

Kanzer (1972) may be correct that Freud needed followers and cobelievers in psychoanalysis because of his incompletely analyzed patriarchal superego that led to his counteridentification with his own critics in the society. However, this early time was also a generative period for Freud and for the psychoanalytic movement in general, and he likely needed complementary minds and the stimulation of other people to further his creative thinking and self-analysis. Freud's group role as father permitted and furthered his own creative wishes, which were so closely allied to his oedipal wishes (Greenacre, 1963).

While Kanzer cast Freud in the role of the group therapist, his behavior in the group was not in accord with the rule and function of the analytic group therapy leader as it has since evolved. Kanzer is aware of the narrowly defined educational and intellectual pursuit of "The Vienna Circle" and the group's need for transference approval from the leader. Reexamined in the light of current clinical group theory it would not be considered therapeutic for unconscious conflicts to be directly pointed out by jealous sibling participants and subsequently hard-won insights to be swept away by Freud's new insights. Kanzer's (1972) view of these events as group therapy probably reflects his transferential reverence for Freud and an idealized notion of both group dynamics and leadership. What seemingly ensued in this group, in my opinion, was in the form of primitive group bonding that cast Freud as teacher, father, and impossible ideal. For Freud his recaptured group transference likely reflected his need for disciples, students, and often wayward or loyal sons. Each of these transference themes evoked in him its own psychic resonance.

It is clear, however, given both his intellect and personality, that Freud wielded enormous intellectual and transference authority over this group and over all of the emerging psychoanalytic movement for the first generation of analysts. As a transference authority and with the authority and status of his being father of the movement, his shadow was cast not only over the Viennese psychoanalytic organization and its various members—that shadow prevails over us and may prevent us from seeing Freud as a man. This exaggerated perception, on the one hand, serves to alleviate anxiety in some of his followers about his theory, his personality, and his errors; on the other hand, his critics overreact to his errors and conflicts to reduce his status, authority, and insights.

As the psychoanalytic movement geographically spread, many analysts decided upon an analytic association, and hence the city and cultural climate in which they lived, based on their perception of closeness or distance from Freud personally (Jacoby, 1983). The factor of proximity to and closeness with Freud as a dynamic has been essentially ignored in the history of the psychoanalytic movement. For example, it is interesting that many who choose the Berlin Institute during the period before World War II were to develop many technical innovations (Gedo, 1986). Such divergent personalities as Fenichel, Melanie Klein, Wilhelm Reich, and Edith Jacobson, all divergent theoretically from Freud, sprung from the same (group) environment of the Berlin Institute.

Perhaps we can now profit from employing Gedo's (1986) distinction between theoretical differences as deviations from the father's word from those arising from complex theoretical disagreements that advance clinical knowledge. Valuable insights emerge from divergent sources. Many of the early group members could deviate from the basic theoretical assumptions of Freud without disrupting their tie to Freud the man. Others in the group lived under the force of their oedipal allegiance to Freud and did not openly think independently until after his death. Some would feel tyranny when there was none or exaggerate the meaning of loyalty to mean personal or intellectual surrender. Still others would be impelled into action, separation from Freud, and separate organizations (groups).

A group dynamics view of the mixture of personalities within the all-male group of intellectual seekers and rebels (Jacoby, 1983) drawn to Freud in the early years would reveal a transference stage for both acting in and acting out. No matter how carefully considered and masterful Freud's restrained remarks might be, they were likely received by these group members as severe narcissistic blows which subsequently aroused various resistances in the group members and further deflected competition with Freud to the other members. There were no overtly passive and dutiful sons in this group for Freud, despite their overt idealized transference. While overtly dutiful, their competitiveness and aggression would later turn against Freud. Given his own psychic disposition, Freud likely counteridentified with his rebellious sons, became their critic, and suffered the torment of the misunderstood and governing patriarch. This was certainly a stage set for dramatic events, no doubt a psychic recipe for the kind of drama of disagreement and theoretical splintering that later occurred in many other analytic training programs.

In sum, the initial period, from 1901 to 1906, the opening stage of the organizational group, was somewhat chaotic with frequent changes in membership (Kanzer, 1972; Gay, 1988); yet it was prolific in terms of papers presented and institutional efforts. An organization was born but there were some individuals, because of their own character needs, who would pay a great price for the prohibitions to discharge real anger and negative transferences directly toward the group leader. Interestingly, the problem of tolerating a negative transference was also a complaint frequently made about the original group as analysts (Jacoby, 1983).

These initial formative events took place at a time when psychoanalytic concepts were in their infancy. Basic ideas such as transference, resistance, and defense had yet to be articulated (Coltrera and Ross, 1967). As a consequence Freud had few conceptual vehicles to express either individual or group dynamics. Even at a later point his theoretical explanations for behavior in groups remain partial (Scheidlinger, 1980), oddly sociological, and devoid of clinical reference. His group paper(s) remain, as Scheidlinger suggests (1980), filled with ideas about social groups, identificatory processes and group contagion, and the nature of bisexual transferences that remain incompletely formulated and overly influenced by the ideas of repression.

The Viennese group itself had a varied composition of personalities and intellectual interests and abilities. Study of some of the members' histories, (i.e., Rank, Tausk, Stekel) would suggest that there was often a reenactment of family dynamics among its members. Freud as the leader and teacher, at this time, welcomed people from various fields to study with him. It is likely, given his own struggle with identifications with his father, that Freud had little appreciation for overtly passive acceptance of his ideas. His need for an organized group around him was probably determined by multiple personal needs which blended with his need to further the growth of psychoanalysis. He clearly valued mutual albeit unequal discussion to further his ideas (Lilleskov, 1972), and while he probably learned from the other members, the exchange of ideas allowed his creative mind to wander over the analytic terrain he had created. There is little doubt that he received narcissistic transference satisfactions from this group, while in his personal life, his disappointment with his own sons continued to grow. Part of Freud's motivation to be a father–leader derived from his dual dissatisfactions—with his sons and with his father (Greenacre, 1963).

After 1906 another stage of this group's existence was characterized by emotional turmoil. For example, charges of plagiarism, an often repeated theme in the history of psychoanalysis, dominated the group at one time (1906–1908) and emotional attacks among the group members increased in frequency (Kanzer, 1972). The idea of "being stolen from" is explained by Kanzer as related to a reversal of the group's appropriation of Freud's brilliant and thorough appraisals of their efforts. However, Freud was himself occasionally guilty of "borrowing" from his students and forgetting the source (Shengold, 1983b). At this juncture some members left the group unable to accept analytic principles, while some left unable to tolerate the idealization of Freud and the compensatory competition among the other members (Gay 1988). Others who left were unable to face the remorseless urn, or, in some cases the virulent and competitive remarks by their group siblings. Freud's technique, and that of many of his early followers, was to interpret directly and quickly unconscious motivation in an event and to give direct advice. And while the "imperatives of the urn" and associational methods may have contributed to a sense of vulnerability of the group members, it was also copied and carried forward as a style of procedure in the organized analytic meetings (Nunberg and Federn, 1962–1975). However, it was clear that Freud most frequently protected the presenter in the original group (Kanzer, 1972; Gay, 1988).

Kanzer (1972) notes that Freud was the most tactful of men in his approach to other people. Often he would go out of his way to avoid inflicting pain and suffering in people he cared about. At the same time that Freud was the open personification of bourgeois manners, he was often guided by his own unanalyzed transference needs and as many of his historians note he had a quick ironic wit often employed in his private descriptions of his colleagues. In addition, during this early proselytizing period up until the 1920s, he seemed preoccupied by a search for loyal members and the spread of his ideas.

Finally, as was inevitable, individual and group discontents came to the surface of the group, especially as the organizational demands outside the group grew more intricate and transference tensions within the group became more complex. Hierarchical transferences within the privacy of the group might have become sufficiently worked upon even without being articulated, because of the support and structure of the group setting. However, the same transferences in an organizational reality can become the occasion for acting out, particularly if the participants in the two settings are the same people.

Among the accomplishments of the early psychoanalytic movement were the establishment of the *Internal Journal of Psycho-Analysis*, the appointment of an editor, the formation of the Zurich group led by Jung, and the impending analytic congress at Salzburg in 1908. The outcome of these external changes was the formal structure of the meetings and the reduction of the direct influence of Freud as the patriarchal leader. But a complex sibling rivalry emerged both within and between the Viennese and Swiss groups, as between two closely born siblings of the same father. Within the groups bitter disputes developed concerning organizational appointments which were often viewed as based upon Freud's special preferences. With the lessening of direct influence and control Freud seemingly gained a different form of transference power and status in the eyes and minds of his disciples.

It is evident that by 1910 Freud sought to disengage himself from the Viennese circle (Gay, 1988). In 1910 the confrontation between Freud, the father, and Adler, the heir, took place. And while Freud himself eased the transition of Adler as president of the analytic association and leader of the group he would later lament, in typical fashion, that he was a "dissatisfied and unwanted old man." In April of 1910, the symbolic overthrow was accomplished by the symbolic removal of the urn and the change in location of the group meetings from Freud's home (Gay, 1988).

In many ways this original group had accomplished its initial task. It had formed itself from a band of adherents into an organization or congregation. It had grown beyond a one-man (totemic) and one-city (nationalistic) structure. However, real separateness from the direct influence of the leader, the giant, the father of us all, would be hard won and did not occur at this time. Interestingly, Adler, who was in the forefront of the movement to remove Freud from the presidency, and in turn became president with Freud's manifest approval, was forced to resign after a few months in office (for multiple reasons). This event itself foreshadowed another group wisdom: the one who would be king is later deposed, just as he deposed the previous king.

Freud, ever mindful of his self-analysis, seemed well aware of his countertransference problems with the Wednesday evening society (Kanzer, 1972; Gay, 1988). He would later comment that the older Viennese analysts proved "a heavy cross to bear" (Freud, 1914a). Still later in the group paper he selflessly reveals how the hatred of the totemic father for his sons increases the envy and aggression of the rivalrous sons (Freud, 1921). Within the limitations of his self-analysis Freud would remain disposed to a painful pattern: the traumatic termination of relationships. This theme—from Freud's own history, and of sibling rivals, Caesar and Brutus, Isaac and Ishmael—was probably acted out by many members in their quest for sibling supremacy. In retrospect there is good reason to propose that the theme of supremacy—sibling, oedipal, and preoedipal—found resonance in the actions of this group.

Organizational activities, at the *International Journal* and the International Psycho-Analytic Association (IPA), though accomplished, often served as screens for competitive transferences. The manifest and latent pathways of communication and power that emanated from "the first group" were often clogged with residual transferences and envy. Yet it was quite remarkable that one small group of members would undertake and accomplish such a multipurpose endeavor.

Within the basic themes and struggles already described in this paper would later be the basis of some of Freud's views in "Group Psychology and the Analysis of the Ego" (1921). Freud would come to better understand "the heavy cross" once his second period of isolation had come to an end and he completed his paper on the history of the analytic movement (Freud, 1914a). In addition, after the deposing of Adler, Freud was able to return to the now expanded Viennese society unlike Adler who formed his own society. The return of the leader to the original group is itself part of Freud's paper on group (1921).

The political, social, and economic unrest that precipitated the onset of World War I influenced the small group of psychoanalysts. The financial and intellectual status of the psychoanalytic movement changed before and after this war. In certain countries there was a period of great interest and growth (i.e., in the war neurosis). And at the same time many younger members of the society were con-scripted into the Army, as were Freud's sons. These events changed the composition of the group as well as Freud's immediate family. Travel was restricted or at best difficult and new members of the society were scarce while "international" conferences were impossible.

After World War I and the economic depression that followed, Freud became relatively affluent as patients returned, many from America. He was always generous to his analytic family, often sup-plying food, money, and patient referrals to less fortunate colleagues. He himself had been the recipient of such gifts during the war. As his international reputation increased he naturally reclaimed his status of the patron alongside that of intellectual patriarch. He referred patients to his students and exercised certain prerogatives by accepting or rejecting prospective analysands. These decisions determined among other things the next generation of analytic and intellectual "bloodlines" and links to the father.

Among the more speculative implications of the impact of Freud's power to accept or reject an analysand is found in Roazan's (1969) study of Tausk's suicide. Overtly, as Roazan (1969) suggests, Tausk's suicide may have in part been precipitated by Freud's decision to reject him as his patient. However, Roazan's explanation is insufficient in explaining this suicide. For some reason, Tausk has also been given the status of an "original" member (Roazan, 1969) although his entrance into the Wednesday circle seems to have occurred in 1909. He seemingly joined when the original group was already embarked on the displacement of Freud as the leader and the post-Salzburg conflicts were at their height (Kanzer, 1972; Gay, 1988). Ironically, it was Stekel who earlier commented (Kanzer, 1972), as the early group discussed suicide, that "no one kills himself who does not wish to kill someone else." Stekel appears to have been sensitive to the defenses against aggression and of the negative transference in that group.

GROUP PSYCHOLOGY AND THE ANALYSIS OF THE EGO

In 1921 Freud published his classic paper on group (Horde) psychology. Strachey (1955) in the introductory notes suggests that Freud worked on this paper from 1919 and a first draft was finished in 1920. Strachey had first-hand knowledge of these facts as Freud handed the paper to him to translate after one of Strachey's analytic sessions (Meisel and Kendrick, 1985). From the collected material presented from divergent sources, there is no doubt that the roots of this paper, Freud's analysis of groups, reaches not only into the well of his self-analysis and his experiences with the Wednesday night group, but also reflects his gifts and inclinations for theory building. It is likely that the initiation of the particular self-analysis that led to this paper occurred in the period immediately after and during Adler's presidency of the International and Freud's writing of the "History" in 1914.

Scheidlinger (1956), in an important review of this paper, addressed himself to the formal theoretical components of Freud's group theory in great detail; the following summary draws freely from his work. When considering the history and development of the first group of analysts and Freud's speculative and ambiguous description of group behavior in 1921, there is a seeming parallel between the early theory and his own experience. The first analytic group struggled to accept Freud as "the one and same object in the place of their Ego ideal" (Freud, 1921). Great psychic drama was played out in an attempt to accomplish this task. Freud may have sought, by his own behavior and naive "group technique," to enhance this occurrence. At the same time in that sociohistorical climate it is likely that the father was more readily idealized than in later times. Scheidlinger (1956) also concludes in his foreword that Freud seems less interested in group psychology than he does with his concept of the ego ideal, later renamed superego. Nevertheless his insights into some groups are astute.

Scheidlinger (1956) describes this essay on groups as having an "armchair" and a somewhat disorganized quality. For example, although Freud mentions "ambivalence," "direct expressions of aggression," and "the powerful civilizing effect of the libidinal ties," many of these crucial ideas are left more incomplete in this paper than in his other writings. Additionally, Freud depicted the imago of the father as the group leader and chief, a revenant of his earlier conception in "Totem and Taboo" (1913–1914). To this definition he adds the concept of the primal leader as uniquely self-centered and cruel, often prone to persecute his sons with at least an intensity equal to their wish to dispose of him. In fact, he argues in terms of the reality principle that the group members' feeling of being equally loved by the leader was an illusion, a wishful restructuring of the opposite.

The collected historical evidence (Jones, 1955–1957; Kanzer, 1972; Gay, 1988) supports the hypothesis that imbedded in Freud's statements about group psychology, when viewed from our current historical vantage, are conflicted internal struggles. Freud is forging an analysis of his experience with groups; he is struggling with the exposition of the (group) superego and is continuing the analysis of his own ego ideal. He reveals the extent of his analysis of his own behavior in the Viennese group and he also anticipated the insight that the father–leader's unconscious feelings impact on the unconscious of the group members.

Within the group paper, Freud discusses group libidinal ties, the wished for and feared murder of the leader by the sons, who must then renounce the idea of taking the leader's place, and how related homosexual themes are transformed into aim-inhibited bonds contributing to group cohesion. Had Freud recognized the deeper level of conflicts within the original group while he was working through his status within the analytic movement? Indications are that a further understanding of a number of complex dynamic issues was emerging. The original group was singularly composed of males (although Anna Freud often sat in on the meeting), and that Freud was early committed to the idea of a bisexual legacy of identificatory processes. Surely he had originally been somewhat cognizant that the façade of sibling aggression acted out in the Wednesday group was a screen for narcissistic and homosexual transferences. Yet he inexplicably clung to his earlier totemic oedipal explanations of the group accepting the leader as the one and same ego ideal as therapeutic. While such an explanation may be effectively repressive for neurotic problems and his clinical explanatory vehicles were limited, this remains a striking scotoma, which lingered without correction in group theory for some time (Scheidlinger, 1982).

Since Freud's clinically useful conceptualization of the ego (1923) and of perversions and narcissism were not clearly formulated at the time of the group paper, he had limited options for explaining dynamics. Did he hope that homosexual ties would remain at a brotherly or higher level and that brotherly love, regardless of its psychological source, aided group social cohesion? If so, it would ideally act to limit the behavior of the father and control the behavior of the sons. However, at the very same time that Freud was working on the group paper he was also working on a paper concerning the dynamics of homosexuality (Freud, 1922). Did he when writing the group paper seek to "protect" himself and the group from his emerging insights into narcissism and homosexuality? Perhaps material in the Freud archives will eventually shed further light on what Freud referred to as his "unruly homosexual component."

As Freud aged, the emergence of an extended analytic family through the international organization may have allowed him some healthy respite from his complex familial relationships, his reactions to his own children's maturation, his own superego struggles, and his disappointments with his Viennese colleagues (Gay, 1988). Not only was Freud insured that his ideas and discoveries would be perpetuated but the continued concern for him and his work allowed the emergence of a "new father" identity in Freud. The new father described in the "Addendum" to his group paper has accepted and renounced the familial totemic role and achieved a more benign relationship to the group in reality as he still sought "the promised land" (Schur, 1972).

FREUD'S GROUP TECHNIQUE

When considering Freud's group technique, we are addressing a complex phenomenon. Freud's character, the social conventions of the time, the image of the father, and Freud's understanding of analytic goals and basic belief systems are very much at work. While we have no exact knowledge of the group interactions, and clinical data are limited, there may be some meaningful connections between Freud the man who described himself as "a conquistador" by nature, who struggled against the tyranny of his own superego, and Freud the man who placed the understanding of his unconscious and his own self-analysis as single-minded goals.

Shengold (1983b) described Freud's character as "heroic in the Aristotelian sense—full of conflict, defect and quirks . . . dedicated to search for the truth no matter where it might lead" (p. 214). In addition we are concerned here with a man whose own family of origin had sensitized him to a variety of transferences and conflicts (Jones, 1953–1955; Kanzer and Glenn, 1983). His intellect was pro-digious as were his gifts for pushing at the limits of his private self-analysis. As Gedo (1986) suggested, he used his own neuroses as a bedrock for not only understanding in general but for the sketching of the stages of normal conflicts as well. He was prone to what Schur (1972) called "revenants," a term referring to the way that events in reality intensely revived the memory and the emotional constellation of an original event. This not only indicates an openness to his own personality but that he cultivated and sought creative outlets for his understanding.

As most creative people are prone to do, Freud probably empath-ically projected his hard-won personal understanding as having ex-planatory value for his patients and others. At the same time he likely projected the accompanying doubt onto his critics. This expands Kan-zer's idea that Freud unconsciously identified with his critics by pro-jection and Gedo's idea that Freud wrote about the self-same things he was working on in his self-analysis. This kind of unconscious bias is also present in the romanticized scenario of the origin of psycho-analysis being revealed in Freud's dreams following his father's death (Schorske, 1961). Whatever the value of these prior explanations, they do an injustice to Freud's emerging analytic capacities and erroneously fall back upon earlier, non-ego psychological models as explanation. However, our purpose here is to consider how Freud probably be-haved in these group meetings and the motives of this behavior. This will be examined from the vantage of the facts we have about the man and in light of our current conceptions of psychoanalytic group dy-namics.

There is no doubt that Freud naturally assumed the role of the father in the group. This role came to him as a result not only of the age differences but also because the members sought him out. He was properly aloof as was the standard of the Viennese father; he stood to the side, and yet maintained the prerogative of the "last word." He controlled the time and place of the meetings and hence their begin-ning and end. His interest in language and his intellectual command of the complexities of spoken and literary German itself further set him apart from the other members. Also, he was accustomed to the self-referential art of free association which he taught to the newer members through the form of alternating free association and the use of the urn. Their turn to speak was determined by chance, relieving Freud of the burden of calling on people. Freud could then assume other group roles and allow his mind to wander. The use of a vase as the center for a group of men may paradoxically seem to be a clinical cliché for going to the maternal "interior."

Freud's cognitive gifts (Holt, 1973) certainly were superior to those of the other members (Gay, 1988) and likely resulted in many varied responses. Schur (1972) remembered being held spellbound during Freud's later lectures by his range and command of concepts. What awe and displaced anxiety the Wednesday men must have felt comparing themselves to Freud's cognitive and intellectual vituosity (see also Shengold, 1983c). This likely enhanced their paternal and narcissistic transferences and ambivalence.

We may also conclude, given the status of his theory at that time (Coltrera and Ross, 1967), that Freud not only believed that the group must accept him as a ideal but that he sought to reinforce this both by conscious and unconscious behavior. At this time, he was never clearly drawn into an argument within the group. Criticism of presentations could come from within the lateral transference figures while Freud protected the presenter. While the criticism was likely to be in his behalf and more cruelly than Freud would have probably done, he would assume the role of the mediator, settling disputes. It is likely that he believed at this time that anger and other negative feelings directed at the leader interfered with the formation of an ego ideal. Many of his analysands would complain later that their anger was never addressed or analyzed (Jacoby, 1983).

Freud's reaction to having been given a medal by his group may serve as a particular point of reference. Today, such gifts might be seen in a different context. Among the many reports of the present given to Freud is Jones' (1955–1957, pp. 13–14) description of the occasion. On May 6, 1906, the group presented Freud with a medallion that bore his portrait on one side and the Sophocles quotation hailing Oedipus as the man "who divined the famous riddle and was a man most mighty." Jones related Freud's emotional "confessing to the group his own childhood fantasy of being a great professor and having a bust of himself engraved with just that line." In such a confession Freud was manifestly self-revealing. He also encouraged the group to support his wished-for greatness as the ideal leader of the group and if it was a true recollection of events, to support his notion of the "uncanny" in the group. At the same time, he avoids the unpleasantness of exploring the underlying defensive aspects of this maneuver.

Other events also contributed to the "idealization" of Freud while firming group boundaries. Group members writing analytic or autobiographical papers while in the group may have been dynamically understood as binding the individual group members to Freud. As part of the ebb and flow of being in the actual group, writing about Freud's ideas kept alive the representation of Freud as the authority. The shadow of this transference authority fell across all organizational group activities outside of the analytic study group. When there are transference and boundary problems due to a mix of organizational and study group interactions it is likely one of the dynamic origins for the concerns for references and priorities of ideas. It is also likely that the constancy of Freud's persona in the professional life of the group members contributed to their perception of him as an intellectual and charismatic leader. Papers written were applications of Freud's principles; presentations were essentially to him and the reworking of Freud's old ideas enabled a secondary tie to the group leader. Errors could be corrected, oversights inserted, and Freud's new ideas would easily leave the neophyte feeling his work was immature and that Freud offered a chance for others to mature.

Because of Freud's own (superego) sensitivity to criticism when considered with the emerging idealizations, the group was likely to adopt an attitude that to reject his idea was to reject him. This form of group bonding usually masks the transference hostility and personal rigidity within the group by finding an external intellectual scapegoat. In his life, total acceptance of his emerging ideas became known as the hallmark of personal loyalty.

Criticism of Freud emanating from outside the group also served to establish a bond for those within the group. Criticism of psychoanalysis aided in the establishment of group boundaries while enhancing the narcissistic feeling of group "specialness." At the same time Freud was tolerant of divergent thinkers within the group (Gay, 1988) as his goals for the group as the leader were different from those of the members. In the early history of the psychoanalytic movement, anyone who would accept his radical ideas in principle was an ally very much needed by Freud. This caused some difficulties when his basic ideas were only partially accepted. His natural "kindness" could also emerge more freely when others were hostile and aggressive. Although he naturally gravitated toward the role of *pacim paternas* in the Vienna Circle as in his family, only at a later stage would he publically criticize, at least in print, those who deviated from his models (among them Adler, Jung, and Rank). Whatever other purpose this may have served, as a group phenomena, Freud's written and verbal criticisms established the negative kinship of those outside of the group, while for those inside the group, these criticisms helped establish a positive identity and kinship.

If we examine the period of time when Adler became president we may consider that Freud eased the way for Adler in an analytical light. To oppose Adler personally in the group would escalate the group's hostility, and foster an early splintering within the group. To accept his new status would allow the group to combine the natural animosity toward the "successful sibling" with the displaced anger at Freud. Bion (1959) later would understand this wish as a natural early group dynamic. However, other interpretations are now available. Given current understanding of the tendency to split the bisexual transference responses within a group, wresting the group from the leader may also be understood as stealing power and stealing the mother's body from the father. Such an unconscious dynamic may be behind the possessive attitudes toward any body politic. A similar (nongroup) insight was offered by Greenacre (1963, pp. 13–22) in her discussion of the Butler–Darwin controversy.

The opposite of splintering within a group is remaining tightly allied. In any group that remains together a core of unconscious agreement and commonality emerges. Without this dynamic core, a proactive group cohesion will not emerge. the fractal emergence of any group core will likely result in occasional splinterings, divergences, and changes in membership. From whatever perspective one views the core of the Wednesday group, the capacity for concern for each other, or, concern for Freud as the first constant object, is likely to be the basic psychic stuff that resulted in their proactive course. The psychic origin of concern is only partially explained by bonding to the primal father. Freud's important and single-minded preoccupation with the image and role of the primal father still remains a basic truth. It was certainly a dynamic part of the shaping of the origin of the psychoanalytic movement and exceedingly important to the group members. In retrospect it may also be correct that there had to be a multiply determined defense against awareness of the maternal transferences in the group.

ESCAPE FROM THE GROUP

Freud's relationships with analytic groups would continue throughout his life. The Viennese Psychoanalytic Society and the International Psycho-Analytic Association, which would be his savior and host in the escape from the Nazis, continued to play significant roles for

Freud and his immediate family. Yet, as he reveals in the postscript
to his group paper, "the new family was only a shadow of the old one"
(1921, p. 135). His poetic understanding of the role of the group
leader expressed in the final section of the group paper also seems
to have self-referential roots.

> The poet who has taken this step and had in this way set himself free
> from the group in his imagination is nevertheless able to find his way
> back to it in reality. For he goes and relates to the group his hero's
> deeds which he has invented. At bottom his hero is no one but himself.
> Thus he lowers himself to the level of reality, and raises his hearers to
> the level of imagination. But his hearers understand the poet, and, in
> relation of their having the same relation of longing towards the primal
> father, they can identify themselves with the hero [p. 136].

Freud's reflective contemplation of his relationship to groups reveals Freud's painful acceptance of the need to and manner in which
he came back to the group. The goal of any good group leader is to
remain self- and empathically analytical. The generative leader strives
to remain imbedded in reality and raise the hearers to the level of
imagination. Freud is now the empathic philosopher and poet: still
sharing the longing toward the primal father that he must share with
the other group members; "he is nothing but himself."

The seemingly disjunctive and melancholy last section of his group
paper avoids the important psychological reality that "the first God"
of the child is the "Mother God"—Freud's longing is more complex
than that for the primal father. This open vista in individual and
group treatment will be faced by Freud's followers.

CONCLUSION

This brief biographical study of the origins of Freud's group paper
adds to our understanding of the creation of Freud's group theory.
Theories are energized and motivated as radical and creative psychic
solutions to internal conflicts and conflict-laden experience. Freud's
self-analysis paved the way not only to a comprehension of group
behavior but to an understanding of how explanatory hypotheses are
formed. Freud's genius for hypothetical constructs set the foundation
upon which later correction and elaboration would stand—and upon
which this paper rests.

In conclusion, any biographer or historian develops a transference
toward the subject of his study that must be continuously analyzed

(Gay, 1988). Freud's self-analysis was limited by his own transferences which he sought valiantly to understand. His writing of papers was one vehicle for self-learning and his need to communicate. It seems that this crucial and guiding paper, which has encouraged the development of psychoanalytic group psychology and psychotherapy, emerged from Freud's incomplete analysis of his own personal conflicts with groups and his role as leader of a radical intellectual group. Beyond the autobiographical elements, Freud's initial and hard-won analytic perspective of group psychology served as an impetus and inspiration to those of us in the field today. Our understanding of the man, and appreciation for Freud's effort, is enhanced by the continuing scholarship and biographical research on Freud's life and work. Advances in our own theories that put his work in historical perspective will lead to further questions, hypotheses, and understanding.

REFERENCES

Bion, W. B. (1959), *Experiences in Groups*. New York: Basic Books.

Coltrera, J., & Ross, N. (1967), Freud's psychoanalytic technique: From the beginning until 1923. In: *Psychoanalytic Techniques*, ed. B. Wolman. New York: Basic Books.

Freud, S. (1913–1914), Totem and taboo. *Standard Edition*, 13:1–162. London: Hogarth Press, 1955.

———(1914a), On the history of the psychoanalytic movement. *Standard Edition*, 14:3–66. London: Hogarth Press, 1955.

———(1914b), The Moses of Michelangelo. *Standard Edition*, 13:211–236. London: Hogarth Press, 1955.

———(1921), Group psychology and the analysis of the ego. *Standard Edition*, 18:69–143. London: Hogarth Press, 1955.

———(1922), Some neurotic mechanisms in jealousy, paranoia and homosexuality. *Standard Edition*, 18:221–232. London: Hogarth Press, 1955.

———(1923), The ego and the id. *Standard Edition*, 19:3–66. London: Hogarth Press, 1961.

———(1937), Analysis terminable and interminable. *Standard Edition*, 23:209–253. London: Hogarth Press, 1964.

———(1939), Moses and monotheism. *Standard Edition*, 23:7-140. London: Hogarth Press, 1964.

Gay, P. (1988), *Freud: A Life for Our Time*. New York: Basic Books

Gedo, J. (1986), Sigmund Freud's character and the definition of psychoanalysis. In: *Conceptual Issues, Essays in History and Method*. Hillside, NJ: Analytic Press.

Greenacre, P. (1963), *The Quest for the Father*. New York: New York Psychoanalytic Institute.

Holt, R. R. (1973), On reading Freud. Introduction. In: *Abstracts of the Standard Edition of the Complete Psychological Works of Sigmund Freud*, ed. C. R. Rothgeb. New York: Jason Aronson.

Jacoby, R. (1983), *The Repression of Psychoanalysis*. New York: Basic Books.

Jones, E. (1953–1955), *The Work and Life of Sigmund Freud*. New York: Basic Books.

Kanzer, M., (1972), Freud, the first psychoanalytic group leader. In: *Freud and His Self-Analysis*, ed. M. Kanzer & J. Glenn. New York: Jason Aronson.

——— Glenn, J. (1983), *Freud and His Self-Analysis*. New York: Jason Aronson.

Krüll, M. (1986), *Freud and His Father*. New York: W. W. Norton.

Lilleskov, R. (1972), A discussion of L. Shengold's A parapraxis of Freud in relation to Karl Abraham. In: *Freud and His Self-Analysis*, ed. M. Kanzer & J. Glenn. New York: Jason Aronson.

Meisel, P., & Kendrick, W. (1985), *Bloomsbury/Freud. The Letters of James and Alix Strachey*. New York: Basic Books, 1924–1925.

Nunberg, H., & Federn, P. (1962–1975), *Minutes of the Vienna Psychoanalytic Society*, 2 vols. New York: International Universities Press.

Roazan, P. (1969), *Brother Animal: The History of Freud and Tausk*. New York: Alfred A. Knopf.

Rose, L. (1988), Editor and translator—Freud and fetishism: Previously unpublished minutes of the Vienna Psychoanalytic Society. *Psychoanal. Quart.*, 58:147–167.

Scheidlinger, S. (1952), *Psychoanalysis and Group Behavior*. New York: N. W. Norton.

———(1956), *Psychoanalytic Group Dynamics: Basic Readings*. New York: International Universities Press.

———(1980), *Psychoanalytic Group Dynamics: Basic Readings*. New York: International Universities Press.

———(1982), The concept of the mother group. In: *Focus on Group Psychotherapy*. New York: International Universities Press.

Schorske, C. (1961), *Fin-De-Siècle Vienna*. New York: Vintage Books, 1981.

Schur, M. (1972), *Freud Living and Dying*. New York: International Universities Press.

———(1983), The background of Freud's disturbance at the Acropolis. In: *Freud and His Self-Analysis*, ed. M. Kanzer & J. Glenn. New York: Jason Aronson.

Shengold, L. (1983a), Freud and Joseph. The meaning of the metaphor of the journey in the "Interpretation of Dreams." In: *Freud and His Self-Analysis*, ed. M. Kanzer & J. Glenn. New York: Jason Aronson.

———(1983b), A parapraxis of Freud in relation to Karl Abraham. In: *Freud and His Self-Analysis*, ed. M. Kanzer & J. Glenn. New York: Jason Aronson.

———(1983c), The background of Freud's disturbance at the Acropolis. In: *Freud and His Self Analysis*, ed. M. Kanzer & J. Glenn. New York: Jason Aronson.

Stamm, J. (1967), The problem of depersonalization in Freud's disturbance of memory on the Acropolis. In: *Freud and His Self-Analysis*, ed. M. Kanzer & J. Glenn. New York: Jason Aronson.

Strachey, J. (1955), Editor's note. *Standard Edition*, 18:67–68. London: Hogarth Press, 1955.

Chapter 17

Reactiveness and Responsiveness in the Group Therapeutic Process

HOWARD A. BACAL, M.D., F.R.C.P.(C)

In an intriguing article that he wrote for the book *Comprehensive Group Psychotherapy*, Mark Kanzer (1971) describes Freud as the first group therapy leader. Kanzer arrived at this idea from what he learned about Freud's leadership of his small group of initial adherents who began to meet with him on a weekly basis in Vienna in 1901, a group that was eventually to become the Vienna Psychoanalytic Society. Although the purpose of this group was an educational enterprise—to discuss the newly emerging ideas about psychoanalysis—Kanzer notes that "therapeutic and personal aspects were never very far from the surface [and] . . . [t]he therapeutic aspects of the society's sessions were further heightened by the fact that the meetings were held in [Freud's] office" (pp. 35–36). In effect, personal matters tended to become explicit as the members of the group shared their own sexual and other personal difficulties in the wake of discussing the analyses of their patients.

The difficulties encountered by this remarkable group of people have since become legend: its operation recurrently broke down, outright revolts were mounted, and a number of dropouts occurred—the most famous one, of course, being Alfred Adler. Freud's well-known seminal insights into group process (Freud, 1921) were apparently not quite matched by his talent as a group leader. He conducted a leader-centered group. His unquestionably superior intellectual and creative stature and the quiet forcefulness of his personality ensured that *his* viewpoints were usually the ones that carried the day—but he

309

also maintained a certain remoteness of posture from those about him. All of this combined to exacerbate the tensions within the group, many of which would appear to have been due to frustrated longings on the part of the members for greater recognition of their own creative capacities by their esteemed leader who, on his part, wondered why they could not all be like the dutiful son, Otto Rank. Rank, of course, eventually became another rebellious defector by creating his own system of psychological thought.

Thus, the attempts of the members of the group to identify themselves with psychoanalysis through their idealizing transference (Kohut, 1971, pp. 37–56) to Freud was not enough to provide them with the nourishment they sought because the group, as led by Freud, did not provide them with the mirroring (pp. 105–142) that they also needed—nor did Freud, of course, interpret this. The main determinant, then, which caused the group to founder repeatedly, was not primarily ideological differences or disagreement, but the shortfall of the group in responding to the individual member's psychological requirements. While therapeutic needs were mobilized in the group, a therapeutic process did not occur.[1] In some ways this group continued to be highly productive despite the loss of some creative members. In some instances, those who left were taking a step toward asserting themselves by joining other groups where they felt they could flourish more creatively—just as individuals who leave their therapy situation may sometimes be taking a comparably positive step.

It is regretful but true that, since then, groups of psychoanalysts in their constituted scientific societies have often not fared much better, as evidenced by the many splits that have occurred in their ranks in the wake of passionately held divergent views. These secessions, too, have sometimes led to creative new developments both for these individuals and for the new groups that they formed. It is also true that, apart from their notorious inability to keep their own "group" house in order, psychoanalysts have, over the years, at least studied their mistakes and have made a number of useful and original contributions to group theory and practice.

For a number of years, my own work in group psychotherapy was strongly influenced by the theoretical and technical ideas elaborated at the Tavistock Clinic, where I trained and taught during the sixties. These ideas comprised essentially those of Wilfred Bion (1959) and Henry Ezriel (1973). Like Freud's Viennese coterie around the turn

---

[1] From time to time, the members of the group apparently used their newly acquired psychoanalytic interpretive skill to say what they thought of each other, but this, of course, is not therapy.

of the century, Bion's early groups at the Tavistock in the late forties consisted of a "mixed bag" of professional people who met to study a fascinating new field—in this case, group dynamics. However, they soon found themselves being "interpreted at" in terms of a collusive, although apparently unconscious, intent to undermine the agreed-upon work task of the group as they struggled with conflicts around their dependency on Bion and their anxiety-laden competitiveness and wish to form an idealized relationship with him. Bion, in thus elaborating his now-famous concepts of dependency, fight–flight, and pairing group assumptions, went one step further than Freud did in his group: he attempted to convey his understanding of the group process to the members. Like Freud, his understanding was formulated from the perspective of his own personal experience of the group, that is, from his own vantage point. Henry Ezriel, probably one of the best-known "defectors" from one of Bion's early groups, evolved a fresh approach of his own to group therapy based on an object-relations model. Ezriel, like Bion, continued to maintain a group process approach in his own work, offering whole-group interpretations based on a common group theme or common group tension. Ezriel specified, in addition, the particular contribution to the common group theme by each member of the group in terms of their interpersonal relations with each other, and especially with himself (Heath and Bacal, 1968). However, his interpretations, like Bion's, were, again, very much in terms of his own (Ezriel's own) experience as the central figure in the process. Put in another way, both group leaders interpreted group process as it impacted or impinged upon them as the object of the group's complex mental states.

While we are in debt to these pioneers of group therapy for teaching us so much about group process, we have also begun to question the validity of the leader-centered perspective of their interpretations. In effect, patients in therapy groups that were conducted along these lines were frequently puzzled by and sometimes protested these interventions—which puzzlements and protests were, consonant with the approach, regarded as manifestations of resistance to the therapist's correct interpretations. The essence of the problem may be expressed by the story of the patient who complained to her therapist that she was unhappy on the ward to which she had recently been admitted. She felt she could not work with the nurses because they just didn't understand her. The therapist replied, "You know, I think they do understand you, they just don't see things as you do." While such perspectives may be offered to the patient in an "understanding," and even warm and kindly, manner, they convey the unmistakeable message that the therapist knows the "truth" about his patient's inner

world and that the patient's subjective experience will not be taken
seriously when it is at variance with that "reality." In effect, traditional
psychoanalysis, in focusing on resistance in the transference to the
therapist, has tacitly supported an approach which accords greater
validity to the therapist's perspectives than to the patient's. As group
psychotherapists, we are well aware that our patients' psychological
growth as individuals can be enhanced by interactive processes where
multiperson perspectives prevail. However, resistance in the classical
sense, that is, that the patient opposes the therapy, is a notion that is
useful only to the therapist who is unwilling or unable to relinquish
the conviction that his own perspective is central. It is an inherently
theory-bound (although not necessarily experience-distant) concept,
and in practice there is no appeal from its dicta.[2] It can have no place
in our therapeutic work except as an indicator that the patient is
anxious about being hurt in ways that repeat childhood traumata.

Self psychology has underscored the importance not only of ap-
prehending as clearly as possible the patient's subjective psychological
states, but also according patient subjectivity greater weight when it
is at variance with the therapist's perspectives. Thus, the antithesis of
the idea that, according to the therapist's view, one is in a state of
"resistance," is the experience of empathic attunement. A sustained
attitude of empathic enquiry on the part of the therapist to the patient's inner experience is regarded as the essential precondition for
a therapeutic process. In the group situation, however, most of the
interactions are not therapist–patient interactions, but member–member
interactions. Since these interactions are not generally modulated by
the discipline that the therapist attempts to apply to his own reactions
(his countertransferences), empathic attunement is not a consistent
feature of the quality of relatedness between members of the group.
An atmosphere of sustained empathic enquiry, therefore, cannot be
expected to prevail in the group. Given that therapist "neutrality" is
a mythical posture, the therapist cannot avoid conveying his preference for the ethos that he believes to be most therapeutic. Should the
therapist take the position that validation of the individual member's
perspective is essential for personal growth? Or should the therapist
take the attitude that the opposition of perspectives is not only inevitable but is to be welcomed if the individual is to develop and
mature? My own view is that both approaches are valid and therapeutically useful in the group and that, in practice, they are not incompatible. It is in this regard that group therapy offers a dimension

---

[2] A therapist may tune in accurately to his patient's inner psychological state, and yet
maintain that the therapist's view is the valid one.

of therapeutic experience that individual treatment cannot provide. While "confrontation" with the therapist's divergent views can sometimes be experienced as "optimally responsive" (Bacal, 1985a) by a patient in individual therapy, it is more often felt as disruptive, since it comes from an idealized figure to whom the patient looks for relatively archaic selfobject recognition ("mirroring"). In group therapy, however, confrontation usually comes from another group member or from the group, and can then more often be accepted and experienced as therapeutic since it is offered by those in relation to whom relatively less disparity is felt (i.e., an alter ego figure in a "partnering" selfobject transference configuration [Bacal, 1985b]).

In the group situation that has the greatest influence on our psychological development, our childhood group matrix, or family group, pervasive attitudes become integral features of personality structure. For purposes of this discussion, I would like to highlight two of them: the assertion of the legitimacy of individual perspectives and needs in relation to the family group, and the assertion of the legitimacy of the requirements of the family group in relation to the individual. The requirements of the family group in relation to the individual child comprise two further components: the specific needs and perspectives of other individuals in the family, and the broad spectrum of group expectations as to how the members should relate to God and their fellow men and women. There are moral precepts with which we are more or less indoctrinated as children by our parents consonant with the family group subculture in which we live.[3] From an object-relations perspective, other individuals in the family group, as well as the family group-as-a-whole (and its extensions in society) become, for the child, objects in relation to which he will feel or will be expected to feel concern, anxiety, and guilt, when he does not fit in with their needs and expectations. From a self psychological perspective, the viability of the group, which all of this tends to ensure, is important to the intactness of the self of the individual child. The family group constitutes the essential selfobject matrix that sustains and nourishes the self of the individual. The health and strength of the child, therefore, always depends to some degree upon the availability of an intact and effectively functioning family group to which he feels he belongs. The individual child needs the family group to

[3] In a well-conducted group therapy situation, three perspectives share center stage: that of the individual, that of the therapist, and that of the group. While the group ethos in the family group is largely determined by the parents (who are normally the leaders of the group), the group therapist will recognize the validity of a group attitude that transcends his own norms or those of the individual members.

expect him to look out for its needs; indeed, the projection of this expectation onto the group in therapy may account for Bion's otherwise peculiar assertion that "the basic assumption in a group about people who meet together in a group . . . is that people come together as a group for purposes of preserving the group" (Bion, 1959, p. 63). An equally compelling determinant for maintaining the group is the preservation of the self structure of the individual member. While the individual and the group depend upon the support of each other for their intactness and vitality, there will be conflicts between their interests and perspectives, and the intensity of these conflicts can be severe.

Many of the problems people bring to therapy can be understood as emanating from antecedent family situations in which, as children, they experienced themselves as being regarded by the parents as parts of, or extensions of, what could be called the "family group self" to such a degree that the expression of their individuality, or their differences from the mainstream ethos of the family group in any way was consistently reacted to severely—sometimes as tantamount to "treason." In such a situation, the children are, in effect, archaic selfobjects of the group; that is, their individuality is regarded as a severe threat to the group's cohesion, and they will inevitably tend to orient themselves to their environment on a false-self basis (Winnicott, 1960), if they do not break away from their family group altogether. In a multitude of somewhat less pathogenically evident ways, children in some family groups are reacted to, more or less allergically, one might say, as "selfish," "bad," or at the very least, "quite wrong," when they "disagree" in one way or another with their parents as standardbearers of their family group's ethos. If, however, the parent regards differences between family members as arising from the tension produced by the intersection of different subjectivities (Stolorow, Brandchaft, and Atwood, 1987), the child will experience himself as really listened to. The family group, as embodied in the authority of the parent-leader, has now loosened its hold on the individual-as-part-of-itself, and instead has taken a step toward offering itself to the child with responsive understanding, from the child's point of view. The family group would then be reliably performing basic selfobject functioning for the individual child.

Let us now turn to the situation of group psychotherapy. In terms of our discussion, an individual comes to therapy because he has difficulty in two sectors of his experience: he is in trouble with other members of the group or with the *group* itself because he does not recognize and/or fit in with its expectations; or he is in trouble with himself because he is not able to find himself and/or assert his own needs in relation to the *group*. Not uncommonly, both problems co-exist.

In the two-person psychotherapy setting, the therapist, as a member of the *group*, does not obviously intrude with his "group" expectations and is expected to intrude minimally with his personal requirements. The setting is therefore conducive to exploring and working through the patient's selfobject needs in relation to a therapist who is experienced by the patient as representing his family group as well as one or other of its members, and where the introduction of the therapist's own needs and standards is usually regarded as countertransference. In contrast, in the group therapy setting, the individual will face other members who will naturally and "legitimately" tend to react spontaneously to him, often without consideration of his needs, as well as asserting their own feelings, thoughts, and needs. Thus, the setting of individual psychotherapy curiously emerges as providing more opportunity for relatively unalloyed exploration of the individual's difficulties as they arise from his experience of inadequate response from the *group*[4] to his needs than does group psychotherapy.

Psychological disturbance in the individual is usually the result of problems he encounters in life due to two determinants: the *group's* reaction to him for not fitting in with their expectations and his experience of inadequate response from the *group* to his particular needs. Group psychotherapy is often particularly useful as a valuable method of treating psychological disorder since this form of treatment is preeminently able to deal with both sectors of disturbance. When we begin to consider the individual in his interactions as a member of a therapy group, the importance of addressing thoroughly both determinants of his distress (as described above) becomes obvious.

When a group of people meets for the purpose of therapy, there is a natural inclination to explore and to confront problems encountered by the individual that arise when he or she reacts inappropriately from the point of view of the needs and expectations of others. Less emphasis and less legitimacy are accorded to the individual's selfobject needs in relation to others and to the group-as-a-whole. Put in another way, interactions between members of the group, whatever their con-

---

[4] Traditional individual analytic therapy does not take advantage of this opportunity, as it tacitly emphasizes the expectations of the *group*, viz., a "maturity–morality." This can never be completely engaged due to its relative silence and because of the relatively unchallengable authority of the therapist in the individual setting. Individual analytic therapy that is informed by self psychological theory does provide more of this opportunity, however, as the recognition of the continuing legitimacy of the individual's selfobject needs in relation to the environment is regarded as an essential aspect of the therapeutic process.

tent and however defended and disguised they might be are, formally speaking, expressed in two modes: "reactiveness" and "responsiveness." Reactiveness, in the group, tends to be the more prevalent one.

Reactiveness and responsiveness reflect different modes of listening to others. Reactiveness is a way of communicating and relating that is relatively experience-distant, and responsiveness is a way of communicating and relating that is relatively experience-near. When reactiveness is operating, the experience of others is registered in terms of a sense of how it affects one's self. The Tavistock groups that were conducted by Bion and Ezriel and their colleagues exemplified this mode of relating, since the leader's communications to the group consistently reflected an understanding of the group process primarily as it affected him. In effect, many other therapy group leaders wittingly or unwittingly tend to foster the use of reactiveness as the predominant communicative mode in the group, even though they may not relate to the group as remotely as the "classical" Tavistock consultant does.

Reactiveness as a way of communicating makes sense in its correspondence to the legitimate expectations that the family group has of the child; that is, it is based on widely accepted norms within the subculture as to how people should behave. In addition, these norms have come to reflect more or less traditionally established psychodynamic theory which addresses itself to the explanation of psychopathology—that psychological troubles are, at base, determined by the persistence of instinctual drives in their archaic forms, or by "narcissistic" needs of one sort or another that the chronological adult has not outgrown. What naturally follows from this emphasis is that the therapy group should ultimately enable the individual patient to renounce or at least modify these primitive ways and grow up. When such a "maturity–morality" dominates the group ethos, group members are tacitly encouraged to react personally to other group members' repetition of pathological childhood interpersonal relationships in current interaction. The task of the therapist, apropos, is to unravel these transference distortions between the group members and between them and himself.

It is this theory of therapy—where transference is regarded as a repetition or projection of early pathological relationships and distorted perceptions that determine interpersonally maladaptive behavior—that underlies, and that intelligibly and inevitably gives rise to, the sort of interpersonal communication that I have called reactiveness. The messages conveyed, whether from therapist or patients (more spontaneously from other group members, more "understandingly" from the therapist) are inevitably going to imply, and sometimes accurately specify, psychopathology, distortion of reality, and an expectation of change. Little or no empathy is required, and the use of experience-distant reactiveness as a communicative mode is therefore both consistent and appropriate.

When, however, the therapist regards transference not as distortion but as the organization of subjective experience (Stolorow et al., 1987, pp. 28–46), he will tacitly foster an intersubjective perspective on interaction in the group. Moreover, in this situation, the mode of interaction that I have called responsiveness will tend to prevail, reflecting an empathic attitude toward other members' experience of the interaction.

Reactiveness, therefore, as a mode of communication, tends to mediate the requirements of the group in relation to the individual, and responsiveness reflects the importance of personal discovery of one's self in relation to the group. Optimal responsiveness (Bacal, 1985a) to the needs of others requires a group ethos or atmosphere in which the group can be experienced as selfobject for the individual, while reactiveness does not.

We would certainly not wish to deprive our patients of the value of the spontaneous expression of their feelings toward each other, which, in addition to providing "grist for the mill" of understanding, may constitute, at times, optimal responsivity for the individual. However, it is important, in my view, that members of the group also be "trained" to respond on the basis of their empathically informed perceptions of others' needs for selfobject functioning. A minimum of optimal responsivity is always necessary for psychological survival; a more or less consistent expectation of it is essential for psychological health. In group psychotherapy, selfobject ties that the individual has with other members, as well as with the therapist and with the group, will provide therapeutic experiences of optimal responsiveness that will foster psychological growth. However, problems in mutual understanding that occur at the intersection of the subjectivities of participants in a therapy group are the order of the day, and experiences of selfobject disruption—frustrating and, at times, enraging—are frequently experienced at these interfaces. The repair of these disruptions, when possible, and their thoroughgoing understanding when harmony cannot be restored, will also constitute significant therapeutic experiences for the members of the group.

The group therapeutic process entails a paradoxical truism. Our patients will mature and grow stronger both from recognizing that others with whom they are closely involved have problems with certain of their needs, attitudes, and behavior, and as a result of feeling entitled to expect everyone in the group to recognize and value their own unique needs and perspectives. Reactiveness is the natural expression of the one, and an ambience of empathically informed responsiveness in the group is required for the other. It is the group leader's task to ensure that the group does not lose sight of the value of either. Perhaps psychoanalysis might even have evolved differently if Freud and his small group of pioneering colleagues had been able to manage a more harmonious balance between the two.

REFERENCES

Bacal, H. A. (1985a), Optimal responsiveness and the therapeutic process. In: *Progress in Self Psychology*, ed. A. Goldberg. New York: Guilford Press, pp. 202–226.
——— (1985b), Object-relations in the group from the perspective of self psychology. *Internat. J. Group Psychother.*, 35:483–501.
Bion, W. R. (1959), *Experiences in Groups and other Papers*. New York: Basic Books, 1961.
Ezriel, H. (1973), Psychoanalytic group therapy. In: *Group Therapy: 1973 An Overview*, ed. L. R. Wolberg & E. K. Schwartz. New York: International Book Corporation, pp. 183–210.
Freud, S. (1921), Group psychology and the analysis of the ego. *Standard Edition*, 18:67–143. London: Hogarth Press, 1955.
Heath, E. S., & Bacal, H. A. (1968), A method of group psychotherapy at the Tavistock Clinic. *Internat. J. Group Psychother.*, 18:21–30.
Kanzer, M. (1971), Freud: The first psychoanalytic group leader. In: *Comprehensive Group Psychotherapy*, ed. H. I. Kaplan & B. J. Sadock. Baltimore: Williams & Wilkins, pp. 32–46.
Kohut, H. (1971), *The Analysis of the Self*. New York: International Universities Press.
Stolorow, R. D., Brandchaft, B., & Atwood, G. E. (1987), *Psychoanalytic Treatment, an Intersubjective Approach*. Hillsdale, NJ: Analytic Press.
Winnicott, D. W. (1960), Ego distortion in terms of true and false self. In: *The Maturational Processes and the Facilitating Environment*. London: Hogarth Press, 1965.

PART VII

Cultural Factors in Psychoanalytic Groups

INTRODUCTION

In chapter 18, Alberto Serrano and Edmundo Ruiz sensitively explore important cultural and transference issues in group psychotherapy, an area previously addressed by Scheidlinger (1968, 1982). Group therapists are interested in ascertaining those qualities which patients, in any one group, may have in common which can contribute to a valuable sense of cohesiveness among members. It is also important to deal with differences in custom and in language (as well as in style) which can create barriers. One of the group therapist's functions is to help the group overcome these difficulties.

REFERENCES

Scheidlinger, S. (1968), Therapeutic group approaches in community mental health. *Soc. Work*, 13:87–95.
———— (1982), *Focus on Group Psychotherapy: Clinical Essays.* New York: International Universities Press.

Chapter 18

Transferential and Cultural Issues in Group Psychotherapy

ALBERTO C. SERRANO, M.D., and
EDMUNDO J. RUIZ, M.D.

A CULTURAL FRAME OF REFERENCE

The role of culture and ethnicity in mental health has been discussed in the early literature, mostly by sociologists and anthropologists. A few mental health clinicians (Castairs, 1965; McGoldrick, Pearce, and Giordano, 1982) have more recently stressed the need to include cultural considerations in the diagnostic and treatment process. Clinical training programs often neglect to discuss the significance of culture and ethnicity. Furthermore, role models available to train and to sensitize mental health professionals and trainees in this area have been few in number. Scheidlinger (1968) among others has stressed the need to be culturally sensitive when using group approaches in community mental health. Bloombaum, Yamamoto, and James (1968) have discussed the problem of "cultural stereotyping among psychotherapists."

We know that generations of immigrants were told of the "melting pot" philosophy. One of the authors (A.S.), who grew up in Argentina, was also educated with the idea that the Americas were a "crisol de razas," something like an "ethnic crucible."

The long-standing myth of the melting pot has been replaced over the last few years by an ethnic pride. While there is a negative side to the ethnic pride which has been at times associated with political posturing and racism, its positive influence has helped clinicians become more aware of how ethnicity and culture "define ways in which people perceive their relationship to nature, institutions, other people and objects." Those "worldviews constitute our psychological orientation in life and can determine how we think, behave, make decisions and define events" (Dawkins, Terry, and Dawkins, 1980, p. 384).

It would be easy to draw the conclusion that each ethnic group can be expected to have different and possibly specific worldviews. Ethnic groups, however, are far from being homogeneous cultural entities and as clinicians we should avoid oversimplifications that would lead to cultural stereotyping.

Following Richard English (1984), it is possible to include four major categories in identifying these worldviews: (1) A *bicultural/multicultural worldview* which "draws upon multiple sources of cultural and socialization experiences" (p. 18). This represents a "bicultural" view where traditional values of the background culture and those of the mainstream society seem to coexist without apparent dominance or replacement. A person with such a worldview is able to utilize "old" and "new" cultural traditions without "melting" them. (2) The *acculturated/assimilated worldview*. Acculturation involves the acquisition of beliefs, attitudes, and behaviors of a social group of which one is not a national member and refers to taking on "values, norms and role expectations of the dominant group" (p. 18). Assimilation is an end state in which primary group ties develop with the dominant group. (3) A *native oriented/traditional worldview* is based upon holding onto symbols, norms, behaviors, values, and beliefs of one's background ethnic–cultural traditions while remaining relatively isolated or impermeable to mainstream influences. (4) A *transitional–marginal worldview* refers to "individuals who are suspended between their original ethnic identity and the mainstream culture" (p. 19). These persons are typically without a strong identification with their cultural roots and have limited adaptive capacity or no commitment to joining the mainstream culture.

We should recognize that these four categories often overlap and that in our clinical observations individual variations are frequently detected across different life cycles and in the context of critical life events.

TRANSFERENCE AND CULTURE

We find it useful to identify where patients as well as therapists function in the spectrum of worldviews just described. Cultural literacy helps us understand symptomatic behaviors within a specific ethnic and cultural context. Such understanding can help minimize the tendency to "pathologize" those behaviors that appear to be outside the mainstream group and to avoid normalizing deviant patterns that "masquerade" as ethnic behaviors.

When patients and therapists are of different ethnic backgrounds, it is mostly their physical attributes that are apparent. They will also display many other characteristic values, customs, and prejudices. "Under these circumstances, and regardless of a conscious effort not to allow it, they [patients and therapists] often create a climate of cognitive dissonance, that can facilitate negative influences on the therapeutic process. . ." (Joseph, 1982, p. 8).

We recognize that a patient's responses to an initial clinical interview are typically influenced by: (1) his psychopathology; (2) his reaction to the initial encounter; and (3) the therapist's reaction to the first interview with the patient. We seldom hear of the significance of cultural differences between patient and therapist as if they either did not exist, or they were unimportant. When cultural issues are the focus of attention in that context, traditionally they have been interpreted as a reflection of negative transference or resistance.

The effectiveness of the therapeutic relationship depends a great deal on the nature of the transferential and countertransferential phenomena which, in group psychotherapy, becomes even more complex than in individual therapy because of the cultural dimension present in each member.

A frequent cause of treatment failure is associated with lack of recognition of the patient's transferential problems or his or her countertransferential reactions. Patients often drop out of treatment when cultural and ethnic issues are not dealt with in treatment and they feel misunderstood by the therapist. This is not to suggest that a successful therapeutic relationship can only be achieved with someone of similar ethnic or cultural background or that minority patients can only be treated by therapists of the same minority group.

We want to underscore that a therapist's effectiveness is greatly enhanced by his cultural sensitivity. Brantley (1983) suggests that such a therapist need not be overidentified with the culture or ethnicity of his patients, but would recognize their significance while examining his own responses to racism.

A culturally sensitive therapist must become aware of and work through his or her own fears and biases about patients of different racial and ethnic extraction. Cultural and language factors often make it difficult for patients and therapists of different backgrounds to establish an effective therapeutic alliance. If future therapists are to become sensitive to the relevance of this dimension, training curricula should include readings, along with supervised experiences on cultural issues. It is well known that patients of foreign origin often prefer to use their native language when they discuss their psychiatric problems. We should note, however, that it is of limited therapeutic value to know a patient's language if one does not understand his cultural values (Collins, Mathura, and Risher, 1984), and that bilingual bicultural competence is far more effective.

MEXICAN AMERICANS AND GROUP PSYCHOTHERAPY

The literature dealing with the use of group psychotherapy with Hispanics, and particularly with Mexican Americans, is rather small. This ethnic group has been frequently viewed as unamenable to psychotherapy and even less to group psychotherapy, possibly because of their traditional reservations about disclosing intimate matters in front of strangers. There is a strong cultural value stating that "La ropa sucia se lava en casa*" Incidently this same argument was heard recently concerning problems in the practice of group psychotherapy in Japan (Wong, personal communication, 1985).

It has been reported that "most hispanos are being treated too often with chemotherapy, by self help, or folk medicine" (Richman, 1985, p. 3). They are frequently disadvantaged and are relegated to poorly financed public services where treatment typically is characterized by excessive use of medication or very brief supportive psychotherapy. These patients manifest a high drop-out rate and have been difficult to engage in traditional psychotherapies. A frequent explanation states that "anglo" standards for psychotherapy do not make sense to them and may separate them from their families.

We need to remember that Mexican Americans, along with other Hispanics, are of mixed ethnic ancestry, and that the Spaniards and Indians had also a long history of interracial marriages. Mexican Americans present a wide range of adaptive patterns with different levels of acculturation and assimilation.

The meaning of mental health or mental illness is different for traditional Mexican Americans. Mental health does not exist as a separate concept; there is no separation between the psychological and the total well-being of the individual. "To feel healthy is to be happy and strong. When one does not feel well, one is more likely to consult

---

*"Dirty clothing is washed at home."

a physician or a folk healer mostly for the physical basis of the condition; such issues need to be well understood by clinicians providing mental health services for this population" (Padilla and Ruiz, 1973, p. 14).

We have stressed thus far that cultural and ethnic issues in patients and therapists need to be considered. We should also recognize that there are differences within a particular culture which can also be identified from one home to the next, with variations even between members of the same family.

CASE EXAMPLE 1

During the war against poverty in the late sixties, centers were established in many areas of the country for the purpose of making a number of services more accessible to low-income populations. This particular case deals with a predominantly Mexican-American population. One of the authors (E.R.), who was then Director of Family Services in Laredo, Texas, selected two Mexican-American counselors, a male and a female. One of them had a college degree, while the other's "qualifications" only included that he lived with his family in the same neighborhood. It had been expected that the clients would feel more at ease with this team. Soon it was found that the response was poor despite their efforts. The few that sought help did not stay long enough to enjoy therapeutic progress. A general meeting with the people from the Barrio was called by the director (E.R.). The neighbors communicated that they would value counseling were it offered by people who could understand their needs in the context of their culture and of their language. Then why were the services offered by this team not utilized?

E.R. and the counselors concluded that counseling *alone* was not a top priority and that people mostly asked for money, food, housing, and transportation to social and health services.

The consensus of the barrio group indicated that the program could not work because the team did not really understand them and their needs.

They criticized the degreed counselor stating that "when somebody graduates from college he typically becomes a different kind of person": "education makes them think like anglos," "they even talk and look like them." As for the neighborhood worker, they felt that this person had very little to offer, "just because they have a salary it does not mean that they are *real* counselors."

In these exchanges with Mexican Americans, E.R., who was born in Mexico, was more schooled and enjoyed a well-balanced bicultural worldview, but was nonetheless challenged for not "really knowing what it is to be poor, live in the barrio and to be surrounded by a dominant culture that is not sensitive to one's needs." ER was able to facilitate better collaboration when he presented himself as open to learning from them about their lives and needs without defensively challenging the assumptions of the barrio group.

CASE EXAMPLE 2

During the Eighth International Congress of Group Psychotherapy in Mexico City in 1984, E.R. led a bilingual process group. The task was to examine initial group stages, to look at transferential issues and racial stereotypes in a multinational group. The meetings lasted for an hour and a half. It was listed in the program that only Spanish and English would be used in this event.

In one of the groups, a Frenchwoman, seemingly unaware of that expectation, joined the session. Her presence forced a change from the bilingual format to include nonverbal communications along with limited use of French with her.

As therapists, we are often confronted with situations when we have to deal with patients of a different background, culture, race, religion. We seek strategies to deal with those differences hoping that they do not become barriers or stereotypes.

While this group did not have time to focus on extensive problem solving it had been designed to explore group interaction across languages and cultures. The goal was to establish a certain amount of group sense, warmth, and a sense of belonging. The ten members that participated in this group represented the United States, Spain, Italy, Canada, Mexico, Argentina, and France.

The group sat in a circle, and as several members started to talk the Frenchwoman felt out of place and said:

F.L.:   Je m'excuse. (Excuse me.) (She tries to get up.)

The group leader remembered some of the French he had learned in college, and dared to say:

Leader: Pourquoi? (Why?)
F.L.:   Je ne comprend pas, je suis française, je parle français. (I do

not understand, I am French, I speak French.)

L.:   Je ne parle pas bien français. (I do not speak French well.)

F.L.:   Tiens! Je me demand de quoi ils parlent. (Well! I wonder what are they talking about.)

L.:   Pourrier vous me rendre un service? (Could you do me a favor?)

F.L.:   Voudriez-vous? (Please?)

L.:   Asseyez-vous un moment, ne vous inquietez pas. (Sit down for a while; do not worry.)

So far, so good, but the rest of the group members needed to be included: Are you going to let her go? E.R. asked. No they answered. So again the question: How are you going to convince her to stay? She was about to reach the door, when one of the members got up and touched her shoulder, to call her attention.

Member: Yo quisiera que se quedara. (I wish you could stay.)

She looked puzzled, and then he repeated the words but this time with the help of his hands.

M.:   Yo (touching his chest) quiero (touching the side of his heart) I want que se quede (pointing to the chair that she had left) you to stay.

The whole group echoed the request.

F.L.:   Merci, vous êtes bien amiable. (Thank you, you are very nice.)

While it had not been an easy group to start, the crisis helped the members become a group rather rapidly. Following this incident the goal of containing her was achieved. The experience was used by the leader to encourage the members to elaborate on their own transferential reactions toward each member, focusing not just on their brief group experience but by sharing their own historical biases about each other. It was interesting that the projected thoughts and feelings we heard were to a large extent based on history and myths as they were manifested by national and ethnic groups, and were typically not related to their own personal experience. It was most useful to identify those biases and to recognize how they influenced behavior in the group experience. The participants were encouraged to express those prejudices, as honestly as they could, and it went something like this:
A Spaniard candidly stated that he felt a strange feeling being in

Mexico, the land conquered by his ancestors. He saw himself as being different from the Mexicans and also ambivalent about their having achieved independence from Spain. He experienced some feelings of superiority while listening to the way Mexicans "kill" the language when they speak Spanish. He also was able to recognize how much Mexicans have departed from the traditional Spanish heritage.

Mexicans, on their side, expressed resentment for the treatment of the Indians by the Spaniards, and were proud of the way Mexicans have proven to themselves that they can run their country better than the Spaniards after gaining their independence. In regard to the Frenchwoman, the Mexicans discussed her in two different ways: an assumed stereotype that being French she must be very romantic and sexually free. They also recognized feelings going back to the time when Maximilian and Charlotte were royal rulers of Mexico, which included the assumption that the French are supposed to be very good at governing, and that their presence gave Mexico a touch of aristocracy. There was also reference to the tragic ending, with Maximilian's execution and Charlotte's insanity.

The Mexicans harbor considerable hurt and anger against the Anglos (Gringos), for the loss of a great portion of Mexican territory. The Anglos on the other side remember well the battle of the Alamo and its consequences.

Argentines were very much in tune with the Mexicans' sentiment in regard to the Spaniards, but seemed more identified with Europe.

This experience is obviously a first step, and to further develop and elaborate the emerging issues, a more extended experience would be necessary.

CASE EXAMPLE 3

This was demonstrated in the following example that took place at the meetings of an Institute and Annual Conference of the American Group Psychotherapy Association in 1975, in San Antonio, Texas. A bilingual (English–Spanish) group was offered and, despite a clear listing in the program, some registrants joined the group with the expectation that it was going to be conducted solely in Spanish.

We soon found that one of the members could not even understand Spanish. As the other members continued the group in Spanish, the leader asked why was it that the members believed that the session was going to be conducted only in Spanish. The majority, including the Anglos who spoke some Spanish, stated that they wanted an experience in Spanish. The one non-Spanish-speaking member insisted on the use of English. At that time the "Chicano" movement was very militant and one of its active members confronted him saying: "Tu hablas Español," and as he got closer to him he touched him on the chest and said, "Yo Juan, tu quien eres" (I am Juan, who are you?)

"Ha!" (surprised)
"Tu hablas Español." (You see, you speak Spanish.)

Everybody laughed but there was a lot of tension in the air.

The leader then invited the group to talk in Spanish for fifteen minutes, after which we were to ask the non-Spanish-speaking member for his understanding of what he thought had taken place. Much to his surprise he was able to give a very close version of the group interaction. Later, and as termination of the group experience came closer, the members switched into English without even realizing it. They seemed to have a need to get closure by employing the language that would include everybody.

CASE EXAMPLE 4

Cultural transferences were experienced in a multiethnic group in reaction to a member's own projections. Strong feelings had developed toward a Japanese woman. Although the tension kept mounting, nobody dared to discuss the conflict. Eventually she brought it spontaneously into the open and was able to discuss her experiences as a group therapist. In the past, as a result of being Japanese she had been the target of resentments and hatred. She then stated that something similar was happening again in this group. This incident evoked many feelings of discrimination in others who could find courage to talk openly about such conflicting issues. One of the members who was a black Catholic sister was then able to disclose that she was proud of being a nun, but that as a black woman she felt frequently stereotyped as being sexually open, something in clear conflict with her vocation.

CASE EXAMPLE 5

In another multiethnic group, E.R. was doing cotherapy with a black clinician. One of the members seemed very defensive about disclosing any facts that would define his race. He appeared to be black but had a very light-colored skin. He also verbalized not wanting to reveal his occupation, but it was later acknowledged that he was a high-ranking officer in the armed forces. Because exploration of racial issues was the main focus of the group experience everybody else seemed accepting of the task and irritated with his resistance. This member was eventually challenged with the racial issue, which was interpreted as his way of excluding himself from the group. A black member then confronted him saying: "You are a Nigger and don't you ever forget it." This expression, coming from one black to another, seemed more tolerable. At that point a southern white woman, in an attempt to appear open-minded, addressed herself to another black member and stated that she "did not have any prejudices against blacks," "as a matter of face," she said, "I like you." The black member reacted very strongly, and said "stop the bull . . . don't give me that stuff, you know that you hate my guts, you southern belle, don't give me that BS." He then related an incident that took place while he was working in a southern hospital: just because he had the "audacity" to sit at the breakfast table with a white female, he was not only fired, but was also threatened with lynching.

CASE EXAMPLE 6

During the Ninth International Group Psychotherapy Congress held in Zagreb in 1986, there was a powerful confrontation between two members in one of the workshops. One of them remained silent for a long time while the other saw in him a "Nazi" whom he blamed for the death of several relatives during the Holocaust. The angry tone and the accusations against him and "his kind" escalated. Tension in the group increased while the "Nazi-looking member" became even more rigid and somber. As the climate reached an explosive point, he finally opened up, talking very loud, in a rage, and to the point of tears. Because of the way he looked he often felt blamed for crimes committed by others and that took place before he was even born. He was quick to remark that his accuser made statements of a discriminatory and persecutory nature against him similar to those the Nazis used to justify their actions against the Jews. The group members experienced a sense of hope and great relief that a resolution of this intense confrontation could develop in less that two hours.

CONCLUSION

Recognition of the cultural and ethnic dimension in our clinical work expands our field of observation and offers us more resources in our efforts at understanding patients and ourselves.

The vignettes attempt to illustrate how the cultural dimension manifests itself consciously and unconsciously in a variety of group experiences. The authors also indicate how dealing with this conflict-laden material openly and respectfully can greatly facilitate group process.

REFERENCES

Bloombaum, M., Yamamoto, J., & James, G. (1968), Cultural stereotyping among psychotherapists. *J. Counsel. & Clin. Psychol.*, 32:99–

Brantley, T. (1983), Racism and its impact on psychotherapy. *Amer. J. Psychiat.*, 140:1605–1608.

Castairs, G. M. (1965), Cultural elements in the response to treatment. In: *Transcultural Psychiatry*, ed. A. V. DeReuck & R. Porter. London: Churchill, pp. 169–175.

Collins, J., Mathura, C., & Risher, D. (1984), Report of the Department of Psychiatry—Howard University. *Hosp. Commun. Psychiat.*, 35:372–376.

Dawkins, M., Terry, J., & Dawkins, M. (1980), Personality and life style factors in utilization of mental health services. *Psycholog. Rep.*, 46:383–386.

English R. (1984), *The Challenge for Mental Health Minorities and their Worldviews*. Austin, TX: The Hogg Foundation for Mental Health, The University of Texas.

Joseph L. (1982), Black therapist, white patient, a report of a conference of the Canadian Psychiatric Association. *APA News*, January 15.

Maldonado-Sierra, E., & Trent, R. (1960), The sibling relationship in group psychotherapy with Puerto Rican schizophrenics. *Amer. J. Psychiat.*, 117:239–244.

McGoldrick, M., Pearce, J., & Giordano, J. eds. (1982), *Ethnicity and Family Therapy*. New York: Guilford Press, pp. 23–28.

Padilla, A., & Ruiz, R. (1973), *Latino Mental Health: A Review of the Literature*, DHEW Publication (HSM) 73-9143. Washington, DC: U.S. Government Printing Office.

Richman, J. (1985), Social class and mental health revisited: Sociological perspectives on the diffusion of psychoanalysis. *J. Operat. Psychiat.*, 16:2–6.

Scheidlinger S. (1968), Therapeutic group approaches in community mental health. *Soc. Work*, 13:87–95.

Yamamoto, J., James, G., & Palley, N. (1968), Cultural problems in psychiatric therapy. *Arch. Gen. Psychiat.*, 19:45–49.

PART VIII

*Research in Psychodynamic Group
Psychotherapy: Theory and Treatment*

INTRODUCTION

Throughout his writings, and in the course of serving as editor of the *International Journal of Group Psychotherapy*, Saul Scheidlinger has clearly supported and encouraged scientific research in the hope of increasing understanding of areas of intuitive clinical practice. This section on research contains three papers: Stone and Stevenson (chapter 19) seek correlations between motivational and experiential factors on the one hand, and group attendance of patients, on the other. This study is one form of clinical research.

Roy MacKenzie and James Kennedy (in chapter 20) devote their efforts to an ethological study which offers a fresh perspective to group theories. Studies of group interaction in other species may provide new insights into human group functioning and group dynamics. Although the application to humans of findings concerning group behavior among primates may be premature, it is nonetheless interesting (and potentially important) to study such phenomena. the close biological relationship of primates and humans (from an evolutionary viewpoint) may be manifested in what appears to be parallel behavior of the two species (in child care, scapegoating, rank order hierarchies, and sexual behavior).

Finally (in chapter 21) Robert Dies considers the critical issue of group therapy research. He encourages further effort toward deeper communication between researchers and clinicians and presses for the development of more effective research methods. These concerns are in keeping with Saul Scheidlinger's objectives.

337

Chapter 19

Seeking Perspective on Patients' Attendance in Group Psychotherapy

WALTER N. STONE, M.D., and F. BEAUMONT
STEVENSON, M.Div.

It is fitting that this study exploring patients' attendance in group psychotherapy be one contribution to a monograph honoring Saul Scheidlinger since many of his theoretical contributions serve as a base from which a self psychological perspective can be understood. Indeed Scheidlinger's consistent exploration of traditional analytic concepts has greatly enhanced our field.

In relation to the present study, two fundamental themes are present in Scheidlinger's work. (1) A consistently balanced effort to distinguish between individual and group dynamics. The group phenomena are the product of the hopes, fears, wishes, and overall psychic structure of the individual in dynamic interaction with others. (2) An effort to distinguish levels of group functioning and thereby refine our thinking about observable phenomena.

Individuals bring to groups their own way of interacting, their fantasies, wishes for nurturance, care. and acceptance, as well as a variety of motivations for help. Groups develop norms, values, and a variety of rules that are conscious and unconscious. Scheidlinger has argued consistently for the need to keep in mind the two perspectives (Scheidlinger, 1955, 1968, 1984). He has had considerable interest in examining individual psychological functioning at an early developmental level. Self psychology has a considerable interest in the same developmental period. However, the two paradigms view development and interpret the phenomena differently. These differences should be the basis for dialogue. It is our hope that this contribution will enhance that process.

Therapists continue to search for satisfactory guidelines in selecting patients who will successfully engage in and profit from group psychotherapy. The problem extends beyond the task of adequately screening and preparing individuals for group treatment. It includes the very difficult assignment of determining the quality of the relationships that the patient will develop with the therapist and with the group, and whether or not these relationships can be utilized in the service of change. With more than a decade of experience applying the concepts of self psychology in group psychotherapy, it seems in order to review the clinical outcome of patients treated in groups led by a therapist with a major interest in disorders of the self.

The therapist utilizing the precepts of self psychology initially strives to achieve a therapeutic atmosphere that accepts and stabilizes the fragile self in relation to an appropriate selfobject. This is accomplished by attending to the patient's inner state, through the process of empathy, and by working with defenses against the emergence of selfobject transferences (Kohut, 1977, 1984). The selfobject as defined by Wolf (1986) is "neither self nor object, but the subjective aspect of a self-sustaining function performed by a relationship of self to objects who by their presence or activity evoke and maintain the self and the experience of selfhood. As such the selfobject relationship refers to an intrapsychic experience and does not describe the interpersonal experience between the self and the other object" (p. 492).

Subsequent to establishing selfobject transferences, primarily formulated as mirroring, idealizing, or alter ego transferences, the patient optimally proceeds to restart growth (Ornstein, 1974). Within the treatment framework the therapist can understand and then explain (interpret) the sequence of the patient's experience of narcissistic injury followed by restorative responses. Through such interpretations the patient gradually increases his capacity to assume self-soothing functions previously assigned to the selfobject. This process, labeled transmuting internalization, results in the patient's increasing capacity to separate from an "external" stabilizer and assume greater self-reliance. This theory recognizes that a developmental need for selfobjects exists throughout the life cycle. Early, primitive needs for selfobjects are transformed into more mature forms. The individual does not outgrow the need for a selfobject, but instead builds a cohesive, firm self structure that is able to manage both internally and interpersonally the ordinary and extraordinary vicissitudes of life, using his or her own resources and age-appropriate selfobjects.

From a self psychological perspective, the therapy group provides some special opportunities as well as dangers in building an optimally functioning self. Patients may utilize the experiences in the group to provide for a variety of selfobjects, which would include the therapist, peers, and the image of the group-as-a-whole. If one element is insufficient or unavailable, another may fulfill the selfobject need (Bacal, 1985; Harwood, 1986). However, each of these selfobjects also may be a potential source of narcissistic injury via empathic failure (Scheidlinger, 1966; Stone and Whitman, 1980). The therapist's initial task, in this framework, is conceptualized as trying to remove resistances to the development of pathognomonic selfobject transferences. Efforts are expended at creating a safe, trustworthy environment where narcissistic injury is recognized and attention is paid to the patient's inner experience rather than expecting "realistic" or appropriate behavior (Schwartzman, 1984).

THE STUDY

This report is one portion of a larger study of the clinical outcome of patients entering into psychotherapy groups led by a senior clinician experienced in working with narcissistic and borderline patients from a self psychological perspective. The twenty patients entering the therapist's groups during a three-year period were the subjects.

The following areas were explored: (1) the patients' initial request for and motivation to enter into group treatment as recorded at the time of diagnostic evaluations; (2) the clinical course of the therapy obtained from the process notes recorded by the therapist after each session; (3) follow-up information provided by interviews with patients no longer in group treatment. These interviews were conducted three-and-a-half years after the beginning of the study period by a second senior clinician.

The groups for which the patients were selected were open-ended and met once weekly for ninety minutes. The members were diagnosed as character disordered, with a preponderance of the diagnoses at the earlier end of the developmental continuum. Patients were added to the groups when openings existed. Preparation for the patients specifically referred for group treatment was generally accomplished in one or two individual sessions. Those who were in individual treatment with the group therapist generally had a more protracted preparatory period.

Traditional ways of thinking about the prospective members' capacity to experience and observe themselves in interaction with others were an essential element in the screening interviews. However, the use of the self psychological perspective led to a specific focus on attachment behaviors. The attachments were examined in relation to the patients' ability, when entering into emotionally important relations, to consider the others as separate and autonomous or, alternatively, as needing idealized or mirroring selfobjects. Additionally, the patients' characteristic responses to the inevitable shortcomings or empathic failures on the part of the selfobject (i.e., withdrawal, anger, somatization) were examined. Careful attention also was paid to the doctor–patient relationship as it emerged in the course of the diagnostic or treatment interviews. Particularly scrutinized was the manner in which the patients initially related their history. A poorly organized or disjointed story was suggestive of a patient's unconscious expectation that the therapist might provide magical understanding and cure. Such a presentation was tentatively evaluated as a signal of the need for a developmentally early selfobject tie (Stone, 1985). Finally, it was expected that the treatment process itself would provide the most salient data.

At the end of the three-year period a rough retrospective classification of the twenty patients' potential to engage in and benefit from group psychotherapy was made from the initial diagnostic information. In the situation where patients had prior individual treatment with the group therapist, that information was utilized. Engagement was conceptualized as a patient's capacity to allow a significant sector of his or her psychopathology to emerge in the treatment process. This was judged by the therapist's assessment of the patient's willingness, both conscious and unconscious, to expose a vulnerable part of himself to scrutiny within the group. Three categories, high, moderate, and weak engagement potential were developed which roughly corresponded with expectations along a continuum of successful to unsuccessful treatment outcome. Such a procedure is fraught with a multitude of biases, but it was a procedure that could be refined in future research.

Sixteen of the twenty patients had been referred specifically for group psychotherapy. The remaining four had initially requested individual therapy, and only after a period of dyadic treatment did they enter a group. All but one of the twenty patients had at least six months of prior therapy. Six were in combined treatment, which included the group or their referring therapist (Stone and Rutan, 1984).

Overall the clinical course of the twenty patients was somewhat poorer than outcome–evaluative reports in the literature (Roback and Smith, 1987). Eleven patients (55%) quit within the first year, three successfully completed therapy, and six were continuing in treatment at the cutoff time of the study. Table 19.1 shows the outcome of the twenty patients in relation to the assessment of their ability to engage. As judged by successful termination or remaining in therapy, the outcome for patients assigned to the high engagement group was more favorable than those in the other categories. Of the six patients in regularly scheduled combined treatment one was a drop-out, three continued in treatment, and two successfully terminated their therapy.

The individuals who terminated were contacted and agreed to an interview with a senior clinician–researcher who was primarily oriented to a group analytic approach to group psychotherapy. The interviews were generally an hour or more in length, were semistructured, and explored the patients' intial reasons for requesting or entering into group treatment, their experience of the process, and their reasons for and reactions to termination. Patients who continued in their group were not interviewed.

Table 19.1
ESTIMATED "ENGAGEMENT" POTENTIAL

	High	*Middle*	*Low*	*Total*
Successful	2	0	1	3
Continuing	2	3	1	6
Drop Out	3	3	5	11
Total	7	6	7	20

The remainder of this report will examine patients at two ends of the "engagement" continuum: (1) those seven patients who were predicted to engage weakly, and (2) those three individuals who were predicted to engage strongly and yet dropped out. It was anticipated that a careful exploration of these two groups would generate further ideas about therapeutic or countertherapeutic elements in the treatment process.

WEAKLY ENGAGED PATIENTS

This group contained seven patients. All but Ms. A. were initially diagnosed as borderline. However, Ms. F. eventually revealed a longstanding delusional system, and her initial diagnosis was changed to schizophrenia. Five prematurely discontinued their treatment, one successfully completed therapy, and one remains in treatment.

Two patients discontinued treatment following their second group meeting. Both of these individuals gave strong indications at the time of their initial interview that they were not prepared to use a psychodynamic therapy group. Ms. A. had initially sought treatment for a perceived crisis. She had begun private treatment but could not continue for financial reasons. Her boyfriend, who was a group patient, recommended that treatment modality as an affordable alternative. she complied but quickly terminated and entered individual treatment at a mental health center. She subsequently deemed this treatment to be successful. In the follow-up interview Ms. A. observed that she liked the group, but it was not what she needed.

The second patient, Ms. B., had asked her individual therapist to refer her to a group. She had a lengthy history of failed individual treatments, and although her interpersonal problems were readily apparent she was primarily interested in receiving advice and direction. She angrily quit after two sessions complaining that her needs were not met. The follow-up interview, which Ms. B. would permit only by phone, was replete with criticisms of the therapist for not providing her or the group with what she perceived as necessary. The sense of narcissistic injury and rage was evident in the phone conversation. These two patients should have been evaluated more thoroughly and not placed in a group. They represent a 10 percent (2 of 20) error rate.

The other five weakly engaged patients, who initially were diagnosed as borderline personality, remained in therapy at least six months in part due to continuing or intermittent individual therapy. Ongoing concurrent individual psychotherapy clearly sustained two patients (Ms. C. and Ms. D.). Both individual therapists reported that these patients frequently discussed quitting their group treatment. It was apparent that the patients were unable or unwilling to talk about these feelings in the group, and they had very limited capacity in the individual sessions to explore the sources for their desire to quit the group. Since the individual therapists felt that the group was important, they took a noninterpretive stance of firmly insisting that the patient remain in group and continue to work on their problems.

For Ms. C. this strategy was crucial in her engagement in her group which continued beyond the study period. In contrast, Ms. D. terminated after nine months, stating that she could no longer afford group therapy. Ms. D. had frequently expressed concern about her precarious financial situation which seemed unchanged prior to her decision to stop. Interestingly, Ms. D.'s individual therapist, who initially had been very firm in recommending group treatment, no longer encouraged her to continue the group therapy. This process was similar to that of a third patient in this group, Ms. E., whose individual therapist maintained an interpretive and nondirective stance. Ms. E. abruptly quit group following a vacation by the therapist, a pattern of withdrawal that she had repeated many times. The individual therapist did not encourage her to return to the group.

The remaining two patients, Ms. F. and Mr. G., intermittently requested individual sessions with the group therapist to manage problems within the group. These temporary solutions consisted of intermittent dyadic meetings lasting two to three sessions. At a manifest level the content was not related to group issues; instead, it was presented as a crisis within the family. Efforts by the therapist to make connections between the family and the group were unsuccessful, and the work remained in the displacement. The family crises cooled down without any specific solutions, most likely as a result of the firming of the fragile self in the patient–therapist relationship, and the patient then would continue in the group without concurrent dyadic meetings.

The outcome of these two patients was mixed. Ms. F. initially requested intermittent private sessions with the group therapist, but later asked for referral to a woman therapist of her own ethnic background. A first referral did not click, but a second therapist proved satisfactory, and Ms. F. entered into regularly scheduled sessions. This therapist reported that Ms. F. revealed a long-standing delusional system, which had previously been unknown. According to the therapist, Ms. F.'s dropping from the group after sixteen months of treatment coincided with her incorporation of the group therapist into her persecutory delusional system.

The second patient, Mr. G., gained considerably from his group experience. This man, in his midtwenties, was referred to group because of severe family problems, anxiety that interfered with his ability to read and retain simple information (there was no evidence of a learning disability), and an inability to sustain romantic relationships. After a period of slightly more than two years of group treatment, occasional series of individual appointments, and a brief, unsuccessful effort at family treatment, he appropriately and reasonably terminated therapy. He had married satisfactorily, his anxiety had diminished, and he was able to concentrate and retain information to a degree that enabled him to enroll in an intensive training program that would enhance his professional capabilities. The resultant time conflict and the general sense of doing much better in his life were the reasons for finishing treatment.

In the follow-up interview, Mr. G. said that he had received a great deal of help from his group therapy. Mr. G. talked about his initial problem as that of anxiety, but he emphasized that through therapy he had learned to accept and deal with the emotional side of himself. In recounting his experience he said: "I described people as flawed pieces of wood that needed sanding. The group was irritated and took exception, and I learned from that. That was the way I thought of myself and other people. I didn't give real emotional feeling to anything." At the time he terminated, Mr. G. was aware that he had more therapeutic work to do. He appreciated the therapist's recognition of that fact, felt understood, and not patronized. He described this interaction as a big boost in that it confirmed his ability to understand himself. Combining information from the follow-up interview with the developmental history, and the treatment process, we can speculate that Mr. G. had defended himself against any anxiety associated with unfulfilled needs, through intellectualization and affect repression. During treatment he gradually achieved freedom in experiencing and expressing affects, and he no longer felt so different or unacceptable. The result for Mr. G. was a significantly enhanced sense of self-esteem and self-cohesion. The remaining vulnerability of the self was in part expressed in his recognition that "a big boost" was so important for him to feel confident with his decision, but substantial gains were nevertheless quite evident.

Overall the five individuals in this subgroup, who remained more than two sessions, had entered therapy with major defenses against their needs for selfobjects. The transferences developed silently, outside the awareness of patient and therapist alike, and seldom were available to be examined collaboratively. In the early treatment phase when the patients were narcissistically injured, they withdrew. When the therapist attempted to empathically explain this process the patients seemed unable to utilize the intervention to restore equilibrium to the fragile self. Not infrequently these patients, in their individual sessions, would discuss quitting the group, but even in this protected dyadic setting they were unable to explore the precipitant that led to their wishes to terminate. The individual therapist was left in a position that required a directive recommendation to continue the group without an understanding of the treatment process or the mechanisms that had produced the disequilibrium. When the therapist did not assume this stance, the patient was likely to discontinue treatment, as illustrated by Ms. D. and Ms. E.

The intermittent individual treatment strategy deserves further examination. Ordinarily, group therapists wish to have patients bring their conflicts into the group and are reluctant to diffuse the treatment relationships by siphoning off affect into individual sessions. For several of these weakly engaged patients the dyadic sessions seem to have been crucial to their continuation in group treatment. The therapist appeared to serve as a selfobject, available to meet the patient's needs. A working alliance between therapist and patient had not developed. Instead, the therapist functioned as a selfobject helping restore the patients' inner equilibrium and firming the damaged and fragmenting self. The descriptions of the family crises could not be understood by the patient as allusions to the group situation, either as transferences or as an aspect of the group reality, and the therapeutic work had to proceed in the arena available to the patient. In essence the patients were unable to utilize traditional transference interpretations, but instead they needed the therapist to serve as a selfobject. From this perspective the therapist's empathic connection temporarily assisted the patient in reestablishing a cohesive sense of self and remaining in treatment.

HIGHLY ENGAGED PATIENTS

Three patients (two women and one man) in the subgroup of highly engaged individuals seemed to be benefiting from participation in their group, and the therapy was proceeding at an expectable rate. Yet all three terminated from group rather abruptly. They thereby present an opportunity to explore the factors contributing to this unanticipated behavior.

These patients were in their middle years and had apparently successful work careers. The women had professional careers which they felt to be satisfactory and successful. Both were divorced, had raised children into adolescence and beyond, and both wished to learn more about their *patterned* behavior of lack of success in finding a new mate. They both seemed to attract men and then have the relationships fall apart. They were not only puzzled by these patterns, but they wished to gain an understanding of their own contributions to the problem. The man, a partner in a successful business, was referred by his marital therapist because of his complaint that he could not feel emotions with his wife. In the preparatory interviews he revealed his secret that he was in the midst of an extended affair and only wanted individual treatment. In a fairly brief period, he terminated the affair and then expressed interest in learning more about how he managed feelings. He saw the group as a good place to learn. The three individuals were all bright and could articulate their therapeutic goals. They seemed to have a capacity to form at least minimally satisfactory relationships, but found that their ability to form long-lasting and genuine intimacy to be short-circuited, a process that perplexed them.

Dr. L. was referred for group psychotherapy following three years of individual therapy. She was primarily concerned with trying to gain a better understanding of her attraction to men whom she felt were stupid and incompetent. She fluctuated in her stance of blaming men to wondering about her role in provoking them. Dr. L. attended group for ten months, where her patterns of controlling, demanding behaviors emerged and were available for exploration. Her tendency to withdraw, whenever she was confronted, was also scrutinized. The context of her quitting was instructive. About six weeks before Dr. L. dropped out, a man successfully terminated his treatment. Dr. L. had missed several days of work because of flu, but she came to the man's final meeting in order to say goodbye. During the meeting she coughed almost continually, and finally chose to leave the meeting early. Dr. L.'s decision to attend at all suggested that she had an increased capacity to relate to a man and could tolerate and work with the painful feelings associated with goodbyes.

The group response to the termination was tumultuous. It was as if this man was the glue that had been holding the group together. Members began arriving late, missing sessions, and/or threatening to stop treatment altogether, although none actually did so. All of this was addressed as a focal issue, and the members eventually were able to use the experience therapeutically.

In this context, Dr. L. specifically examined her compulsive care-taking as a way of remaining in control and above her feelings. She began to face the loneliness underneath the surface and her belief that the group tumult meant that she would be unable to obtain the responses she desired. In this process, she reported a dream fragment. She was shopping for doctors; she came to see the therapist; she felt disappointed. The remainder of the dream was obscure. Her associations were to disappointment with the group and worries that new members would interfere further with chances for intimacy. In the session prior to the therapist's vacation, Dr. L. commented that she was thinking of stopping. She brought up the fact that her bill was delinquent and wondered if that was a manifestation of her disappointment with the therapy. Dr. L. criticized the therapist for not making the group "better."

Following the one-week vacation, Dr. L. sat silently until very near the end of the meeting when she announced that this would be her last session. Considerable pressure was brought to bear, and she agreed to attend for another month, but she quit following the next meeting. She felt that the therapist was incompetent, which seemed to mean that he would not respond the way she wished. The therapist felt that Dr. L.'s termination followed from a feeling that the therapist's "nonresponsiveness" was a narcissistic injury which was added to the sense of loss of safety within the group. Flight was her characteristic solution.

In the follow-up interview Dr. L. responded to the question inquiring about reasons for joining the group by stating, without elaboration, that her individual therapist had recommended it, as if she had not made a choice herself. She felt she had learned that she could not control herself or others as much as she thought and, indeed, was affected by others' caring and/or anger. Dr. L. said the group had helped her become more compassionate, but she was anxious prior to each meeting. She was angry that she had not been told to remain in the group longer, but recognized she had chosen to leave. Dr. L. added that she felt she was in the wrong group. Members were "sick" and she did not feel that way about herself. She wished to be with people who were more like her, namely, those who were aware of feminist issues and were struggling with relationships. Indeed, Dr. L. reported that she subsequently joined and was pleased with belonging to a women's support group.

Dr. L. seemed to have actively engaged in the group treatment with neurotic level conflicts. However, the combination of another patient's termination, the resultant group turmoil, and the therapist's vacation, evoked a regression, and brought forth a wish for more mirroring, both from the therapist and from the group. In addition Dr. L. seemed frightened by seeing the "sick" parts of others (most likely unacceptable aspects of herself), which took place in the context of the group not serving as a viable selfobject. Dr. L. "solved" her problem by extricating herself from the treatment and locating a group that was "more like her." In this respect the apparent twinship transference was a defensive warding off exposure of earlier deficits in the self.

Mr. M. had been partly described above. His course of treatment, over eight months, was essentially unremarkable, and he seemed to be making excellent progress. He was examining his considerable discomfort to warm and caring exchanges directed to him. Several weeks before terminating, Mr. M. told the group of a dream told to him by his son. In the dream his son had portrayed Mr. M. as nonresponsive and unemotional in the face of an accident in which several family members were injured. Mr. M. used this dream to convey his expanding awareness of how others saw him. The following week he reported how he had been firm but not punitive with his son regarding his completing homework. Afterwards the two of them had spent a half-hour thoroughly enjoying one another. Mr. M. cried as he talked about how meaningful this experience was for him.

Two weeks later Mr. M. took a week's vacation and never returned to the group. He left messages that he would miss sessions, and when the therapist called to inquire what was happening, he cited a work schedule conflict as the reason for his not returning. He did not say goodbye to the other members. The therapist's initial tentative formulation attempting to account for Mr. M.'s leaving centered around the increasing intimacy both out and inside the group which frightened him, and shame about crying and exposing strong feelings. But the departure was rather perplexing.

In the follow-up interview, Mr. M. discussed his experiences in considerable detail. He explained that he was trying to get in touch with and practice sharing his feelings. He had come to recognize how he put up walls by establishing control and the group members had seen what he was doing. "I came to see it as others saw myself, and this was astounding." Mr. M. stated that he had gained insight but not change. He could not be specific about why he had left when he did, merely noting that he felt burned out with therapy. However, like Dr. L., he commented about the tensions within the group. "One person left and then another said he was going to leave and didn't; then he changed his mind again. It was beginning to disintegrate. It was not cohesive." These responses are very similar to those of Dr. L., and although rather vague, they are supportive of the notion that the selfobject functions of the group-as-a-whole serve to stabilize the self even for the more developmentally advanced members. Recognition of the significance of these events to all members might have enabled the therapist to more persistently interpret responses to the changes, help members stabilize their sense of inner disruption, and prevent drop-outs.

The third patient, Ms. N., had undergone several periods of therapy in the past. She was a divorced woman who had a successful professional career as an educator. She had been referred by a therapist–friend specifically for group psychotherapy. In the screening interviews Ms. N. described with great clarity her pattern of becoming intensely involved with a man, leading to engagement on three occasions, and then watching the relationship deteriorate prior to marriage. Ms. N. seemed partially aware that she compulsively took care of others. One of the precipitants for seeking treatment was her termination of her engagement to a severely disabled man. She had minimized his disability until shortly before the wedding date when she suddenly became very anxious that she would spend her life caring for his physical needs. A second precipitant was the departure for college of her youngest child, which she said evoked an "empty nest" syndrome.

Not unexpectedly, Ms. N. assumed a caretaker role, and at the same time talked about needing to change because her children were gone. Progress was signaled by her direct challenge of the therapist when she felt he had not paid attention to her. Ms. N. did this with considerable pride, recognizing that she no longer was as self-sacrificing and in the caretaking, compliant mode as she had been. The others joined her in recognizing this achievement. In the third month of treatment Ms. N. missed a meeting to do an errand for a friend. Her "explanation" was merely that she should be charged for the missed meeting, in conformity with the group contract. Unfortunately neither the therapist nor the members pursued this matter. Two weeks later Ms. N. abruptly announced she was terminating in order to be home with her daughter during the summer vacation. In the brief time available to explore this decision, Ms. N. realized that she could remain in treatment and still be with her daughter, but she nevertheless decided to stop. There was no overt clue from the process notes deepening the understanding of this abrupt termination.

In the follow-up interview Ms. N. reported that her initial anxiety and depression had abated in the four months of treatment and she decided to quit. She had begun to learn about her interpersonal problems: "I was good at offering other people support, but not good at reaching out and asking others to support me. I didn't reveal much of myself, only the problem. I'm more closed than I thought." She continued: "My basic way of dealing with things is to allow things to happen to me. I let others take the lead." Ms. N. was frightened by the possibility she would be like a member who had been in the group for five years. She was unable to clarify precisely why she stopped, but commented about the group process: "We seldom went for two weeks without having a new member; therefore we didn't have continuity." [This was not an accurate perception of the group events.] Ms. N. reported that she would continue to work on her problems in a group setting by intermittently participating in weekend encounter groups.

From the perspective of self psychology this patient controlled situations through her caretaking. This enabled her to feel accepted and simultaneously to strengthen a fragile self by receiving recognition for her behavior. In fact it seems that she had assumed this role, which resulted in a feeling of greater self cohesion and a diminution of symptoms. However, further involvement, perhaps like Dr. L., carried with it the potential for loss of self in an extended treatment. Dropping out protected her from that "fate."

DISCUSSION

What can be learned from these clinical experiences to further understanding of group processes and the individual's participation in group psychotherapy? Scheidlinger (1984), utilizing traditional psychoanalytic concepts, describes patients' reactions to belonging to a group as a "universal human need to belong, to establish a state of psychological unity with others, represents a covert wish for restoring an earlier state of unconflicted well-being inherent in the exclusive union with the mother" (p. 6). The maternal object functions are need satisfying. At the earliest developmental levels, the maternal object is a part object, and at later stages of development she is experienced as a whole object (Scheidlinger, 1968). Similarly, in the early developmental phases, or under regressive forces, the "group members are believed to perceive people in an undifferentiated way . . . as objects are sought out primarily for the purpose of relieving tension" (Scheidlinger, 1968). These formulations are very similar to those of the psychology of the self, but differences appear in understanding the meaning of the observations and the schema for the individual's future development.

Self psychologists conceptualize these processes as selfobject needs. The object is experienced as part of the self and is to function to help maintain a sense of inner stability and continuity. These selfobject needs mature along their own developmental track and do not develop into object relations as formulated in the traditional psychoanalytic framework. In this paradigm transferences are not seen as a product of conflict, but rather as an effort to establish a particular kind of relationship—the selfobject tie—from which the patient will be provided a second chance to grow (Ornstein, 1974). Yet if self psychology is a more generalizable psychology it should clarify some clinical situations that did not readily fit within other theoretical frameworks.

The experiences of the three patients categorized as highly engaged are particularly instructive, since their terminations appear to represent a failure of the selfobject function of the group-as-a-whole. Previous authors (Stone and Gustafson, 1982) have suggested that entry into a group is fraught with anxieties regarding the potential for narcissistic injury. A considerable part of the early interactions can be conceptualized as efforts to establish a safe environment. This could be formulated at a level of adequate mirroring or of a merger with an idealized selfobject. These developmental levels would fit with the patient's particular deficit in the cohesion of the self, and the group, therefore, would provide an excellent arena in which these problems could be recreated and then worked through, via transmuting internalization. For other individuals, with a less precarious self, the dynamics of joining a group would reawaken some of these issues and might provide opportunities for further strengthening the self, but would not be the primary treatment focus. With the establishment of a more developmentally advanced group these issues would move into the background and conflicts involving separate individuals, such as oedipal level conflicts, would move into the foreground.

These three highly engaged individuals all seemed to be strongly reacting to the loss of a sense of the group as a reliable selfobject. Similar responses to group instability from an object relations perspective have been described by Hawkins (1986). Each person commented about their sense of loss of continuity and cohesion and expressed feelings that the group was disintegrating. Most likely the fairly apparent gains these patients made took place against the backdrop of a cohesive group, but continued growth was thwarted by the change in the group environment supporting the self.

It could be argued that underneath a surface adjustment these patients' apparent success was a vulnerable self that could not maintain a sense of cohesion in the face of the group disruptions. That seems most likely with Ms. N., but may be valid for the others as well (Horwitz, 1984). As Menninger (1959) noted three decades ago, the group-as-a-whole concerns and core issues must be taken into account in examining dropouts. Scheidlinger's (1955) exploration of identification in groups also is relevant here: "not unlike the child's preoedipal identifications with the maternal figure, the collective perception of unity—the forcefulness of the group become sources of ego support" (p. 671). If the perception of unity is disrupted, the group may no longer be experienced as a place where affects can be calmed and/or needs for calming met. Since these patients' terminations were unexpected, the main focus of attention should have been the group, and the therapist's efforts should have been focused on reestablishing the group equilibrium and restoring a sense of safety.

What remains to be answered is the question, so thoughtfully raised by Scheidlinger (1984), of how to measure the relative balance of each of the two major forces; that is, those emanating from the individual and those from the group. One distinct possibility is that the regressive pressures in the group may have overridden a fairly cohesive self and led to the patients' experience of a potential for internal disruption.

Two patients, who terminated from their treatment groups, continued in their quest to use groups as a therapeutic vehicle. These efforts could be viewed from the perspective of the psychology of the self as efforts to maintain an inner equilibrium through a search for a selfobject. Dr. L. sought out a support group that would serve as a twinship transference, and Ms. M. planned to join a series of encounter groups which would not threaten the more precarious self with the potential loss through merger.

At the other end of the continuum are those patients whom we accept into our groups and whom we know represent a high risk to discontinue. These patients, often diagnosed in the narcissistic –borderline spectrum, are particularly vulnerable to injuries to the self and often erect many "difficult" defenses against therapeutic engagement (Pines, 1975). They may respond to the group experiences as real and not containing vestiges from the past. Yet these patients generally develop selfobject ties to the therapist and the group-as-a-whole. Only when there has been a disruption of such relationships, followed by an effort on the patient's part to restore his or her inner equilibrium, does it become apparent that a selfobject transference had been activated.

Some of these individuals come with readymade magical transferences which are doomed to disappointment. This seems to be the most likely explanation for understanding the woman (Ms. B.) who angrily quit after two sessions. The therapist, during the screening sessions, did not appreciate the intensity of the magical expectations, and may have inadvertently supported them by admitting her into the group. The angry quitting was not only an act of retaliation, but was an attempt to restore the patient's precarious equilibrium.

Of considerable interest are those patients who remained, but had been predicted to do poorly. The recommendations in the literature for combining individual with group treatment seems validated by this small sample (Horwitz, 1980; Wong, 1980; Rutan and Alonso, 1982). However, the cases bring into focus several clinical and theoretical relevant points. The patients who were in ongoing concurrent treatment were not at a stage where they could utilize interpretation. Instead the therapist had to rely on the tie between the patient and himself to strongly reenforce continuation in the group. This was successful, until, as illustrated by Ms. C., the therapist changed his stance and no longer encouraged continued attendance. Patients in treatment with nondirective analytic therapists are likely to quit under similar circumstances when a more directive intervention might help them remain (Ms. E.). At a later time, when there had been therapeutic growth, these patients might be able to examine the precipitants for wishing to leave. They would no longer require the therapist's directive interventions, but could work within an exploratory–interpretive framework.

Two patients signaled their defenses against awareness of the transference (Gill, 1982) by seeking intermittent individual sessions. In these meetings the allusions to the group setting were clear, but could not be utilized by the patient. Thus the chief process that sustained the patient most likely was the acceptance by the therapist of the individual's need to discuss family crises. This act probably restored the disrupted selfobject tie to the therapist. The usual clinical recommendation is for therapists to resist seeing patients individually because such meetings will diffuse the transferences. For patients with severe character pathology such a recommendation seems counterproductive.

In conclusion, one further observation emerges from this study. The group therapist, as has been frequently observed, is also vulnerable to narcissistic injury. This appears to be greater in groups than in individual treatment. Therapists respond to patients' disruptive behaviors as if their group was being destroyed, and as a result they are likely to experience countertransferential responses that are difficult to contain. The highly engaged patients' abrupt terminations seemed especially perplexing, and their behavior evoked a good deal of self-examination and self-doubt in the therapist. There is no antidote to this except increased self-understanding and increased understanding of the patient and of the group processes. Yet almost all patients seemed to have gained something valuable from their group experience. Such gains should not be discounted in the essential process of reviewing our work, and we need to recognize that we are not capable of preventing all such responses. We certainly could benefit from more systematic follow-up evaluations, but we will always be faced with the complexities of human interaction that prevent our fully knowing the inner world of our patients.

REFERENCES

Bacal, H. (1985), Object relations in the group from the perspective of self psychology. *Internat. J. Group Psychother.*, 35:483–501.

Gill, M. M. (1982), *Analysis of Transference*, Vol. 1. New York: International Universities Press.

Harwood, I. (1986), The need for optimal, available caretakers: Moving towards extended selfobject experience. *Group Anal.*, 19:343–360.

Hawkins, D. M. (1986), Understanding reactions to group instability in psychotherapy groups. *Internat. J. Group Psychother.*, 36:195–203.

Horwitz, L. (1980), Group psychotherapy for borderline and narcissistic patients. *Bull. Menn. Clinic*, 44:181–200.

——— (1984), The self in groups. *Internat. J. Group Psychother.*, 34:519–540.

Kohut, H. (1977), *The Restoration of the Self*. New York: International Universities Press.

——— (1984), *How Does Analysis Cure?* Chicago: University of Chicago Press.

Menninger, R. W. (1959), Observations on absences of member patients in group psychotherapy. *Internat. J. Group Psychother.*, 9:195–203.

Ornstein, A. (1974), The dread to repeat and the new beginning—A contribution to the psychoanalysis of the narcissistic personality disorder. *The Annual of Psychoanalysis*, 2:231–248. New York: International Universities Press.

Pines, M. (1975), Group therapy with "difficult" patients. In: *Group Therapy 1975: An Overview*, ed. R. Wolberg & M. L. Aronson. New York: Stratton Intercontinental.

Roback, H. B., & Smith, M. (1987), Patient attrition in dynamically oriented treatment groups. *Amer. J. Psychiat.* 144:426–431.

Rutan, J. S., & Alonso, A. (1982), Group therapy, individual therapy, or both? *Internat. J. Group Psychother.*, 32:267–282.

Scheidlinger, S. (1955), The concept of identification in group psychotherapy. *Amer. J. Psychother.*, 9:661–672.

——— (1966), The concept of empathy in group psychotherapy. *Internat. J. Group Psychother.*, 16:413–424.

——— (1968), The concept of regression in group psychotherapy. *Internat. J. Group Psychother.*, 18:3–20.

——— (1974), On the concept of the "mother group." *Internat. J. Group Psychother.*, 24:417–428.

——— (1984), Individual and group psychology—are they opposed. *Group*, 8:3–11.

Schwartzman, G. (1984), The use of the group as selfobject. *Internat. J. Group Psychother.*, 34:229–241.

Stone, W. N. (1985), The curative fantasy in group psychotherapy. *Group*, 9:3–14.

——— Gustafson, J. P. (1982), Technique in group psychotherapy of narcissistic and borderline patients. *Internat. J. Group Psychother.*, 32:29–47.

——— Rutan, J. S. (1984), Duration of treatment in group psychotherapy. *Internat. J. Group Psychother.*, 34:93–109.

——— Whitman, R. M. (1980), Observations on empathy in group psychotherapy. In: *Group and Family Therapy: 1980*, ed. L. R. Wolberg & M. L. Aronson. New York: Brunner/Mazel.

Wolf, E. S. (1986), Selfobject transferences: An overview. *Psychiat. Annals*, 11:491–493.

Wong, N. (1980), Combined group and individual treatment of borderline and narcissistic patients: Heterogeneous versus homogeneous groups. *Internat. J. Group Psychother.*, 30:389–404.

Chapter 20

Primate Ethology and Group Dynamics

K. ROY MACKENZIE, M.D., F.R.C.P.(C), and JAMES L. KENNEDY, M.D.

Interest in the biological understanding of disordered behavior has resulted in significant advances in the treatment of major psychiatric syndromes. At the same time, the energy and creativity devoted to such research has bypassed a compelling field of equally rigorous biological investigation. Ethology is the study of animal behavior under natural conditions. Basic interactional and social group behaviors have been identified for many species. Bowlby (1988) has reviewed the importance of this approach for understanding both human development and psychopathological states, commenting: "These research programs [ethology] are as firmly rooted in biology as are those of the physiological psychiatrists who have improperly kidnapped the label 'biological psychiatry' " (p. 2).

Ethological field studies of primates document a variety of common behavioral characteristics. The stereotypic nature of these suggests the effect of biologically determined mechanisms. Often such behavioral patterns are apparent at a young age, long before they are functionally required. Animals reared in isolation, without social cues, will still exhibit rudimentary social behavior. Crook (1981) comments:

> [C]omplex group processes result from relationships between individuals established through repeated sequences of interactions. These interactions are often quite characteristic of species and are clearly rooted in genetically inherited dispositions that lead to the activation of performance mechanisms in defined motivational circumstances. Relationships arise through social learning that leads to interactions occurring with motivational rewards ultimately of biostrategic (i.e., reproductive)

357

significance between particular individuals rather than between others. The higher-order relationship and group behaviors are thus based upon the maintenance of elaborately learned traditional programs of behavior within which the units of expression are often highly characteristic of the species concerned [p. 91].

Cheney, Seyfarth, and Smuts (1986) present evidence to support the theory that primate cognitive capacity is more highly developed in regard to social behavior than to nonsocial tasks. "[T]his argument suggests that during primate evolution group life exerted strong selective pressure on the ability to form complex associations, reason by analogy, make transitive inferences, and predict the behavior of fellow group members" (p. 234). Many social behaviors of the higher nonhuman primates, chimpanzees and gorillas, are recognizable for their similarities to human behavior.

Contemporary studies of genetic composition utilize powerful methods for identifying and comparing DNA sequences. Humans belong to the primate order which is primarily composed of the monkeys and apes. Within this order, the hominoids, including humans, chimps, and gorillas, show high similarity in their genetic material. Examination of the chromosome banding patterns among these species reveals remarkable similarities. The differences can be accounted for in terms of a relatively small number of inversions or fusions of chromosomal fragments. If the pieces are reshuffled to a common arrangement, the banding patterns are virtually 100 percent homologous (Yunis and Prakash, 1982). Analysis of the DNA nucleotide sequence by hybridization techniques (Sibley and Ahlquist, 1987) indicates that chimpanzees and humans have a 98.4 percent correspondence in DNA sequences. Gorillas and humans have 97.7 percent correspondence. Baboons, in a different family within the primate order, share 93 percent correspondence in DNA sequence with humans. A spectrum of similarity can be created by noting that two separate species of chimpanzee (*Pan paniscus* and *Pan troglodytes*) have 99.3 percent DNA sequence congruence.

These observations, combined with analyses of various protein amino acid sequences, all lead to the conclusion that humans, chimps, and gorillas arose from a common ancestor 6 to 8 million years ago. There is little evidence for major qualitative differences in the structure of proteins among the hominoids. It is quite conceivable that the differences among these species are due to differences in gene regulation, as opposed to gene products. If certain behavior patterns in humans are under genetic control, one might hypothesize that these behaviors arose from a behavioral ancestry common to chimps, gorillas, and humans. The similarity of behavioral patterns among the hominoids may be underrecognized and underexploited as a means to understanding normal and pathological behavior in humans.

The set of social behaviors of interest for this chapter are those believed to be under substantial genetic control. The actual emotional "language" appears to be relatively simple. However, even a limited set of basic communication patterns may be utilized in complex combinations. The existence of a "hard wired" system for communication of interpersonal intent may be considered a necessary evolutionary development to support higher order socialization processes (Plutchik, 1980). In humans, cultural expectations may lead to a masking of certain affect states and the process of attributing meaning to interpersonal events will be influenced by prior life experience.

Studies of human facial behavior indicate a set of basic emotional display patterns which are used universally and are unaffected by cultural or social influences. These patterns include those demonstrating happiness, sadness, anger, fear, surprise, interest, and disgust (Darwin, 1872; Ekman, Friesen, and Ellsworth, 1972). Specific neuromuscular patterns have been identified which control these displays of emotion. The same facial mechanisms are found among other members of the primate species, with similarities throughout most of the group-living mammals.

Inherited propensities for behavioral patterns can be studied by examination of identical twins. The Minnesota study of identical twins reared apart indicates correlations ranging from 0.39 to 0.58 in primary personality dimensions such as social closeness, stress reaction, and aggression (Tellegen, Lykken, Bouchard, Wilcox, Segal, and Rich, 1988). A study of childhood shyness reports: "2-year-old children who were extreme in the display of either behavioral restraint or spontaneity in unfamiliar contexts revealed that by 7 years of age a majority of the restrained group were quiet and socially avoidant with unfamiliar children and adults whereas a majority of the more spontaneous children were talkative and interactive" (Kagan, Reznick, and Snidman, 1988, p. 167).

D. Stern (1985) has identified childhood behavioral dimensions such as irritability, arousal, and affiliative behaviors. This increasing body of knowledge supports the notion that many aspects of human interaction are rooted in the operation of biologically determined behavioral sequences. Wilson (1978) summarizes: "behavioral genes . . . probably influence the ranges of form and intensity of emotional responses, the thresholds of arousals, the readiness to learn certain stimuli as opposed to others, and the pattern of sensitivity to additional environmental factors that point cultural evolution in one direction as opposed to another" (p. 47).

The biologic components which have been identified here represent basic interactional patterns. Any comparative study of humans with other primates must take into account the importance of language development. In the human an expanded repertoire of symbolic meanings and associational connections results in a more complex process by which meaning is derived from social experience. To view this as superimposed upon biologically controlled communication mechanisms does not in any way detract from an appreciation of the magnificence of the mind. Hinde (1983) suggests that it is precisely because the relationships and social structure of the higher primates are less complex than the human case that they provide basic principles in the dynamics of social behavior.

SOCIAL BEHAVIOR OF HIGHER PRIMATES

The material in this section is drawn from the expanding field of current ethological investigations (Eibl-Eibesfeldt, 1975; Bowlby, 1982; Hinde, 1983; Smuts, Cheney, Seyfarth, Wrangham, and Struhsaker, 1987). Much of the original primate social behavior data was based upon the study of primates held in captivity and therefore reflected the impact of incarceration and social isolation. Ethologists describe behavior at two levels of complexity. The first of these deals with specific brief communicative acts of a sterotypic nature which reflect genetically determined neuromuscular activation mechanisms. The second level describes how these basic units of behavior are utilized in complex social relationships. This higher order perspective is less sterotypic in nature and involves an awareness of the social system in which it is occurring.

Because of the tendency to anthropomorphize, discussions of animal behavior may selectively focus on single dimensions which resemble human behavior. Each species shows its own unique combination of behavioral characteristics, and within a species, different subpopulations may vary significantly. It is believed that at least some of these differences are mediated by genetic differences. Ethological studies indicate that a social system requires the presence of mechanisms for dealing with two fundamental functions: cooperation and competition. Walters and Seyfarth (1986) state:

> Most primates live in groups. There are numerous potential benefits in sociality, including increased protection from predators, cooperative

events for food resources, and collective rearing of offspring. Group life also provides an opportunity for long-term cooperative relationships. At the same time, however, sociality entails a number of costs, since group-living animals must compete with one another for scarce resources such as food, water, and mates. Life within a primate group is thus delicately balanced between competition and cooperation [p. 306].

Mother–Child Bonding

The most powerful affiliative behaviors occur between mother and child. Bowlby's (1982) studies of the primate mother–infant "behavioral system" reveals the complex and reciprocal nature of this early experience of communicating. An interactive process occurs in which the infant smile functions as an elicitor of maternal response and in which the mother's positive facial expression provides reassurance to the infant. Thus, a subtle, visually mediated process consolidates maternal–child bonding. This is reinforced by the quieting effects of touching and skin contact in addition to feeding. Childhood temperamental traits interact with the nurturing environment. This bonding process is quite time sensitive. When initiated early in the neonatal period it results in the development of a strong and enduring mother–child bond. However, the longer the delay after birth, the weaker the bonding effects. As the infant matures the mother systematically promotes independence. This releases the adult animal for other social tasks including further reproduction.

These themes of affiliation and autonomy intertwine to explain the social attachment process and the "secure base effect." A child who is confident of the availability of protection, help, and reassurance is thereby freed to explore the environment and test independence. In the absence of this, primates (including humans) show two major categories of pathological bonding. "Anxious resistant attachment" is characterized by separation anxiety, clinging behavior, and reluctance to explore. "Anxious avoidant attachment" is reflected in compulsive self-sufficiency or persistently angry and delinquent behavior. Attachment patterns appear to be established early and to become more entrenched with time.

Interruption of early nurturing relationships produces a sterotypic response pattern, beginning with protest, followed by despair and sadness, eventually leading to a state of withdrawal and nonresponsiveness. These human and nonhuman primate responses are evident at all ages but are most marked in the young. They may be lessened in severity when other animals, usually close kin, function as maternal surrogates. In chimps, the withdrawal patterns associated with severance of the maternal–child relationship is associated with high infant mortality during the ensuing year (Goodall, 1986).

Affiliative Behaviors and Social Cooperation

Affiliative behaviors are signaled by close physical contact as well as spatial proximity. Greeting rituals of embracing and lip-smacking signal interactional safety. Grooming is an important mechanism for consolidating interpersonal bonds. Animals which are closely affiliated spend a considerable portion of time carefully searching each other's coats for insects and lice, particularly in areas which are inaccessible to the recipient. While this behavior has a "preventive health care" component, it also serves an essential bonding function. Grooming behavior is associated with lower levels of aggression. More dominant animals receive more grooming. This forms a link between affiliative behaviors and the maintenance of a dominance hierarchy. Kinship has an important influence on affiliative behaviors. The closer the blood ties, the more intense the bonds.

Another important dimension has to do with the differences between species in regard to which sex migrates from the tribe of rearing. These innate patterns have an effect upon affiliative interactions within the group. Same-sex animals who remain in the home tribe demonstrate greater affiliative bonding and higher dominance status. Migrant animals have their main affiliation bonds with opposite-sex animals except those of their own group which have migrated with them. For example, chimpanzee females migrate to other tribes when they reach late adolescence, and male chimpanzees left in the tribe of origin demonstrate a high degree of bonding behavior. Gorilla males migrate and gorilla tribes are characterized by high levels of female affiliation. These examples illustrate some of the complexity involved in understanding primate social behavior.

The higher primates demonstrate varying patterns regarding stability in choice of sexual partners. In chimps there is relative promiscuity with a broad mixing of partners. However, as a female approaches ovulation, dominant males have higher priority and frequency. giving them greater procreative success. Gorilla groups consist of a single alpha male who controls sexual access. Adolescent males are driven from the troop as they mature. In general, affiliative grooming patterns parallel sexual access priorities. Across species of primates, the strength of bonding in specific adult pairs varies considerably.

Primates also demonstrate altruistic behavior, technically defined in the ethology literature as an animal performing an act which clearly puts him or her at risk in order to assist another animal. Such acts reveal the power of affiliative bonds. This has presumably evolved to protect genetically related individuals, who tend to receive more of the altruistic acts (Hamilton, 1964).

Aggressive Behaviors and the Dominance Hierarchy

Aggression occurs at a higher level of intensity with male animals and is more likely to result in physical harm, although this is not common. Most injuries occur during circumstances involving animals of different tribes. Female primates also show considerable dominance aggression. There is a common misconception that aggressive behaviors are more characteristic of males. Male patterns tend to be episodic and more intense, while female patterns are more frequent but of lower intensity. The older literature reflects a selective attention to high-volume episodes rather than the actual frequency of aggressive behaviors. Females may fight fiercely if the stakes are high; for example, if offspring are threatened. Females also tend to show more aggressive behaviors in the absence of males.

All primates demonstrate a well-developed system for dominance behavior. The threat display of a dominant animal includes such components as a hard stare, teeth baring, piloerection, heightened posture, chest thumping, and in the case of chimps, stamping, branch-waving, and "arm over" charges. All of these behaviors are familiar to parents of young boys.

There are also sterotypic patterns indicating submissive behavior. These include a sheepish "appeasement grin," crouching posture, lowered gaze, and begging hand gestures. These submission display behaviors quickly bring aggressive encounters to a halt by signaling who is the winner. Submissive behaviors have a vital social function in preventing the escalation of aggressive behavior. These interpersonal display behaviors signal dominance status and stabilize the social system, just as a salute demonstrates with fine distinction the command levels in the military.

Dominant and submissive behavioral displays are used to signal the "formal" dominance relationships. Maturity, size, and conditioning are critical ingredients in determining dominance contests between two animals. Aggressive and submissive display behavior is the principal mechanism for resolution of dyadic dominance contests. Severe fights and physical harm are the exception, although less dominant animals show greater anxiety in the presence of dominant animals. This is in contrast to acts involving animals outside the tribe where aggressive behavior may be fatal. A number of the reported cases of chimp infanticide appear to be associated with infants born of recently migrated females in which the question of paternity might be in doubt.

In the majority of primate species, all males rank higher than all females. This is most striking when there are dimorphic differences in physical build. In species where females more closely approach males in size, the dominance system is more sexually heterogeneous. Males appear to be more reactive to the dominance process. Dominance contests are more violent and there is greater jockeying for dominance rank. The introduction of a strange animal or other change in membership elicits a stronger ranking response from males than females. Dominance systems in females are clearly present but not as obvious. Female dominance hierarchies tend to be more stable over time. The gradient of the dominance hierarchy tends to be steeper in smaller tribes. In large tribes, "class" distinctions appear between high, middle, and low subgroups but with less rigid differences within each class (Hausfater, 1975).

Another feature of the dominance system is that of scapegoating. The process of "redirected threat" occurs particularly as a mechanism for diffusing aggression amongst high ranking animals. The loser of a dominance contest may become irritable and act aggressively toward an individual of lower rank. This mechanism serves to contain aggression amongst the most powerful animals where there is the most tension and where aggressive acts are likely to be more dangerous. The lowest ranking member of the group receives the greatest number of aggressive actions and demonstrates the highest levels of anxious behavior. Van Lawick-Goodall (1971) has also documented the tendancy of chimpanzee groups to expel members who are deviant from the norm. For example, a chimp with polio was ostracized by the group and finally abandoned.

Coalition Formation

The "formal" dominance relationships between individual animals are only one ingredient in establishing the "real" dominance hierarchy system within the social group. This depends on socialization processes where complex coalition negotiations play an important part. Males will actively seek support from other animals by utilizing begging gestures and appeasement grins which indicate a cooperative and nonhostile intent. Grooming behaviors, food sharing, and sexual preference may be used to consolidate coalitions that support dominance rank. Preferred female mates of a dominant male will rise more quickly within the female dominance system. Offspring of dominant parents are more likely themselves to be dominant, irrespective of their age or size. Kinship is thus a powerful mechanism for coalitions. Since these complex negotiation activities are dependent upon the relative role of the various participants in the larger system, they are inherently less stable and subject to change. A great deal of the social behavior can be seen as attempts to increase status through coalition negotiation and dominance displays.

The advantages of higher status are obvious. Dominant animals or groups of animals have better access to food resources. They have greater reproductive success and are able to provide greater protection for their young. At the same time, the ritualized nature of dominance contests and the social acceptance of the ranking system provides a component of social stability. This conservative function not only provides a degree of social predictability and security but also individual safety. One function of a dominant animal is to serve as a referee in preventing dominance contests from becoming too violent. Similarly, the inherent mechanisms for dominance decisions are highly dependent upon individual recognition and acceptance of the outcome of ranking contests. Thus dominance processes, while ostensibly a reflection of individual merit, in fact are part of a complex social control system.

In summary, affiliative bonds form the basis of social cooperation. This is a critical survival function in regards to acquisition of food, sexual access, rearing of young, protection from threat, and quieting anxiety. Affiliative patterns between adult animals are highly correlated with kinship. The strongest of these kinship links are based on innate mother–child bonding mechanisms. Grooming behaviors serve as an important mechanism for reinforcing affiliation. The dominance hierarchy is largely maintained through threat and submission displays. Redirected aggression to low dominance animals appears to serve as a diffuser of dangerous aggression among high ranking animals. Affiliative behaviors interact with dominance behaviors in creating mechanisms for coalition formation. Coalitions and negotiations determine the real outcome of dominance competition and serve as a stabilizing group force. These processes account for many features of the social structure.

RELEVANCE TO PSYCHOTHERAPY GROUPS

The intent of this section is to apply some of these findings from the higher primate social behavior literature to psychotherapy groups (Kennedy and MacKenzie, 1986; MacKenzie, 1990). Features reflecting social behavioral predispositions will be identified. The therapist may find that these ideas offer an additional perspective for understanding group events. However, the direct application of this material in making therapeutic decisions is not yet warranted.

In higher primates, kinship bonds have a stabilizing effect on social organization. This is such a pervasive primate phenomenon that it raises a question as to the appropriateness of focusing therapeutically on the individual. Even family systems approaches generally deal only with the nuclear family. While there are reports of extended family network approaches, these tend to be the exception, not the rule. The extended kinship group has greater depth of both support and tension release opportunities as well as intergenerational normative expectations. Western culture has tended to move away from these traditions, perhaps to its detriment.

The criticism might be offered that therapy groups do not provide a social environment based on kinship ties as found in higher primate societies. However, time spent closeted together in early sessions results in increasing levels of trust and a sense of belonging. The emphasis in therapy groups on serious personal topics stimulates a recreation of family of origin issues and "turns on" old response patterns. Thus, the therapy group eventually comes to resemble more closely a family structure, but in this case a composite structure based on the original families of all the members.

Numerous authors have identified stages of group development which appear in a variety of human social systems (Tuckman, 1965; Beck, 1974; MacKenzie and Livesley, 1983). The "stage hypothesis" generated from this work provides a description of mechanisms by which a cluster of diverse personalities can be transformed into a social system. The ability to form a cohesive and functional group of individuals constitutes an important survival resource. The following discussion centers primarily around the first two stages of group development. These two stages are readily observed and mastery of them is crucial to the development of an effective interactional therapeutic climate. A set of guidelines for recognizing these stages also helps the leader to more readily identify group regression. Regression is a predictable event at times of leader or membership change, when difficult members block the group progress, or when the stress of addressing individual psychopathology increases tension. At these times one sees the reemergence of phenomena characteristic of stages 1 and 2. Throughout this section we will refer back to the principal axes of cooperation and competition which have been defined in the primate literature.

Affiliation to the Group

Stage 1 has been termed the "engagement" stage. In this stage the task consists of forming a group which has a common purpose and which is perceived by the members to have value. The question of membership must be answered bilaterally. The individual must want to be a member and the group must accept the individual. In human groups, this stage is characterized by early self-disclosure of a limited nature which provides an opportunity for the members to recognize that there are similarities amongst them. Conflict is inhibited and a generally positive emotional tone is characteristic of the first stage.

These stage characteristics may be compared with those found in higher primate social groupings. "Lip-smacking" and "silent grin" facial displays are used as typical greeting rituals. These behaviors are drawn from the appeasement behavior categories. Van Hooff (1967) comments: "As a rule the posture facilitates nonhostile approach between the individuals and this may be achieved by an appeasing or reassuring effect on the partner. . . . The display may reflect a conflict between the tendency to flee and the tendency to approach" (p. 254).

McGrew (1972) noted that nursery school children when placed in newly formed groups demonstrated shyness and "nervous caution," accompanied by a spectrum of behaviors such as lowered head and avoidance of eye contact, which are characteristic of primate appeasement patterns. Similarly, studies of adult therapy groups reported by MacKenzie and Livesley (1983) indicate rising levels of interpersonal warmth and cohesion, coupled with low levels of conflict during initial sessions.

It may be hypothesized that if a social system is to become established, these rituals have an important function in facilitating social acceptance before the potentially disintegrating effects of conflict occur. Appeasement behaviors and greeting rituals dampen or delay the emergence of dominance conflict. In human groups, most emphasis has been placed upon verbal content themes emphasizing similarities and universality (e.g., "I didn't think anyone else could have such thoughts"; "it is a great relief to know I'm not the only one").

Such themes at the level of symbolic verbal interaction appear to be an extension of an underlying mechanism to appear nonthreatening. At the verbal level, the covert message is that because we share similar interests, experiences, or reactions, we can understand each other and therefore get along together. Such comments are of a general and global nature yet are interpreted as an indication of high similarity. The mechanism of allowing these assumptions to go unchallenged appears to achieve the same function as the greeting rituals expressed in chimpanzee facial and postural behavior. Such displays, at either the verbal or nonverbal level, indicate an adherence to rules of social behavior and thus indicate basic interactional safety.

MacKenzie and Livesley (1983) suggest that the task for the leader early in the group's life is to maintain an atmosphere in which there is low interpersonal threat and conflict and in which the cohesion-forming functions of affiliation behaviors can be maximized. This may include dampening of conflict themes, modeling empathic concern, promoting member-to-member interaction patterns, and ensuring that all members participate to some extent. Such an atmosphere could also be described as one in which there is a high frequency of "appeasement" behaviors. In primates, one analog of such an atmosphere is a high degree of grooming behavior and close physical proximity. A verbal analog of such behaviors is an emphasis upon commonly shared experiences, beliefs, and assumptions. It is interesting to speculate that therapy techniques such as closeness of seating, the use of exercises employing physical contact, and early marathon sessions may be reinforcing innate social affiliation mechanisms.

Conflict and Competition

The second stage of social system development is characterized by competition, conflict, and anger. This conflict or "differentiation" stage is also concerned with the clarification of group normative regulations about how the group should operate. Whereas the first stage dealt with issues of cooperation, the second stage deals with issues of competition. The recognition of differences among members generates a climate of confrontation and turmoil. The group task at this stage is to develop an effective mode of conflict resolution. A prolonged competitive and unyielding approach will result in group fragmentation.

Stage 2 provides a demonstration of dominance hierarchy formation. While it is true that group members are able to report dominance rankings at a very early point in the group's life (Buirski, 1980), there appears to be an implicit assumption that such issues will not be tested until the group has to some extent become cohesive. In the conflict stage, this process of differentiation becomes overt. In the higher primates, dominance issues are resolved on a dyadic basis in relationship to size, strength, and maturity. In the psychotherapy group, these dominance contests are waged primarily through verbal interaction, commonly taking the form of statements of opinion which are strongly justified. This verbal process may be accompanied by subtle or not so subtle nonverbal behaviors incorporating dominance and submission characteristics. The ranking function of these may at first go unnoticed.

The formation of a dominance hierarchy is a predictable process in normal group development. The inherent conservatism of a dominance hierarchy provides a stabilizing effect which lends support to the group system and allows energy to be redirected toward personal learning. The members can turn toward introspective work less preoccupied with competition between the leader and each other. In some ways it is paradoxical that a process which is based upon recognition of individual differences is at the same time incorporated into a ranking process which seems to bind the individual to a level in the social system.

While there are advantages to the dominance system, there are also problematic issues in its emergence in a therapy group. The extent of dominance contests can become damaging to the individual, especially if they are interpreted as personally rejecting or delivered with intent to harm. Members who are on the bottom of the dominance system are particularly susceptible to these effects. Yet, by the very nature of this process, if some are to be high, others must be low. Those members at the upper end may experience positive self-esteem effects, particularly if this is a unique position for them compared to outside social contexts. This idea of "winners and losers" will be repugnant to some democratically inclined therapists. However, the universal existence of this ranking process suggests that therapists need to be aware of the positive and negative implications.

A significant concern, for example, is that the gradient of the dominance hierarchy not be excessively steep. The amount of control and attack behavior directed toward those lower in the hierarchy could be deleterious, especially if lower ranking members view those higher in the system as having total and absolute authority. The group leader, as one at or near the top of the dominance hierarchy, will set an example regarding appropriate levels. A group based upon a more egalitarian posture is likely to allow greater individual development than one based on more authoritarian principles (Lewin, Lippitt, and White, 1939). The inherent conservatism of a dominance hierarchy may have beneficial stabilizing effects.

Undoubtedly, cultural expectations influence the nature of the dominance structure. It is useful to consider how culture-bound our therapeutic stance may be. Is it the role of therapy to promote social change or to enhance adaptation of the individual to social circumstances? Do people living in cultures where status levels are rigidly defined become less or more reactive to dominance issues in a therapy group? Should we be concerned with the appropriate use of appeasement behaviors as much as with assertion training? In the primate literature, appeasement serves a vital social function in defusing dominance aggression, so that it is unusual for dangerous fighting to occur. While it is beyond the scope of this chapter to address these issues in any depth, they are intertwined with a consideration of the social function of the dominance hierarchy.

By virtue of the role of designated leader, the therapist is assumed to have a high, initially probably the highest, dominance position. Challenge of leadership control and status is to be expected. If this is lacking it suggests that the differentiating process has been inhibited. One of the functions of the dominant animal in primate groups is to govern the level of violence inherent in dominance contests. Similarly, in therapy groups the leader has a crucial function in dampening the extent of interpersonal challenge and in facilitating its resolution. The expected outcome is that differences can be accepted and used in the learning process rather than being inhibited or denied. Thus, the leader's role might be to tolerate and nurture the negative atmosphere of the conflict stage while at the time actively working with it to further interpersonal learning.

MacKenzie and Livesley (1983) have described the importance of identifying differences of opinion as a mechanism for both clarifying personal positions as well as promoting conflict resolution. This concept of "differentiation" is inherent in the process of ranking which underlies the creation of the dominance hierarchy. Mastery of this stage is indicated when differences can be acknowledged, but also tolerated and used as the basis for further exploration.

High rank will foster an attitude of respect for the leader's skill and knowledge. It will allow the leader to function as a stabilizing force whose control of group process is acknowledged. This will provide system stability and a sense of safety. However, the power of rank can be abused. The high intrusiveness of a charismatic leader is associated with an increase in group casualties (Lieberman, Yalom, and Miles, 1973). Members may be drawn into more active or revealing participation than they can tolerate. At times, harm is produced because of a component of aggression or shaming in the therapist's behavior which is interpreted by a vulnerable patient as victimization. High leader control of group process is also associated with poorer outcome because it inhibits member activity.

In higher primate groups the dominant animal inhibits the activities of other animals. Almost immediately upon removal of the alpha male, other animals begin to show higher levels of aggression and lower levels of appeasement behaviors (Kummer, 1971). This suggests that the leadership behavior repertoire is present but not utilized. If these findings are translated into the group therapy context, one could say that self-actualizing tendencies may be inhibited by an overly controlling or dominant therapeutic style. This raises interesting questions regarding optimum therapist behavior. Recent work in individual therapy suggests that therapist clarification statements are generally more effective in promoting patient self-exploration than statements of confrontation or interpretation. However, the latter become effective if the patient is in an affectively open state before they are delivered (Winston, 1988). In summary, the power associated with the designated leader role places the therapist high on the dominance hierarchy. This position brings with it both advantages and liabilities, many of which are rooted in evolutionary mechanisms.

Scapegoating

In nonhuman primate groups, weak or abnormal individuals are at risk of being relegated to the lowest positions on the social ladder. Here they suffer the greatest number of contest losses, including difficulty in access to food supplies and sexual opportunities. When tension is elevated among high-ranking animals, irritability and aggression is frequently displaced onto animals in lower rankings. Thus, they receive the greatest number of "redirected threats." Similar phenomena can be identified in schoolchildren, where obesity, deformity, or racial difference may result in scapegoating phenomena.

In therapy groups, the scapegoating process is understood as a mechanism to contain hostile and aggressive impulses which threaten to disrupt the system (Wright, Hoffman, and Gore, 1988). It is hypothesized that the scapegoat serves as an absorptive sink for projection of avoided, negatively valued, and aggressive issues. By ganging up on the offending member, the group can become unified. For the group, therefore, the scapegoating process may be accompanied by a decrease in tension: "we all know now what the problem is"; and an increase in cohesion: "now we can all agree again." The marked use of such projective mechanisms indicates a group in a highly defended position. Such a state is inherently unstable since the logical solution, to get rid of the offender, also undercuts the defense and necessitates finding another locus for the affect.

The scapegoating process is particularly likely to occur in therapy groups during the second stage when confrontational identification of differences is at its height. This is the time when the ranking process is most active and tension between high-ranking group members will be most evident. Thus, deviant or low-ranking members are most at risk during this stage, when there is most polarization along the dominance axis. Frequently, the designated leader becomes the focus for confrontation at this point. In accordance with ideas developed originally by Freud (1921), this is sometimes conceptualized as an attack upon the father figure. Primate studies suggest that such events might be understood as one manifestation of the dominance process.

As Scheidlinger (1982) has argued, it is a misuse of the term *scapegoat* to refer to leadership challenge. Indeed the very opposite is the case. Scapegoating is more likely to occur when direct leader challenge is inhibited. Lewin et al.'s (1939) classical studies of leadership indicate that the authoritarian leadership style is more likely to be accompanied by scapegoating amongst members. This is explained as a displacement from reactions to the leader which are too threatening to be expressed directly. Such a rationale might be considered as one application of the primate phenomenon of "redirected threat" found when tension among high-ranking animals is elevated.

Not only weak and submissive group members may become the butt of the scapegoating process. Frequently the member who expresses deviant ideas draws upon himself the wrath of the members. Members who are most likely to do this tend to be impulsive and insensitive in their approach, yet quite intuitive at picking up the nuances of group process. They will identify in words issues which the rest of the group would rather avoid. By identifying potentially troublesome matters, they threaten the stability of the group system. Thus a resonance is set up between the actions of these "divergent" members and the implicit recognition by the others that the problem identification is accurate. The interactional pattern is completed by the use of projective mechanisms to "blame" the scapegoat for the group tension. This is an example of basic interactional behavior that is extended into symbolic constructs in the human. However, the end result is a similar displacement of affect.

The cohesion developed during the engagement stage constitutes an important sustaining factor during periods of increased conflict in the group. New members are at particular risk if introduced when the group is dealing with stage 2 issues. The difficulties the group is experiencing may be quickly displaced onto a new member, who is least acquainted with the support function which the older members will be able to recall. In a more general sense, any change in group composition will result in an intensification of the dominance ranking process. Thus, new members must always be considered at risk for adversive experiences which might lead to premature termination. This is in keeping with the clinical wisdom of admitting new members in twos or threes to provide support during the engagement process.

Low positions in the dominance hierarchy predispose to dysphoric states of depression and anxiety (Price, 1967). This is particularly the case if a loss of rank has occurred. The group context has power to heal diminished self-esteem, but in the reverse direction it may be severely damaging. In the Encounter Group study (Lieberman et al., 1973), members who were group casualties usually cited severe group attacks as a major factor. These were particularly upsetting if the therapist participated. When dominance issues are strongly expressed, the therapist should be prepared to modulate the effects if this is not adequately done by other group members.

Two simple intervention techniques are particularly helpful. Support directed toward the recipient will be useful since it indicates the availability and concern of the therapist. This may be an adequate response to allow the "victim" to integrate the experience. The therapist may need to actively intervene in order to control the strength of the scapegoating process; for example, by calling for a "time out," or directly requesting less intensity or a change of focus. In the heat of therapy, the therapist may take satisfaction from the idea that somewhere in the African bush a gorilla alpha male may be struggling with the same issues for the same reasons.

A more specific technique is to align with the "deviant" quality which is being attacked. By highlighting the value of a different approach or perception, the therapist is not only supporting the scapegoat, but also leading the way to a mechanism for resolving differences. This theoretical perspective also enables the leader to appreciate the activities of the scapegoat as a useful group contribution. The therapist can thus avoid an implicit alliance with the group criticism. Family therapists, in particular, will appreciate the paradoxical nature of such an aligning maneuver.

Coalition Formation

The array of higher primate coalition-forming techniques described in the first section are regularly observed in human social settings. Common gestures such as the salute or the begging hand are drawn directly from our primate repertoire. Coalitions serve an important function in diffusing raw dominance contests. They are also responsible for promoting a complex social structure.

Reciprocal altruism is found throughout the animal kingdom (Hamilton, 1964). It is dependent on the capacity to remember the individual involved in helping events, and on the likelihood that there will be occasions for future reciprocity. Altruistic behavior creates a tension between immediate gratification and long-term advantage. Coalitions demand negotiating skill and interactional flexibility. They require accurate assessment of others. The relevance of these skills to social functioning is clear.

The need for deception is inherent in the tension which develops from delayed gratification. Deception in the ethology literature is considered an important social skill. Indeed, successful coalition negotiation is dependent on the ability to dissimulate and detect dissimulation in others. Ekman et al.'s (1972) studies of the leakage of nonverbal cues in facial behavior indicate how sensitive we are to nuances of expression, even if we don't respond overtly. Empathy can be defined as the ability to understand the other's position. An often unrecognized component of this process is the detection of hidden meaning. These mechanisms contribute to the development of object relations. One interesting current theory holds that repression may be conceptualized as self-deception; a necessary skill if one is to deceive genuinely (Trivers, 1985; Nesse, 1988).

The process of coalition negotiation both enhances affiliative bonds and contributes to the establishment of the "real" dominance hierarchy. These techniques are involved in the development of a complex social system. While the language of ethology may sound crude to our therapeutic ears, the phenomena described are highly sophisticated and part of our primate heritage.

SUMMARY

The ethological literature contains observations concerning the behavioral characteristics of nonhuman primates in groups. Despite the applicability of this material to understanding human social behavior, the findings have not been widely recognized in the group literature.

Social behavior in the current ethology literature is considered under three categories: (1) affiliative behaviors and social cooperation, including maternal–child bonding; (2) aggressive behaviors and the dominance hierarchy, including redirected aggression; and (3) coalition formation. This primate material is utilized to illuminate both theoretical and practical issues in group psychotherapy. The purpose of this review is to draw attention to the biologic propensities at work beneath complex social behaviors. This perspective offers some alternate explanations for common group phenomena. Ethological studies of the higher primates are at an early stage of development. While some promising hypotheses are being explored, direct application of these ideas to clinical work is premature.

REFERENCES

Beck, A. P. (1974), Phases in the development of structure in therapy and encounter groups. In: *Innovations in Client-Centered Therapy*, ed. D. A. Wexler & L. N. Rice. New York: John Wiley.

Bowlby, J. (1982), *Attachment and Loss*, Vol. 1, 2nd ed. New York: Basic Books.

——— (1988), Developmental psychiatry comes of age. *Amer. J. Psychiat.*, 145:1–10.

Buirski, P. (1980), Toward a theory of adaptation of analytic group psychotherapy. *Internat. J. Group Psychother.*, 30:447–459.

Cheney, D., Seyfarth, R., & Smuts, B. (1986), Social relationships and social cognition in nonhuman primates. *Science*, 234:1361–1366.

Crook, J. H. (1981), The evolutionary ethology of social processes in man. In: *Group Cohesion: Theoretical and Clinical Perspectives*, ed. H. Kellerman. New York: Grune & Stratton.

Darwin, C. (1872), *The Expression of Emotions in Man and Animals*. London: John Murray.

Eibl-Eibesfeldt, I. (1975), *Ethology: The Biology of Behavior*, 2nd ed. New York: Holt Rinehart & Winston.

Ekman, P., Friesen, W. V., & Ellsworth, P. (1972), *Emotion in the Human Face*. New York: Pergamon.

Freud, S. (1921), Group psychology and the analysis of the ego. *Standard Edition*, 18:67–144. London: Hogarth Press, 1953.

Goodall, J. (1986), *The Chimpanzees of Gombe*. Cambridge, MA: Harvard University Press.

Hamilton, W. D. (1964), The genetical theory of social behavior. *J. Theoret. Biol.*, 7:1–52.

Hausfater, G. (1975), Dominance and reproduction in baboons (Papio cynocephalus), a quantitative analysis. *Contrib. Primatol.*, 7:20–68.

Hinde, R. A. (1983), *Primate Social Relationships*. Sunderland, MA: Sinauer.

Kagan, J., Reznick, J. S., & Snidman, N. (1988), Biological bases of childhood shyness. *Science*, 240:167–171.

Kennedy, J. L., & MacKenzie, K. R. (1986), Dominance hierarchies in psychotherapy groups. *Brit. J. Psychiat.*, 148:625–631.

Kummer, H. (1971), *Primate Societies*. Chicago: Aldine & Atherton.

Lewin, K., Lippitt, R., & White, R. K. (1939), Patterns of aggressive behavior in experimentally created "social climates." *J. Soc. Psychol.*, 10:271–299.

Lieberman, M. A., Yalom, I. D., & Miles, M. B. (1973), *Encounter Groups: First Facts*. New York: Basic Books.

MacKenzie, K. R. (1983), The clinical application of a group climate measure. In: *Advances in Group Psychotherapy: Integrating Research and Practice*, ed. R. R. Dies & K. R. MacKenzie. New York: International Universities Press.

——— (1990), *Introduction to Time-Limited Group Psychotherapy*. Washington, D.C.: American Psychiatric Press, Inc.

——— Livesley, W. J. (1983), A developmental model for brief group therapy. In: *Advances in Group Psychotherapy: Integrating Research and Practice*, ed. R. R. Dies & K. R. MacKenzie. New York: International Universities Press.

McGrew, W. C. (1972), *An Ethological Study of Children's Behavior*. New York: Academic Press.

Nesse, R. M. (1988), The evolutionary functions of repression. Paper presented at American Psychiatric Assoociation Meeting, Montreal, Canada.

Plutchik, R. (1980), *Emotion: A Psychoevolutionary Synthesis*. New York: Harper & Row.

Price, J. (1967), The dominance hierarchy and the evolution of mental illness. *Lancet*, ii:243–246.

Scheidlinger, S. (1982), On scapegoating in group psychotherapy. *Internat. J. Group Psychother.*, 32:131–143.

Sibley, C. G., & Ahlquist, J. E. (1987), DNA hybridization evidence of hominoid phylogeny: Results from an expanded data set. *J. Molec. Evol.*, 26:99–121.

Smuts, B., Cheney, D., Seyfarth, R., Wrangham, R., & Struhsaker, T. (1987), *Primate Societies*. Chicago: University of Chicago Press.

Stern, D. N. (1985), *The Interpersonal World of the Infant: A View from Psychodynamics and Developmental Psychology*. New York: Basic Books.

Tellegen, A., Lykken, D. T., Bouchard, T. J., Wilcox, K. J., Segal, N. L., and Rich, S. (1988), Personality similarity in twins reared apart and together. *J. Pers. Soc. Psychol.*, 54:1031–1039.

Trivers, R. (1985), *Social Evolution*. Menlo Park, CA: Benjamin/Cummings.

Tuckman, B. W. (1965), Developmental sequence in small groups. *Psychol. Bull.*, 63:384–399.

Van Hooff, J. A. R. M. (1967), The facial display of the Catarrhine monkeys and apes. In: *Primate Ethology*, ed. D. Morris. London: Weidenfeld & Nicholson.

Van Lawick-Goodall, J. (1971), *In the Shadow of Man*. Boston: Houghton Mifflin.

Walters, J., & Seyfarth, R. (1986), Conflict and cooperation. In: *Primate Societies*, ed. B. Smuts, D. Cheney, R. Seyfarth, R. Wrangham, & T. Strusaker. Chicago: University of Chicago Press.

Wilson, E. D. (1978), *On Human Nature*. Cambridge, MA: Harvard University Press.

Winston, A. (1988), Three studies examining patient affective and defensive behavior in brief dynamic psychotherapy. Paper presented at Society for Psychotherapy Research Annual Conference, Santa Fe, NM.

Wright, F., Hoffman, X. H., & Gore, E. M. (1988), Perspectives on scapegoating in primary groups. *Group*, 12:33–44.

Yunis, J. J., & Prakash, O. M. (1982), The origin of man: A chromosomal pictorial legacy. *Science*, 215:1525–1530.

Chapter 21

Clinician and Researcher: Mutual Growth through Dialogue

ROBERT R. DIES, Ph.D.

It has become increasingly fashionable to blame the limited empirical foundation for group psychotherapy on the failure of clinicians and researchers to collaborate in their efforts to understand this complex treatment modality (Dies, 1979, 1983a, 1986; Bednar, Corey, Evans, Gazda, Pistole, Stockton, and Robison, 1987). Implicit in this allegation is the proposition that if only practitioners and researchers would engage in mutual dialogue and cooperative investigation, then the field of group psychotherapy would be significantly advanced. Underlying this assertion is the assumption that there is in fact a fundamental lack of meaningful communication *and* that both parties are actively responsible for this breach.

Even as early as three decades ago, Bennis (1960) addressed the interpersonal problems in group research. He noted that "social scientists who conduct research on small group behavior and psychotherapists who conduct groups observe and are concerned with similar phenomena. And yet, for the most part, they do not read the same journals, usually do not attend the same meetings, and more usually appear to have a difficult time communicating with each other" (p.

Dedication. The theme of this chapter is in keeping with Saul Scheidlinger's long-standing and outstanding efforts to bridge the gap between clinical and scientific inquiry. His influence on the field of group psychotherapy has been profound, but undoubtedly pales in significance compared to his impact on the lives of so many people he has touched, both personally and professionally. My contribution to this volume is written out of love and deep respect for a man who has served as a role model par excellence and a caring and compassionate friend.

65). Twenty years later, in an influential overview of fundamental problems in the group literature, Hartman (1979) still highlighted the basic gulf between researchers and clinicians. This schism has been described in relatively benign terms as a form of mutual dissociation (Dies, 1983a) or more pejoratively as an outright rift within the field (Coché and Dies, 1981). At the very least, there is fairly widespread consensus among contemporary reviewers that an "attitude problem" exists between researchers and clinicians. Therapists are portrayed as distrustful of researchers and critical of their investigations as trivial, irrelevant, and fraught with insurmountable methodological and conceptual pitfalls. Researchers, on the other hand, are depicted as harboring equally negative and stereotypic views of clinicians as defensive, unsystematic, and overly speculative (Coché and Dies, 1981; Dies, 1983a). There are even conjectures regarding the underlying dynamics fueling these contentious reactions. Bennis (1960) interprets the practitioner's presumed opposition to research as reflecting "powerful unconscious resistance" (p. 75), whereas Parloff (1967) describes the "defensive bases" for the researchers' "seemingly maladaptive behaviors" (p. 237).

It appears reasonable to conclude on the basis of the prolonged history of reports on the basic split between scientists and practitioners, and the prevalence of this argument among current reviews of the literature, that there is indeed substantial validity to the basic theme; namely, that the lack of dialogue between investigators and clinicians plays a principal role in forestalling notable progress in our understanding of group treatments.

The primary goal of this chapter is to challenge this viewpoint. An attempt will be made to refute this basic *myth* by critically examining contrary evidence and by proposing alternative interpretations to account for the current status of the empirical literature. Despite the fact that many reviewers, including the author, have endorsed this myth for many years (Parloff and Dies, 1977; Hartman, 1979; Dies, 1979, 1983a, 1985b, 1986; Dies and Riester, 1986; Bednar et al., 1987), there is convincing evidence that this supposition is not entirely accurate, and that it may serve only to maintain an illusion of noncollegiality that perpetuates an unhealthy tension within the field. Ironically, this state of dissonance may be even more insidious than the presumed communication defect from which it derives. Certainly, there are many practitioners who are neither consumers nor purveyors of research, but their disinterest does not block progress within the field if other clinicians and researchers are actively exchanging ideas.

It is much more constructive to view the clinical and research perspectives as simply alternative methods for attempting to discover the uniquely therapeutic properties of group treatments. Neither the clinicians nor the researchers have a monopoly on the "truth," nor do they necessarily occupy a superior vantage point on group process or outcome. Rather, they share a deep commitment to understand complex group phenomena and often employ strikingly parallel operations. They both begin with empirical observations from which generalizations are abstracted and treatment or manipulative hypotheses are deduced, applied, and subsequently validated empirically. Kiesler (1981) explains that what has differentiated the researcher from the practitioner is whether the inductive–deductive logical process operates implicitly or explicitly, and whether systematic or unsystematic observation occurs. "Both the science and practice of psychotherapy involve at their core a hypothesis-testing procedure" (pp. 213–214). One obvious illustration of the scientific approach to clinical phenomena is Freud's astute analyses of psychopathology and the therapeutic conditions fostering symptomatic amelioration. Meehl (1978), one of the major proponents of the statistical over the clinical approach, conveyed his respect for Freud's brilliance by stating: "There is not a single experiment reported in my 23-volume set of the standard edition of Freud nor is there a *t* test. But I would take Freud's clinical observations over most people's *t* tests any time" (p. 817).

Fuhriman, Drescher, and Burlingame (1984), in their treatise on conceptualizing group process, remind us of the parable of the blind men and the elephant and suggest that "as clinicians and researchers of the system called 'group' we find ourselves in an awkwardly similar situation—only our eyes are open and the elephant is human" (p. 427). Sometimes the empirical and clinical viewpoints converge so that there is relative isomorphism in the descriptions of central parameters of group process, but there are also major discrepancies in our understanding of the constellation of ingredients promoting therapeutic gain. Even when clinicians and researchers are in perfect accord, however, it is still possible that the patients have an entirely different sense of the reality of the group. Using cohesiveness as an illustration, we may find that a group characterized by interpersonal friction and open displays of anger may not "feel" especially *cohesive* to some patients, yet the capacity of group members to withstand the confrontation and strain may, from the clinician's and researcher's points of view, be a genuine measure of the strength of the members' interpersonal bond (Dies, 1985a). Truly, the meaning of group process depends on the unique outlook of the observer.

Careful consideration of the parable of the blind men and the elephant reveals that the metaphor falls far short of clinical reality. The problem is not simply that our comprehension of the elephant called "group" is limited, but that in our field we have a veritable parade of pachyderms performing in what may, at times, seem like a "circus of group psychotherapies." Although we have certainly witnessed a gradual decline of interest in the exotic or sensationalized facets of group process (Bednar and Moeschl, 1981), we are still confronted with a bewildering array of therapeutic techniques, clinical settings, and clientele. Thus, we have "inpatient pachyderms" such as those that inhabit revolving door facilities in which our favorite group concepts (e.g., cohesiveness) seem completely irrelevant, and others that reside in long-term treatment centers in which a group ecology can evolve and such pivotal concepts as cohesion, catharsis, and family reenactment seem entirely apt. In our procession, too, we have our "outpatient pachyderms" differing in terms of duration, composition, and diagnosis, and guided by various "ringmasters" who vary in their therapeutic *focus* along the individual/interpersonal/group-as-a-whole continuum, or in their *style* in terms of active–nonactive, transparent–opaque, or gratifying–frustrating (Rutan and Stone, 1984). Some call themselves psychoanalysts, others existentialists, and others still favor labels such as object-relations therapists, transactional analysts, or cognitive-behaviorists.

High above our promenade of elephants, in one ring of our circus, we have the trapeze artists (i.e., our theoreticians), deft at lofty conceptualization and fancy aerial acrobatics, but whose appreciation of the elephant is restricted by their failure to interact with the beast. In another ring we have our animal trainers (i.e., our researchers), clever at demonstrating intricate behavior-reinforcement sequences, but who often lose their sense of the elephant because of their preoccupation with moment by moment acts. And, in center ring, we have various artists (i.e., our practitioners) who entertain us as they interact with the pachyderm; they can report what it is like to "be" with an elephant, but their understanding may be compromised by their failure to adopt the theorist's capacity for abstraction and integration, and the researcher's talent for systematic operationalization.

In all three rings of our circus we have dedicated performers. A few even stand out for the sheer artistry of their presentations, be they clinician or researcher, psychoanalyst or psychodramatist, but their comprehension of the elephant is significantly shaped by the type of experience and training they have acquired over the years. Disadvantaged by their exposure to a modest range of pachyderms, most of our performers have only a limited awareness of the species.

Despite their considerable acumen, their viewpoints remain regrettably myopic.

No wonder the simple parable of the blind men and *the* elephant seems so incomplete. The profusion of theoretical, contextual, personalistic, and even serendipitous factors that contribute to the panorama of group psychotherapies virtually defies comprehensive integration and synthesis no matter how talented our clinical–investigative team. Therefore, before we cast aspersion on either the clinicians or the researchers for their respective roles in our "circus of misunderstanding" about group treatments, we should examine the thesis that the lack of communication across party lines is really the central etiology of the developmental lag within the field.

THE MYTH OF NONCOMMUNICATION

Is there a fundamental lack of communication between psychotherapists and investigators that is predominantly responsible for the insufficient progress within the field, or is the sluggish evolution of our empirical understanding a natural outgrowth of the sheer complexity of group treatments, as implied in our examination of the allegory of the blind men and the elephant? To answer this question, we will first present three lines of evidence that contradict the charge of noncommunication: (1) the professional identities of the "opposing factions"; (2) documentation of considerable discourse within the profession; and (3) alternative interpretations of the presumed "attitude problems."

Professional Identities

It would appear on the basis of the proposed "gulf" between researchers and clinicians (Hartman, 1979; Dies, 1983a) that we are discussing divergent factions within the field, namely those mental health practitioners who actually conduct the treatments and those investigators who evaluate the psychotherapy, but who are not themselves clinicians.

In point of fact, the preponderance of the published research has been contributed by investigators who also have a substantial investment in group work with clinical populations. Thus, even a brief perusal of research articles will reveal that in a significant percentage of the studies the principal investigator has also been one of the group psychotherapists. Similarly, the reviews of the empirical literature have been promulgated largely by professionals who spend extensive portions of their time actually conducting treatment groups in a variety of private practice, outpatient, and inpatient settings (Lieberman, 1976; Bednar and Kaul, 1978; Parloff and Dies, 1977; Yalom, 1985; Kansas, 1986; MacKenzie and Livesley, 1986). Moreover, these same research-oriented clinicians can be found supervising individual practitioners, consulting with various agencies on treatment techniques, and providing intensive workshops on psychodynamic group process and other approaches to therapeutic interventions.

To be sure, there are researchers who are considerably less clinically seasoned than the main contributors to the empirical literature, but even in these cases it is highly unlikely that they are complete neophytes. Undoubtedly, there is a broad spectrum with "pure clinicians" and "pure researchers" anchoring either extreme. Although this continuum is heavily skewed toward the clinical end, almost no one occupies the far right. At the very least, it is clear that the dichotomy of clinician *versus* researcher is a fallacy, and that it is more fitting to think of clinicians who vary in their degree of commitment to systematic research in their efforts to refine their understanding of group treatments.[1]

Documentation of Discourse Within the Field

Challenging the assumption that researchers and clinicians represent different professional identities does much to refute the notion that the failure to communicate is a fundamental problem within the field. Evidence of substantial "scientist–practitioner" dialogue regarding group treatments would obviously bolster the argument even more that "noncommunication" is a myth.

The appeals for more effective integration of research and practice have echoed throughout the literature for decades. As early as 1952, Saul Scheidlinger (cited in Scheidlinger [1982]) began his efforts to

---

[1] The author is deeply indebted to Dr. Kathryn Reed Dies for her invaluable feedback on this chapter. In particular, she picked up on the author's vacillation about whether or not there is actually "noncommunication" within the field. The answer, of course, is "yes" and "no." Informational exchange is not occurring between many clinicians and empirical investigators, yet there is also substantial dialogue among others. Thus, it cannot be said that researchers are being denied access to practitioners and their settings, and this observation precludes the possibility of blaming "pure clinicians" for limiting progress on group treatments. The "myth" is that "noncommunication" inhibits research productivity.

"bridge the gap" between the research and clinical perspectives within the field. There is indisputable evidence that his entreaties, and those of others, have not gone entirely unheeded. For example, in 1967 Saul Scheidlinger chaired one of the first panel discussions on the integration of research and practice (Scheidlinger, 1967), and since that time there have been scores of similar symposia designed to reduce the chasm between the empirical and clinical viewpoints. Thus, many of the principal journals on group methods have periodically dedicated special issues to research, including for instance, *Small Group Behavior* (Dies, 1978b), the *Journal of Applied Behavioral Science* (Dies, 1979), the *Journal for Specialists in Group Work* (Dies, 1985b), and the *International Journal of Group Psychotherapy* (Dies, 1987). These journals, as well as others devoted almost exclusively to group psychotherapy (e.g., *Group; Group Analysis; Group Psychotherapy, Psychodrama, and Sociometry*; and *Social Work in Groups*), are published mainly for practitioners and yet contain hundreds of research articles that are subjected to increasing editorial pressures to make empirical findings pertinent to clinical practice. Moreover, most of the published *reviews* of group research contain concrete recommendations for improving clinical interventions. During the last fifteen years alone, approximately 100 surveys on various facets of group process and outcome have been published to facilitate communication within the field.[2]

Ironically, the first volume in the American Group Psychotherapy Association's (AGPA) Monograph series, launched during Saul Scheidlinger's presidency of AGPA, was devoted to the integration of research and practice in group psychotherapy (Dies and MacKenzie, 1983). The succeeding Monographs on group therapy with children, adolescents, and the elderly all incorporate integrative reviews of the research literature with clear implications for clinical application. Moreover, an increasing number of "how-to-do-it" manuals are available for clinicians on how to incorporate research instruments into their therapeutic work (MacKenzie and Dies, 1982; Corcoran and Fischer, 1987).

In addition to the hundreds of "bridge-building" publications in the area, there is substantial evidence at professional meetings (such as AGPA's annual conference) of scientist–practitioner communication. Although there are certainly specialized interest groups, there is no question that empirical presentations are widely attended by clinicians, and that researchers are actively involved as participants or presenters in a broad assortment of workshops on group therapy.

---

[2] An extensive list of these reviews, organized by category, is available from the author upon request.

Again, these are not different "breeds" of professionals, but mental health experts who vary in their commitment to scientific methodologies.

These observations of mutual exchange run counter to the notion that there is a communication failure between researchers and clinicians within the field. Certainly, by virtue of the sheer number of publications and presentations at various professional meetings, it is clear that opportunities for dialogue are quite plentiful. Thus, Bennis's (1960) quip, cited earlier in this chapter, that scientists and practitioners do not read the same journals, attend the same sessions, and frequently have a hard time communicating with each other, is at present far less accurate, at least on two of the three counts.

Although the indictment about troubled communication has focused mainly on the issue of clinician versus researcher, there is reason to believe that the deficiency is more pervasive, that is, not only across party lines, but substantially within party lines as well. Thus, clinicians are failing to communicate with fellow practitioners, and researchers are not conferring sufficiently with fellow scientists. Scheidlinger (1982, 1987) has noted, for example, that even at the level of defining group psychotherapy and such basic intervention strategies as "interpretation," there are major disagreements and misunderstandings. Similarly, prominent researchers (Kaul and Bednar, 1986) have criticized colleagues for their failure to learn from prior investigations and for continuing to design studies with identical methodological imperfections and anachronistic conceptualizations.

No doubt the generic communication problem within the field is significantly related to a "communication explosion." Thus, each year there are over 600 publications on various aspects of group treatments, and this figure is escalating at a geometric rate (Dies, 1979). Even more shocking is a discovery the author made several years ago that during one five-year period, articles on group therapy appeared in nearly *four hundred* different national and international publication outlets. In the face of this overwhelming proliferation of material on group treatments, it is quite unlikely that the only communication failure will be defined by the presumed scientist–practitioner split. Nonetheless, it is possible that the "attitude problems" we mentioned previously might contribute differentially to the defective dialogue.

Alternative Interpretations of the "Attitude Problems"

One component of the dispositional difficulties would suggest that practitioners harbor rather negative sentiments toward research.

Findings from opinion surveys would lend some credence to this claim; Coché and Dies (1981) and Dies (1983a) found that clinicians were indeed quite critical of research as superficial, conceptually bankrupt, methodologically flawed, and inapplicable to the actual treatment situation. However, we should promptly emphasize that these seemingly unfriendly critiques are not unique to group practitioners, but are prevalent among scientists as well. Bednar, one of the principal chroniclers of the empirical literature on group psychotherapy (Bednar and Lawlis, 1971; Bednar and Kaul, 1978; Kaul and Bednar, 1986) is even more iconoclastic than clinicians in stating that "researchers have essentially failed to advance knowledge in the last three decades despite inordinate improvement in research methods. Contemporary research efforts are addressing questions already answered while ignoring the more crucial issues plaguing the group disciplines" (Bednar et al., 1987, p. 101). There are, of course, more optimistic perspectives on the contributions of research to practice (MacKenzie and Dies, 1982; Dies, 1983b, 1986; Yalom, 1985), and several illustrations will be highlighted at the conclusion of this chapter. Thus, we will see that notable progress has been forged in understanding factors that contribute to effective group process, leadership dynamics, and therapeutic outcomes. Nevertheless, it is clear that the disappointments with the quality and conclusiveness of research findings are not without some historical substance.

Rather than suggesting an "attitude problem," however, it is more likely that the clinicians' fault-finding reflects an accurate appraisal of large segments of the research literature, not a stereotyped and biased viewpoint. It would appear that practitioners are not unjustifiably against research, they are simply against "bad" research. Obviously, they are not alone in that evaluation, since a majority of scientist–reviewers are also strongly critical of the accumulated research literature. To place the primary responsibility for the "attitude problem" at the doorstep of the practitioner would be a gross misrepresentation.

In fact, a moment of reflection would suggest that rather than being vigorously against research, group psychotherapists have been amazingly tolerant. For years investigators have systematically challenged widely accepted clinical realities. Bednar and Lawlis (1971) observed, for example, that it was only after six decades of clinical practice that scientists were finally able to conclude that "the converging evidence is consistent with the view held by many practitioners that group therapy is a valuable tool of the helping professions" (p. 814). Similarly, researchers have regularly dashed many of the most cherished clinical constructs. To illustrate, Bednar and Kaul's (1978) review of the literature questioned the utility of the construct of "cohesion," and Bloch and Crouch (1985) found little to support the proposition that the "curative factors" were indeed curative, and more recently Piper and Perrault (1989) concluded that despite positive endorsement in the clinical literature, the research evidence for the benefit of pretherapy training or contracting was not especially impressive.

In the midst of these rather negative messages, it is no wonder that researchers and their findings are not always viewed dispassionately by their practitioner counterparts. On the other hand, can you imagine what it must be like to be the "Scrooge" of the group treatment literature. Investigators would much rather (because of their own commitment to group psychotherapy as a viable and vital treatment modality) be the bearers of glad tidings than the pallbearers of treasured clinical concepts.

Certainly, there are many opportunities for research-oriented clinicians to document meaningful therapeutic change and to discover the unique dimensions of group process that foster clinical gain. We have learned from our mistakes and our setbacks, and refined our research methodologies accordingly. As we have elevated the sophistication of our research, the yield has become increasingly productive (Dies, 1979; Gazda, 1984). But the road to discovery is fraught with major obstacles. The role of systematically operationalizing therapeutic interventions, the struggles to concretize elusive clinical phenomena using available research tools, and the painstaking efforts required to gain entry into clinical settings in the face of patient, therapist, and administrative resistance, and to control the host of variables infringing on group treatments, is not without its frustrations and disillusionments. No wonder that many researchers have taken the easy way out and resorted to short-term, simplistic outcome investigations with nonclinical populations (Dies, 1983a; Dies and Riester, 1986). Thus, "discouraged by the complexities of group therapy research, investigators have generally taken refuge in isolated environments in which control of experimental variables is more feasible; research on non-patient groups and small-scale investigation of a limited range of variables have been the most fashionable retreats" (Dies, 1983a, p. 1). The unfortunate consequence of this defensive escape is that the contributions of research to practice are thereby severely compromised.

It would be relatively facile at this point to censure investigators for their counterproductive withdrawal from the clinical context, or to reproach practitioners for their resistance to systematic and empirically grounded examination of their work. Traditionally, these are part and parcel of the allegations proffered to document the "attitude problems" we have been considering. However, there is a much more benign interpretation of the "resistance–retreat" (or fight–flight) phenomenon manifested by practitioners and researchers, and that is that *both* are deeply committed to their patients' welfare and primarily concerned with optimizing immediate therapeutic outcome. We know that the strictures of "scientific rigor" and the dictates of "personal crises" and flexible clinical management are often quite incompatible.

After all, when clients are embroiled in interpersonal conflicts and experiencing serious emotional turmoil, they are reluctant to sacrifice valuable treatment time to complete research measures. Moreover, their experiential framework will make it difficult for them to shift to the more objective perspective required to complete most research measures (Dies, 1985a).

Although we know that research validation is an essential step toward refinement of clinical practice, and that we are facing mounting pressures from policy-makers, health care underwriters, and consumers to demonstrate empirically that continued support of mental health service is worth the investment (Dies, 1983a), it still is not comfortable to be involved in research. We know that research is often intrusive—clinicians know it, researchers know it, and patients certainly know it. These reactions are not a function of an "attitude problem" against research per se, but rather an uneasiness about participating in a scientific endeavor which may conflict with moment by moment patient needs or the natural evolution of therapeutic group process.

From this, we can see that practitioners are not only against "bad research" (as noted earlier) but also opposed to "being researched." Once again, however, that disquietude is shared by the scientists who are just as committed to client welfare, and do not relish being "intruders" any more than either the therapist or patient enjoy being intruded upon. Instead of denigrating the practitioner as being "antiresearcher," or the investigator as "anticlinician," it is much more favorable to regard both of their positions as "proclient" or "protreatment." Such an interpretation is far less likely to maintain the unhealthy clinician versus researcher tension that overshadows the profession. It follows from this, that it is imperative for empirically oriented practitioners to consider how best to improve the nature and quality of the research enterprise to reduce its invasive features. Indeed this chapter is dedicated to reducing some of the misgivings and miscommunications within the field with the hopes of fostering a healthier dialogue about scientific validation of group treatments.

We have seen that researchers and practitioners cannot be dichotomized into opposing factions, that there is substantial evidence of meaningful exchange within the profession, and that "attitude problems" may not be as rampant as previously suspected. Indeed, the presumed "noncommunication" may be a myth, not so much based on reality, but a convenient "strawman" used to account for the limited progress within the field (Parloff, 1967). A major thesis of this chapter, however, is that other *constraints* are much more salient in explaining the slow evolution of understanding about group psychotherapy. Let us explore some of those additional stumbling blocks.

CONSTRAINTS THAT HAMPER PROGRESS

There is almost universal agreement that the major impediment to rapid progress within the field is the absolute complexity of group treatments. We find, for example, that the bulk of the empirical investigations published each year (approximately 100 to 150) are simple outcome probes that employ comparatively few groups in short-term treatment facilities or in settings where the "clients" have been specifically recruited for a targeted symptom (e.g., anxiety or depression) or a personal growth experience (Dies, 1979, 1983b). Moreover, a significant percentage of the studies use "captive audiences" (e.g., inpatients or undergraduates enrolled in intensive laboratory groups), and are focused mainly on adults, not children (Dies and Riester, 1986) or adolescents (Tramontana, 1980; Azima and K. Dies, 1989), and apply correlational procedures with linkages made between simple self-report process and outcome measures without follow-up assessments. Research on traditional psychodynamic concepts (e.g., interpretation or transference), compared to studies of cognitive –behavioral interventions, is relatively scarce. Long-term, large-scale, and programmatic investigations within routine clinical settings are inordinately rare. Finally, an overwhelming majority of the investigators do not continue to pursue a research career; indeed, there are only a handful of scientists whose names appear regularly in the empirical literature. All of these "compromises" are symptomatic of the scientist–clinicians' efforts to cope with the staggering array of variables confronting them in group research, and to gain a modicum of control over the intricacies of group treatment. Yet, there are still other factors that impinge on investigators to make empirical evaluation of group psychotherapy even more enigmatic. Some of these surplus constraints are outlined in Tables 21.1 and 21.2. Obviously, the distinction between "researcher" and "clinician" is artificial, as we have already seen, but the tables were constructed, more or less, with the two extremes of our scientist–practitioner continuum in mind.

Intrinsic Constraints

These constraints relate to various personal and professional factors within the individual investigator. Most central are those apprehensions, shared by researchers and clinicians alike, about "contaminating" the therapeutic process.

As the *insider* within the group system, the clinician–evaluator is naturally dedicated to providing maximum benefit to each of the group members in terms of the alleviation of distress and improvement in maladaptive patterns of interaction. The "threat" of research is that it will infringe on patients' needs, divert the therapeutic process, encroach on valuable time, and generate resentment among the group members, not only toward the research measures but also toward the therapist for permitting this unwelcome invasion into their private domain. No wonder that group psychotherapists are disinclined to participate in research. Moreover, often unfamiliar with the research instruments and uneasy about how to address the questions, challenges, and anxieties raised by their group members (Dies, 1983a), most psychotherapists simply avoid becoming involved in evaluation. Although many clinicians genuinely believe in the value of scientific investigation of group treatments, the prospect of "being researched" is an entirely different matter.

As the *outsider* to the group system, the investigator who is not also the clinician is quite cognizant of the potential to trespass on valuable treatment time and to intervene at particularly inopportune moments in the ebb and flow of intensive group interaction. After all, the researcher is well aware that group members may be wrestling with painful personal predicaments and facing constructive challenges from comembers regarding troublesome interpersonal styles. That is why patients are involved in treatment in the first place, not to take time from corrective emotional experiences and enlightening interpersonal feedback to fill out a questionnaire for the sake of scientific advancement. Therefore, despite their deep commitment to experimental investigation, researchers are genuinely conflicted about intruding on profoundly personal issues.

To cope with this professional dilemma many investigators have either shunned process research entirely (and administered measures only before and after treatment); incorporated very simplistic but face valid self-report instruments; or intervened only infrequently in the group's development. The retreat to the safety of the experimental laboratory (i.e., through analogue research and investigations of t-

TABLE 21.1
Constraints on Researchers

Intrinsic Constraints

Personal
—Discomfort about intruding on group process
—Concern over resistance–anger from therapist–patients
—Discouragement resulting from previous failures to detect significant findings
—Uneasiness with stereotype of researcher as a "nonclinician," insensitive, manipulative
—Demoralization as the only researcher in a predominantly service-oriented setting

Professional
—Awed by enormous complexity of group process
—Fundamental respect for the therapist–client contract and the priority of treatment concerns
—Concern over violating confidentiality
—Conflict over "pure science" and field research (e.g., "don't contaminate the process")
—Conflicting role demands as clinician and researcher (i.e., inability to integrate both)
—Lack of specialized research skills, training, knowledge of instrumentation
—Limited clinical experience or training
—Inability to disentangle conflicting results

Extrinsic Constraints

Administrative
—Publish or perish (i.e., pressures to produce numerous publications)
—Pressures to conduct only certain types of studies (e.g., program evaluation)
—External restrictions stemming from anti-research biases

Contextual
—Inability to monitor design issues (e.g., comparison groups, levels of therapist training, patient matching)

—Practical problems arising from the sheer complexity of group treatments (e.g., drop-outs, inattendance, medication)
—Patient–therapist resistance–noncompliance
—Limited access to clinical settings (i.e., patient and therapist samples)

Resource
—Limited funding to support research (e.g., instruments, computer costs, consultants)
—Conflicting role demands limiting available time (e.g., teaching, committee work)
—Lack of role models of research colleagues
—Lack of support staff, assistants
—Instrumentation problems (e.g., inadequate process measures, flawed leadership measures)
—Restricted access to auxiliary services (e.g., library, computer) or space
—Limited publication outlets for dissemination of findings, space limitations

TABLE 21.2
Constraints on Clinicians

Intrinsic Constraints
Personal
—Concern over client resistance, anger, acting out
—Fear that research cannot be justified to the patient–consumers
—Anxiety regarding the exposure of personal inadequacies, limitations, misunderstanding
—Feelings of possessiveness regarding clinical domain
—Apprehension about criticisms from clinical colleagues

Professional

—Awed by enormous complexity of group process
—Fear about impact of research on the contract, therapeutic alliance, transference
—Deep commitment to client welfare and treatment concerns
—Concern over violating confidentiality
—Conflicting role demands as clinician and researcher (i.e., inability to integrate both)
—Fundamental belief that research and practice are incompatible
—Limited research experience or training
—Lack of exposure to convenient research instruments or assessment strategies

Extrinsic Constraints
Administrative

—Heavy service demands
—Pressures from third-party payers to document treatment efficacy
—Limited external rewards for research (e.g., promotion, tenure)
—Pressures to conduct only certain types of studies (e.g., program evaluation)

Contextual

—Practical problems of monitoring individual patient needs within the research contract
—Patient resistance, noncompliance
—Setting not conducive to research (e.g., client flow, scheduling)

Resource

—Loss of income due to time given over to research (and limited outside funding)
—Conflicting role demands limiting available time (e.g., supervision, consulting)
—Lack of role models, research colleagues
—Limited support staff, assistants
—Instrumentation problems (e.g., inadequate process and outcome measures)
—Restricted access to auxiliary services (e.g., library and computer facilities)

groups with student trainees) are also manifestations of the researchers' reluctance to interrupt intensive therapeutic work.

On the other hand, investigators are also aware that research has immense potential to improve the quality of group treatment programs in general, and the practitioner's own interventions in particular. The literature is replete with illustrations of how clinical investigators have refined their treatments as a function of systematic feedback from group members via research instruments. Azim and Joyce (1986), for example, found that satisfaction with group treatments increased after program modifications were implemented based on evaluations from former patients. Similarly, Slocum (1987) demonstrated the value of a pregroup measure to assess and then to address faulty perceptions regarding group treatments, whereas Hisli (1987) found that the routine administration of process measures could actually facilitate therapeutic outcome. The value of research instruments to improve practice as been presented for many years (Dies, 1978a, 1983b, 1987; MacKenzie and Dies, 1982; Dies and Riester, 1986; Azima and K. Dies, 1989), and these authors have shown how to integrate measures into group treatments in ways that are not invasive. A recent volume by Corcoran and Fischer (1987) entitled *Measures for Clinical Practice*, for example, lists over 125 "rapid assessment instruments" to evaluate problems commonly encountered in clinical practice, and the authors demonstrate how to select, administer, score, and interpret these measures as part of the treatment process. Nevertheless, data-based clinical practice is not widely evident. There are noteworthy trends within recent literature of specially designed and empirically grounded treatment programs, but these are largely short-term and symptomatically focused interventions (Lewinsohn and Clarke, 1984), and not especially manifest in more generic treatment settings. Similarly, Coché has observed that "it is a peculiar phenomenon that while a large percentage of the American population receives psychotherapy from private practitioners, there is hardly any research from this form of service delivery" (1983, p. 95).

It has been argued that the very survival of psychotherapy as a profession depends on the active integration of research and practice (Parloff, 1980). Although the emphasis on accountability may ultimately force clinicians to routinely present evidence of the efficacy of their group interventions (Dies, 1985b), the preponderance of practitioners have not been eager to jump on the bandwagon to build research measures into their clinical work. Our brief examination of the intrinsic constraints has shown that the perceived incongruence between experimental and clinical realities is most salient in explaining this hesitation. To interpret the clinicians' *resistance* as related to un-conscious dynamics (e.g., hidden fears about exposure, power strug-gles relating to authority issues), or the investigators' *persistence* about research as similarly based on subliminal motivations (e.g., voyeurism about clinical phenomena without real involvement), as many have opined, does little to foster rapprochement within the field. There are sufficient legitimate and conscious reasons to account for the irresolution about integrating research and practice. As we shall see, these include external constraints as well.

Extrinsic Constraints

Examination of Tables 21.1 and 21.2 also reveals a wide panorama of outside pressures that thwart expeditious integration of research and practice within the group field. Some of these are closely related to the internal constraints we have already explored, such as the *con-textual* restraints growing out of the complicated nature of group treatments and the host of pragmatic problems of monitoring intricate treatment issues within a reasonably controlled investigation.

Other external constraints are *administrative*, such as the heavy de-mand for service. Then, too, in many settings pressures to demon-strate treatment efficacy prevent meaningful research on therapeutic process, since it is more important to show that "it works" in order to generate funding for mental health programs, than to demonstrate "why it works." From the practitioner's point of view, incentives for research participation may be minimal compared to the rewards of clinical involvement (personal satisfaction and financial remunera-tion). In contrast, many investigators may readily acknowledge the outside incentives for research in the form of "publish or perish," but anyone who has conducted an empirical investigation knows that the rate of investment can be quite costly. The difficulties with experi-mental controls and the amount of time required to execute a "sci-entific" study may encourage many investigators (especially tenure-seeking apprentices) to withdraw to the security of the laboratory environment for a guarantee of more scientifically elegant and promptly consummated research findings.

Unquestionably, the most serious extrinsic constraints on group research relate to limited resources; that is, basically issues of time and money. There is really very little that has to be clarified: most research endeavors that are designed to advance the field of group treatments are very time-consuming and costly. In one of the benchmark studies in the field, for example, the principal investigator, freed of most of his other professional responsibilities, devoted most of his time to the research project (Lieberman, Yalom, and Miles, 1973). Similarly, his coinvestigators were required to expend enormous portions of their time in the research. The project required several years to complete, substantial endowments from a wide range of institutions, foundations, and private benefactors, major commitment of time from a huge cadre of support personnel and consultants, countless hours of computer time, and a volume of nearly 500 pages to disseminate.

Although the preponderance of research on group interventions is not of this magnitude, it is clear that most studies require a substantial investment of time by a central investigator and a corps of ancillary personnel; indeed, the main budgetary allocation is generally for salary reimbursements. It would appear from our examination of the multitude of intrinsic and extrinsic constraints that it is virtually impossible for the average mental health professional to build research into a busy clinical practice. However, as we shall soon see, this is not an accurate representation. The type of research projects we have been presenting are primarily those designed to meet the canons of scientific rigor. There are other models of investigation that allow research to be incorporated efficiently into service delivery (Dies, 1983a).

We will examine this possibility briefly in the next section on myths about integrating research into practice. It seems fitting at this point to conclude our review of evidence contradicting the presumed communication deficit, and the various "constraints" on research endeavors, with the following example. There is a scene in Lily Tomlin's Broadway hit *The Search for Signs of Intelligent Life in the Universe* (Wagner, 1986) in which one of the central characters is confronting her psychotherapist:

You're sure, Doctor?
Premenstrual syndrome?
I mean, I'm getting divorced.
My mother's getting divorced.
I'm raising twin boys.
I have a lot of job pressure—
I've got to find one.
The ERA didn't pass,
not long ago I lost a very dear friend,
and . . . and my husband is involved . . .
not just involved, but in love, I'm afraid . . .

with this woman . . .
Who's quite a bit younger than I am
And you *think* it's my *period*
and *not* my life?

    This quote wonderfully captures the basic theme of this chapter.
Thus, in the face of the unquestioned complexity of group treatments,
compounded by an astonishing array of intrinsic and extrinsic pressures that impose upon research-oriented clinicians, it seems just as
therapeutically imprudent to endorse "noncommunication" as the
central etiology of the limited progress within the field. In fact, as we
hinted earlier, it is conceivable that this myth has done just as much
to jeopardize growth by fostering unhealthy tension as any real failure
of clinicians and researchers to communicate about collaborative ventures.

    The final section of this chapter represents an effort to bring an
even closer alliance between "researchers" and "practitioners" who
are still disinclined to consider empirical evaluations in actual clinical
practice. As we shall see, research is possible even for those group
psychotherapists whose training, philosophical biases, and heavy service commitments keep them from exploring any involvement in systematic investigation of their treatments.

EIGHT COMMON FALLACIES ABOUT INTEGRATING
RESEARCH AND PRACTICE

There are a multitude of misunderstandings that undoubtedly plague
mental health professionals and prevent them from engaging in empirical evaluation of their group treatments. A few of the more salient
fallacies will be identified, along with recommendations for overcoming the faulty assumptions and behavioral inhibitions that preclude
active research participation.

*Fallacy 1: Comparatively Little Progress is Evident in the Empirical
Literature and Significant Advancement is Unlikely in the Foreseeable
Future*

Contrary to widespread opinion among many practitioners and to a
certain extent research-oriented critics, there is abundant documentation of progress within the field. It is not feasible to provide a

substantive review at this point, and it is clear that many issues are insufficiently explored, nevertheless, there is little question that group psychotherapy is as effective, if not more so, than alternative treatment modalities for a wide range of individuals seeking relief from stressful and maladaptive conditions (Dies, 1986; Kaul and Bednar, 1986). Although we are certainly less confident about the particular therapeutic forces promoting change, encouraging signs are beginning to emerge. For example, contemporary researchers are generally showing that with short-term group therapies, actively structured treatment sessions are usually superior. Thus, in a recent update of the literature, the author examined fifty studies on therapeutic structure published between 1980 and 1987. Twenty-eight of these articles compared directive and less directive treatments of various types, with nearly 86 percent of the outcomes favoring the more structured interventions (Dies, 1988). These investigations also showed that many patients can be helped equally well by several forms of active treatments, but that specifically tailored group therapies may be even more effective. Proper matching of patients and treatment may ensure more positive and enduring results by providing skills for maintaining treatment gains, and possibly foster unique therapeutic outcomes. The author's update indicated that in twenty-two of the fifty investigations, differential structure could not be established, and that 77 percent of these studies failed to detect main effects for treatment; nonetheless many interaction effects were ascertained to support conclusions regarding individualized treatment outcomes.

Research on group processes promoting clinical improvement (using only the research on "therapeutic factors" as an illustration) suggests there are no universal change mechanisms, but rather a range of factors that operate across clinical settings, diagnostic compositions, and phases of group development (Yalom, 1985; Dies, 1988). Different patients may benefit from various therapeutic ingredients even within the same group (Lieberman, 1989), and what may be more important is the availability of multiple sources of learning within sessions rather than any limited set of common dimensions (Lieberman, 1983). Furthermore, research consistently shows that there is a confluence of nonspecific factors (e.g., cohesiveness) working in concert with cognitive (e.g., self-understanding), affective (e.g., catharsis), and behavioral ingredients (e.g., interpersonal learning, social skills acquisition) to facilitate therapeutic gain (Dies, 1988). It is clear that the "therapeutic factors" may be too global a set of conditions to capture adequately the specific learning mechanisms that operate in group treatments (Bloch and Crouch, 1985).

Progress has also been made in identifying broad parameters of therapist style that promote group climates conducive to symptomatic change (Dies, 1983b), as well as discovering potentially harmful interventions that may precipitate deterioration in more vulnerable group members (Dies, 1983b; Dies and Teleska, 1985). There is widespread agreement that the research methodologies have become increasingly sophisticated (Gazda, 1984; Kaul and Bednar, 1986), and that researchers are addressing more frequently the types of problems encountered by clinicians in their therapeutic routines. Although this brief summary does not do justice to the current state of the literature we can see that the empirical findings often have considerable relevance to the clinical setting.

Fallacy 2: Research Is Not Applicable to Clinical Practice

There are several ways to respond to this opinion. First, reviews of the empirical literature, with concrete recommendations for clinical practice, can be found on a wide range of central topics. These surveys cover such issues as pregroup training, patient attrition from dynamically oriented groups, leadership, member roles, structure, and therapeutic factors.[3] Even without becoming involved in systematic evaluation, it is possible to be an educated consumer of research findings.

Second, research instruments can be used to monitor group process and individual patients in ways that are not feasible in everyday clinical practice. Benefits include the detection of potential drop-outs or therapeutic casualties (Dies and Teleska, 1985; Slocum, 1987), clarification of client goals and structuring the group process (MacKenzie and Dies, 1982), understanding perceptions of therapeutic interventions (Dies, 1983b), and enhancing therapeutic outcome (Hisli, 1987).

Third, research is becoming increasingly important as outside forces regarding accountability press clinicians to demonstrate the efficacy of their treatment interventions. Although many practitioners resist empirical assessments as an imposition, it is clear that they are already conducting informal evaluations that would satisfy most external demands for documentation, if only they would specify their methods more precisely and introduce systematic and repeated measurement into their clinical work. Nelson (1981), for example, offers pragmatic guidelines for implementing data-collection procedures into empirical clinical practice. Similar prescriptions are offered by

---

[3] Once again, this list of reviews is available from the author upon request.

other authors for group therapies with adults (MacKenzie and Dies, 1982), adolescents (Azima and K. Dies, 1989), and children (Dies and Riester, 1986).

Fallacy 3: It Is Not Feasible for Clinicians in Small Practice Settings to Engage in Meaningful Research

The rebuttal to this statement hinges on the definition of "meaningful research." Understandably, most practitioners are not going to become involved in large-scale research designs with multiple comparison groups and rigorous experimental controls, nor are they likely to become invested in small-scale projects with the goal of disseminating their results to the professional community. On the other hand, if the words *meaningful research* can be interpreted to denote "clinically significant," then every group therapist can be involved in meaningful empirical evaluation. The systematic assessment of even one group, or even one patient for that matter, can have important implications for the therapist's understanding of that individual's response to treatment. Thus, we are not referring to traditional scientific inquiry to advance knowledge within the field, but evaluation research that will facilitate decision making about appropriate interventions.

Elsewhere, the author outlines steps for practitioners to follow in conducting comparatively simple, yet extremely valuable, evaluations in their practical settings (Dies, 1983a). Most clinicians would be surprised to learn that if they took only three relatively elementary steps in assessing their group interventions, their "study" would already surpass the level of sophistication of many of the published reports in the literature. Thus, Dies and Riester (1986), in their review of group psychotherapy for children, demonstrated that *replication* (collecting pre/post change scores on several groups); *multiple assessments* (going beyond the simple pre/post design to evaluate progress at regular intervals throughout treatment and in follow-up); and *process evaluation* (gathering information on group climate, patients' perceptions of therapeutic factors), would not only upgrade the quality of clinical service, but also produce results that could make a meaningful contribution to the literature.

Fallacy 4: Research Will Disrupt the Group Treatment Process and Patients Will Object to the Research Instruments

Whether or not systematic evaluation is experienced as "intrusive" by group members depends on the therapist's own conviction that the measures represent an integral component of treatment, the nature of the therapeutic contract regarding instrumentation, the face validity and timing of the instruments being utilized, and on how the findings are integrated into a meaningful treatment plan for each patient (outcome) and the group-as-a-whole (process). Numerous articles have been written to assist practitioners in building empirical assessments into their clinical work (Dies, 1978a, 1983a; Nelson, 1981; Dies and Riester, 1986; Corcoran and Fischer, 1987; Azima and K. Dies, 1989).

MacKenzie and Dies (1982) provide a detailed list of the potential advantages and disadvantages of objective instruments, and give concrete recommendations for avoiding problems that might arise from their use. Despite popular opinion, research interventions do not have to be experienced as invasive. In fact, the sensitive, open, and flexible application of empirical measures can significantly enhance the quality of service by promoting more intensive involvement in group sessions, objectifying clinical changes and perceptions of group process, facilitating communication about treatment issues, and collecting more information from patients than is normally possible within group sessions.

Although many clinicians are worried that patients may become preoccupied with the "research" or take the opportunity to "act out" their feelings through noncompliance with the measures, neither possibility is likely if the contract regarding evaluation is forthright, clear, and negotiated (Dies, 1978a; MacKenzie and Dies, 1982). Besides, patients' reactions to the research measures can be integrated into any discussion of transference, therapeutic resistance, and counterproductive acting out just as any form of feedback is handled.

Fallacy 5: There Is No Reason for ME to Become Involved in Group Evaluation

We have already noted that pressures to document therapeutic efficacy are growing within the mental health professions. Moreover, we have argued that empirical evaluation does not have to be experienced as emanating from outside authority, but rather as a perfectly natural choice for clinicians given the numerous advantages inherent in the systematic assessment of one's own work.

We know from many investigations that patients are more likely to prefer individual over group psychotherapy, despite the relative parity of the two modalities in terms of therapeutic effectiveness (Dies,

1988). We also know that group therapists are often unaware of potential drop-outs as well as group members who may be having an adverse reaction to therapy (Lieberman, Yalom, and Miles, 1973; Roback and Smith, 1987). Within the last several years the author has identified eight studies in which patients' and practitioners' perceptions of "therapeutic factors" were compared, and found that marked discrepancies frequently appeared (Dies, 1988). Thus, Schaffer and Dreyer (1982) discovered huge dissimilarities between staff members and patients in an inpatient facility, whereas Morran and Hulse (1984) and Bonney, Randall, and Cleveland (1986) found significant differences in less disturbed clients. The latter authors, for example, concluded that "therapists chose items for clients that the clients did not choose for themselves as helpful. *The therapists generally saw growth where the clients felt pain*" (p. 318).

Although it may be humbling to discover that our own evaluation of group process and outcome is not entirely congruent with that of the patients, these various findings strongly suggest the importance of using careful evaluation to objectify one's understanding of the treatment process; such an approach might allow the clinician to sort out "therapeutic blind spots" from "patients' defensive functioning." It has also been argued that therapists can refine their appreciation of their own interventions by soliciting systematic feedback from group members (Dies, 1983a,b).

Fallacy 6: It Is Inconvenient, Time-Consuming, and Costly to Integrate Research into Practice

The complaint about "inconvenience" would certainly diminish, if not disappear entirely, if the clinician was able to view evaluation as an ego syntonic means for improving clinical interventions. Naturally, if evaluation was expensive and disruptive to a busy schedule, most service-oriented clinicians would simply avoid the activity. However, most rating forms, self-report inventories, and questionnaires are not costly nor do they require undue time to complete. Valuable treatment time does not have to be sacrificed (Dies, 1983a). Moreover, the clinician does not have to invest inordinate quantities of time or energy in any facet of administration, scoring, or interpretation of measures; these responsibilities could be shifted to a receptionist or a student who is hired for an hour each week to summarize the materials. In reality, the exigencies of many practice settings make it exceedingly difficult for clinicians to spare even a few hours each week for evaluation (for these group psychotherapists Number 6 is not a fallacy!).

The amount of time to "gear up" for the integration of research into practice would require a few hours a month in reading, identifying appropriate measures, and consultation, but the long-range benefits of such an investment seem well worth the minimal time and effort required. Many resources are available for identifying measures, besides those we have already noted. For example, there is a comprehensive five-volume set of test critiques (Keyser and Sweetland, 1986) which reviews hundreds of valuable instruments. Specialized knowledge of statistics or experimental methods is not essential to employ most of these measures.

Fallacy 7: It Is Not Possible to Evaluate Traditional Therapeutic Concepts That Are Important to Me as a Clinician

Certainly one of the central skills within the armamentarium of most group psychotherapists is the capacity for effective interpretation of individual and group dynamics. The meaning of "interpretation" is clearly a function of one's theoretical predilection, but there have been a variety of efforts to operationalize this facet of therapeutic intervention by practitioners and researchers alike. From the clinical perspective, for example, Scheidlinger (1987) recently attempted to differentiate interpretation from other aspects of "meaning attribution" including explanation and facilitation, clarification, and confrontation. As a true "scientist–clinician" he states "that an interpretation, no matter how elegantly conceived, is merely an hypothesis, subject to confirmation or refutation" (p. 349). Schlachet (1985) goes a step further by providing a list of ten validating criteria in group treatments that might serve as corroborating evidence for therapeutic interpretations (e.g., depth of response, anxiety reduction, group participation). Researchers have, in fact, introduced empirical measures in an effort to evaluate such clinically based operationalizations. There are many studies on interpretation (e.g., Dies [1983b] review) as well as numerous investigations of "insight-oriented" group treatments (Roback, 1972; LaPointe and Rimm, 1980; Elizabeth, 1983). Investigators have similarly explored other seemingly elusive psychoanalytic concepts such as transference (O'Day, 1973; Burrows, 1981) and unconscious group process (Karterud, 1989), and conducted projects to explore the value of psychodynamic treatment models for specific diagnostic groups (e.g., borderline patients by Kretsch, Goren, and Wasserman [1987]). Although it may be more difficult to conduct empirical evaluations of these more traditional constructs, it is certainly not impossible.

Fallacy 8: I Can Find Another Reason to Avoid Systematic Evaluation of My Clinical Practice

There is no question that this is possible, but perhaps many readers at this point will not feel so compelled to pursue this path and the "myth of noncommunication" will truly be an issue finally laid to rest. Although the gap between evaluation research in clinical practice and rigorous scientific inquiry may continue to exist, the findings from these complementary approaches may provide a broader foundation for refining our understanding of the intricacies of group treatments. More importantly, the systematic evaluation of group psychotherapy will ultimately lead to improvements in service delivery so that the real beneficiaries are those patients whose pain and troubled inter-personal patterns lead them to seek our therapeutic guidance.

REFERENCES

Azim, H. F., & Joyce, A. S. (1986), The impact of data-based program modifications on the satisfaction of outpatients in group psychotherapy. *Can. J. Psychiat.*, 31:119–122.

Azima, F. J. C., & Dies, K. R. (1989), Clinical research in adolescent group psycho-therapy: Status, guidelines, and directions. In: *The Group Therapies for Adolescents*, ed. F. J. C. Azima & L. H. Richmond. Madison, CT: International Universities Press.

Bednar, R. L., Corey, G., Evans, N. J., Gazda, G. M., Pistole, M. C., Stockton, R., & Robison, F. F. (1987), Overcoming the obstacles to the future development of research on group work. *J. Special. Group Work*, 12:98–111.

——— Kaul, T. J. (1978), Experiential group research: Current perspectives. In: *Hand-book of Psychotherapy and Behavior Change: An Empirical Analysis*, 2nd ed., ed. S. L. Garfield & A. E. Bergin. New York: John Wiley.

——— Lawlis, G. F. (1971), Empirical research in group psychotherapy. In: *Handbook of Psychotherapy and Behavior Change*, ed. A. E. Bergin & S. L. Garfield. New York: John Wiley.

——— Moeschl, M. J. (1981), Conceptual and methodological considerations in the evaluation of group psychotherapies. In: *Advances in Psychological Assessment*, Vol. 5, ed. P. McReynolds. San Francisco: Jossey-Bass.

Bennis, W. G. (1960), A critique of group therapy research. *Internat. J. Group Psychother.*, 10:63–77.

Bloch, S., & Crouch, E. (1985), *Therapeutic Factors in Group Psychotherapy*. Oxford, UK: Oxford University Press.

Bonney, W. C., Randall, D. A., & Cleveland, J. D. (1986), An analysis of client-perceived curative factors in a therapy group of former incest victims. *Small Group Behav.*, 17:303–321.

Burrows, P. B. (1981), The family-group connection: Early memories as a measure of transference in a group. *Internat. J. Group Psychother.*, 31:3–24.

Coché, E. (1983), Change measures and clinical practice in group psychotherapy. In: *Advances in Group Psychotherapy: Integrating Research and Practice*, ed. R. R. Dies & K. R. MacKenzie. New York: International Universities Press.

—— Dies, R. R. (1981), Integrating research findings into the practice of group psychotherapy. *Psychother.: Theory, Res. & Pract.*, 18:410–416.

Corcoran, K., & Fischer, J. (1987), *Measures for Clinical Practice*. New York: Free Press.

Dies, R. R. (1978a), The human factor in group psychotherapy research. In: *Group Therapy 1978: An Overview*, ed. L. R. Wolberg, M. L. Aronson, & A. R. Wolberg. New York: Stratton Intercontinental Medical Book Corp.

—— (1978b), Therapy and encounter group research: Issues and answers (Special Issue). *Small Group Behav.*, 9:163–172.

—— (1979), Group psychotherapy: Reflections on three decades of research. *J. Appl. Behav. Sci.*, 15:361–373.

—— (1983a), Bridging the gap between research and practice in group psychotherapy. In: *Advances in Group Psychotherapy: Integrating Research and Practice*, ed. R. R. Dies & K. R. MacKenzie. New York: International Universities Press.

—— (1983b), Clinical implications of research on leadership in short-term group psychotherapy. In: *Advances in Group Psychotherapy: Integrating Research and Practice*, ed. R. R. Dies & K. R. MacKenzie. New York: International Universities Press.

—— (1985a), A multidimensional model for group process research: Elaboration and critique. *Small Group Behav.*, 16:427–446.

—— (1985b), Research foundations for the future of group work. *J. Special. Group Work*, 10:68–73.

—— (1986), Practical, theoretical, and empirical foundations for group psychotherapy. In: *The American Psychiatric Association Annual Review*, Vol. 5, ed. A. J. Frances & R. E. Hales. Washington DC: American Psychiatric Press.

—— (1987), Clinical application of research instruments: Editor's introduction. *Internat. J. Group Psychother.*, 37:31–37.

—— (1988), Issues in group leadership. Paper presented at the American Group Psychotherapy Association meeting, New York.

—— MacKenzie, K. R. (1983), *Advances in Group Psychotherapy: Integrating Research and Practice*. New York: International Universities Press.

—— Riester, A. E. (1986), Research on group therapy with children: Present status and future directions. In: *Child Group Psychotherapy: Future Tense*, ed. A. E. Riester & I. Kraft. Madison, CT: International Universities Press.

—— Teleska, P. A. (1985), Negative outcome in group psychotherapy. In: *Negative Outcome in Psychotherapy and What To Do About It*, ed. D. T. Mays & C. M. Franks. New York: Springer.

Elizabeth, P. (1983), Comparison of psychoanalytic and a client-centered group treatment model on measures of anxiety and self-actualization. *J. Counsel. Psychol.*, 30:425–428.

Fuhriman, A., Drescher, S., & Burlingame, G. (1984), Conceptualizing small group process. *Small Group Behav.*, 15:427–440.

Gazda, G. M. (1984), *Group Counseling: A Developmental Approach*, 3rd ed. Boston: Allyn & Bacon.

Hartman, J. J. (1979), Small group methods of personal change. *Ann. Rev. Psychol.*, 30:453–476.

Hisli, N. (1987), Effect of patients' evaluation of group behavior on therapy outcome. *Internat. J. Group Psychother.*, 37:119–124.

Kansas, N. (1986), Group therapy with schizophrenics: A review of the controlled studies. *Internat. J. Group Psychother.*, 36:339–351.

Karterud, S. (1989), A comparative study of six different inpatient groups with respect to their basic assumption functioning. *Internat. J. Group Psychother.*, 39:355–376.

Kaul, T. J., & Bednar, R. L. (1986), Experiential group research: Results, questions, and suggestions. In: *Handbook of Psychotherapy and Behavior Change*, 3rd ed., ed. S. L. Garfield & A. Bergin. New York: John Wiley.

Keyser, D. J., & Sweetland, R. C. (1986), *Test Critiques*, Vol. 5. Kansas City, MO: Test Corporation of America.

Kiesler, D. J. (1981), Empirical clinical psychology: Myth or reality? *J. Consult. & Clin. Psychol.*, 49:212–215.

Kretsch, R., Goren, Y., & Wasserman, A. (1987), Change patterns of borderline patients in individual and group therapy. *Internat. J. Group Psychother.*, 37:95–112.

LaPointe, K. A., & Rimm, D. C. (1980), Cognitive, assertive, and insight-oriented group techniques in the treatment of reactive depression in women. *Psychother.: Theory, Res., & Pract.*, 17:312–321.

Lewinsohn, P. M., & Clarke, G. N. (1984), Group treatment of depressed individuals: The 'Coping with Depression' course. *Advances Behav. Res. & Ther.*, 6:99–114.

Lieberman, M. A. (1976), Change induction in small groups. *Ann. Rev. Psychol.*, 27:217–250.

——— (1983), Comparative analyses of change mechanisms in groups. In: *Advances in Group Psychotherapy*, ed. R. R. Dies & K. R. MacKenzie. New York: International Universities Press.

——— (1989), Group properties and outcome: A study of group norms in self-help groups for widows and widowers. *Internat. J. Group Psychother.*, 39:191–208.

——— Yalom, I. D., & Miles, M. B. (1973), *Encounter Groups: First Facts*. New York: Basic Books.

MacKenzie, K. R., & Dies, R. R. (1982). *CORE Battery: Clinical Outcome Results*. New York: American Group Psychotherapy Association.

——— Livesley, W. J. (1986), Outcome and process measures in brief group psychotherapy. *Psychiat. Annals*, 16:715–720.

Meehl, P. E. (1978), Theoretical risks and tabular asterisks: Sir Karl, Sir Ronald, and slow progress of soft psychology. *J. Consult. & Clin. Psychol.*, 46:806–834.

Morran, D. K., & Hulse, D. (1984), Group leader and member reactions to selected intervention statements: A comparison. *Small Group Behav.*, 15:278–288.

Nelson, R. O. (1981), Realistic dependent measures for clinical use. *J. Consult. & Clin. Psychol.*, 49:168–182.

O'Day, R. (1973), Training style: A content-analytic assessment. *Hum. Rel.*, 26:599–637.

Parloff, M. B. (1967), A view from the incompleted bridge: Group process and outcome. *Internat. J. Group Psychother.*, 17:236–242.

———— (1980), Psychotherapy and research: An anaclitic depression. *Psychiatry*, 43:279–293.

———— Dies, R. R. (1977), Group psychotherapy outcome research 1966–1975. *Internat. J. Group Psychother.*, 27:281–319.

Piper, W. E., & Perrault, E. L. (1989), Pretherapy preparation for group members. *Internat. J. Group Psychother.*, 39:17–34.

Roback, H. B. (1972), Experimental comparison of outcomes in insight- and non-insight-oriented therapy groups. *J. Consult. & Clin. Psychol.*, 38:411–417.

———— Smith, M. (1987), Patient attrition in dynamically oriented treatment groups. *Amer. J. Psychiat.*, 144:426–431.

Rutan, J. S., & Stone, W. N. (1984), *Psychodynamic Group Psychotherapy*. Lexington, MA: Collamore Press.

Schaffer, J. B., & Dreyer, S. F. (1982), Staff and inpatient perceptions of change mechanisms in group psychotherapy. *Amer. J. Psychiat.*, 139:127–128.

Scheidlinger, S. (1952), Freudian group psychology and group psychotherapy. *Amer. J. Orthopsychiat.*, 22:710–717.

———— (1967), Current conceptual and methodological issues in group psychotherapy research: Introduction to panel—Part I. *Internat. J. Group Psychother.*, 17:53–56.

———— (1982), *Focus on Group Psychotherapy*. New York: International Universities Press.

———— (1987), On interpretation in group psychotherapy: The need for refinement. *Internat. J. Group Psychother.*, 37:339–352.

Schlachet, P. J. (1985), The clinical validation of therapist interventions in group therapy. *Internat. J. Group Psychother.*, 35:225–238.

Slocum, Y. S. (1987), A survey of expectations about group therapy among clinical and nonclinical populations. *Internat. J. Group Psychother.*, 37:39–54.

Tramontana, M. G. (1980), Critical review of research on psychotherapy outcome with adolescents: 1967–1977. *Psycholog. Bull.*, 88:429–450.

Wagner, J. (1986), *The Search for Signs of Intelligent Life in the Universe*. New York: Harper & Row.

Yalom, I. D., (1985), *The Theory and Practice of Group Psychotherapy*, 3rd ed. New York: Basic Books.

PART IX

Overview and Future Prospects

In 1980, Saul Scheidlinger summarized the state of the art of both theory and therapy concerning psychoanalytic group dynamics. Now, in this volume, a number of group therapists and theorists, directly influenced and encouraged by him, offer their concepts and experiences in essay form as a means of celebrating the first forty years of Scheidlinger's contributions. True to his objectives, we hope to advance understanding of group theory and practice by devoting our energies and expressing our ideas on subjects about which we are all concerned.

In 1980, Scheidlinger was somewhat discouraged when he concluded that we have:

> [R]ich and creative, yet disappointingly disparate minimodels . . . [I]t is apparent that a satisfactory integration of the very complex variables at work in groups has so far evaded the efforts of even our best thinkers. [W]e have to content ourselves at present [1980] with "limited domain" theorizing. This more circumscribed approach involves concentrating in depth on specific concepts . . . and trying to evolve connecting paths if not true bridges between them [pp. 285–286].

Scheidlinger (1980) noted that most psychoanalytic group theorists in the early 1980s agreed that there is an ongoing interaction "between *individual personality* and *group process* manifestations on overt and covert levels" (p. 286). Different explanations come to mind as we attempt to understand specific issues concerning the nature of these relationships. "[W]*hat* interacts (self, ego, personalities, leader, members, shared emotions); *why* the interaction (motivation, direction); *how* the interaction (depth level, process, mechanism); and, above all, which of the interacting elements are of primary and which are of secondary importance" (p. 286).

In 1982 Scheidlinger dared "a glimpse at the future." Regarding theoretical advances up to that point, he noted that there was the beginning of a trend to move away "from an earlier, almost chauvinistic adherence to competing ideological camps. Seasoned clinicians of all persuasions have begun to move towards a new pragmatism, eclecticism, and search for commonalities among the varied psychotherapies" (p. 238). It was more clearly understood that there are certain therapeutic factors common to all treatment interventions. One manifestation of this can be noted: increasingly, group therapists borrow from analytic theory and psychoanalysts have become more interested in group dynamics and social factors. Scheidlinger (1982) quoted Parloff's (1979) admonition that it was essential to question "what kinds of changes are affected by what kinds of techniques, applied to what kinds of patients, by what kind of therapists under what kind of conditions" (p. 303).

I agree that such questions are vital, but they can only be meaningfully considered by further efforts in specific directions. We need more precise definitions and effective data collection methods as well as more systematic approaches to data analysis. It is becoming increasingly possible to do such research since techniques are improving for gathering and storing data (for example, the use of videotapes and computerized information storage). These provide the raw clinical material in a form useful for evaluating and testing hypotheses. Increasingly sophisticated methods are emerging which can help us seek consensual validation despite the complexity and the dynamic nature of the material we study. For example, utilizing and developing specific rating scales, and the training of observers to make judgments are promising (Luborsky, 1984).

As we enter the final decade of the twentieth century it is encouraging that increased communication is under way between representatives of different schools of therapy. Issues are less polarized and overlapping areas are contemplated from various perspectives. For example, in this volume, Horwitz describes how a former dichotomy (*group-as-a-whole* focus versus *individuals in the group* emphasis) has developed beyond the "either/or" stage to a "working through" involving the effective use of *both* perspectives in appropriate combination, determined by the needs of the particular group and the individuals in it. There are other examples, in this book, which reflect the application of various orientations and combined theories to generate more meaningful and inclusive hypotheses.

Other promising insights relate to the newer infant research which has begun to yield important early life psychological data. At first glance, this recent work appears to be meaningful mainly from the vantage point of intrapsychic psychology; however, I believe that intrinsically related to subjective experiences, which become "registered" as memories within the minds of individuals, are phenomena also intimately related to group experience.

Often group members experience emersion in or differentiation from the group matrix in a manner probably somewhat parallel to the phenomenological fusion or process of psychological separation of the youngster from the mother. For example, Kosseff discusses (chapter 8) the likelihood that, from earliest life, all individuals probably embank archaic memory traces which begin to collect as the neonate emerges from a subjective state of mother–infant fusion. These engrams become more specific as the child matures and resolves symbiotic promptings. Such memory traces become still clearer and more specific as there is growth toward autonomy and selfhood. Undoubtedly this is not a simple direct unidirectional progression since the vicissitudes of living generate movement backward and forward as far as perceptual and emotional development is concerned. This pattern of progression and regression also relates probably to what occurs in group situations, thus generating a potentially significant group therapeutic experience. In other words, I believe that the mother-group (Scheidlinger, 1974) properties of the group matrix create subjective parallels to the child's early life experiences of fusion with the mother and eventual separation from her. These concepts are expressed by Kauff, Kibel, Kosseff and Tuttman. They are stimulated, in part, by the British school of object relations, by ego developmental psychology, and by Scheidlinger's concepts. The sources of such conceptualizations go back to Freud's (1930) "oceanic feeling," Balint's (1968) "harmonious interpenetrating mix-up," Mahler's (Mahler, Pine, and Bergman, 1975) "symbiosis–individuation" phases, Jacobson's (1964) and Greenacre's (1971) appreciation of selfness reinforced through the experiencing of similarities with others and differences from others. It is promising and exciting that we see a new perspective concerning the relationship between group dynamics and intrapsychic factors which leads to therapeutic application and an important potential vista for further research and understanding.

There is another sense in which we are probably on the way to achieving better understanding of the relationship between these realms through the testing of specific hypotheses. For example, measurements of group characteristics such as "cohesiveness" may be correlated with manifestions of intrapsychic factors operating within group members. This involves comparing "macrostructure" on the group level (dealing with group dynamics) with "microstructure" of individual group members on the intrapsychic dynamics level. Such data may be ascertained by noting and evaluating each individual's memories, free associations, dream productions, and by tracking of verbalizations and affects as they make up that person's communications and projections in the course of group sessions. Such methods can be used to study individual dynamics and their impact upon the qualities and characteristics of the group in which these individuals participate. Exploring such connections may help us better conceptualize and comprehend the specific contributions of group members and leader to identificatory processes and degrees of cohesiveness. (The chapters of Bacal, Kauff, Kibel, Kosseff, and Stone all deal with such issues.) This approach may help us develop and test hypotheses, refine concepts, and clarify our formulations that may be applicable to overlapping realms. I believe that such concerns are appreciated by many of the contributors to this volume and that we are addressing connections between group and individual dynamics. The possibility of ongoing progress in the next decade is enhanced by the increasing application of object relations theories (Tuttman, 1981), particularly the concepts of: (1) The British Middle School, especially the work of Balint, Guntrip, and Winnicott; (2) and Melanie Klein's ideas as modified and elaborated by Bion, Ganzarain, and Kernberg; (3) ego developmental psychology, applying the theories of Mahler, Jacobson, and others; (4) the gradual evolution of the concepts of Self, including Kernberg and Kohut; and (5) the applications of recent infant research including G. Klein and D. Stern.

Although we increasingly appreciate the primacy of object relatedness as the meaningful context for sexual and aggressive drive concepts, we have not as yet advanced an integration of social psychology and psychoanalysis (although I continue to believe that the work of Leo Berman, Erik Erikson, and David Rapaport may yet help us advance this line of theorizing). It is likely that the recent focus on relational factors in psychoanalytic thought (rather than a drive–discharge model) provides a framework more relevant to the realities of the group milieu, an atmosphere rich with human relationships and interpersonal experiences. In addition to compatibility for theorizing, the social and interpersonal involvement quality of group therapy situations is an important reason why this mode of treatment is likely to play an ever-increasing role in the decades ahead. This is especially important in an age of increasing alienation.

Many, including Scheidlinger, have noted how, increasingly, in our society, individuals seem to suffer greater isolation. There is a dramatic tendency toward family disruption and personal detachment, an absence of meaningful communication and interaction. Although this is distressing, it may indicate the likelihood that group treatment will become still more important. Group settings are more frequently employed for child care, for patients suffering serious diseases, and for the increasing geriatric population.[2] The care of young children whose parents both work is increasingly delegated to the preschool

---

[2] This is interesting because the first use of group treatment in the United States involved groups of tubercular patients (Pratt, 1917).

group. Treatment of substance abusors and codependents utilizes group formats. Recently evidence suggests that specifically designed group therapy can be a potent instrument in dealing with specific pathologies (to be described below) as well as in the treatment of social problems. The chapters of Kibel and Kosseff illustrate such applications. In my opinion, the work of Robert Liberman (Liberman, DeRisis, & Meuser, 1989) and others demonstrate how productive a group format can be when utilized in an institutional setting, along with other forms of therapy. There is evidence that patients with serious social deficiencies can learn, in controlled group settings, more adaptive means of relating and developing social skills. This can dramatically improve functioning. Such methods (Liberman et al., 1989) have gained support because they are often more effective and less costly than intensive dyadic care. Furthermore, there is a trend toward increasing use of group methods in industry, education, administration, and government.

We still do not have an all-inclusive theory of group and individual dynamics. Perhaps it is not possible to conceptualize one grand theory which is completely applicable to both realms. Let us consider some possibilities:

1. It might be necessary to acquire more detailed and specific information before we can hope to formulate an applicable overall theory. In any event, we are building bridges and making meaningful connections at an ever more rapid rate. Our research methods and findings as well as our conceptualizations are becoming more encompassing and productive.

2. Perhaps the processes, mechanisms, and dynamics involved in the two realms (intrapsychic and group) may not be the same in every way or completely interchangeable. (It has been suggested that the physical laws governing subatomic particles may differ from those dealing with molecular behavior. In an analogous way, the laws may differ to some extent in the two psychological areas.) Perhaps it is an overly ambitious and naive assumption when we hypothesize that the same principles are at work in both psychological realms (intrapsychic and group).

Would the consequences be dire if we could not utilize an all-inclusive theory in comprehending group and individual processes? Is not the important consideration rather to advance our understanding of the manner by which people relate in terms of intrapsychic, interpersonal, group and societal factors and to strive to further comprehend the relationships among these realms? I believe (Tuttman) that there are group processes involved in the early development of intrapsychic elements within the individual. This hypothesis requires additional study. In any event, our goal is to (1) advance understanding; (2) to further the effectiveness of our work as group therapists and (3) to apply group process understanding to society on behalf of the general welfare.

Saul Scheidlinger has been catalytic in advancing group psychodynamic theory and in generating research ideas and improved techniques, in the course of his efforts over forty years thus far. Regardless of whether or not we arrive at an all-inclusive theory, it is clear that his contributions have been enriching and highly productive. Whether a single integrative theory is possible is only for the future to determine.

Completely aside from the issue of advancing theory (very important to Saul Scheidlinger and all of us), it is also crucial that we exploit the powerful, psychoanalytic group techniques in seeking still more effective approaches to alleviating human suffering. It is in keeping with Scheidlinger's and our own value system to encourage psychodynamic group practitioners to address more fervently the important, if not devastating, social crises afflicting our world today. Can the group as therapeutic agent help in the struggle to deal with: homelessness, unemployment, abandonment, and poverty; the consequences of family disruption including child care issues; the elderly, ill and relatively well; victims of substance abuse and addiction states; those suffering terminal illness; the devastation of chronic disease and physical disabilities (AIDS, herpes, malignancies, etc.); psychiatric disabilities (caused by schizophrenia, Alzheimer's, mental deficiency); and the loneliness and pain of social isolation which afflicts the widowed, divorced, hostages, and their loved ones. Withdrawal of governmental social service support necessitates economically feasible, effective methods for addressing such important issues. Group dynamic treatment has much to offer.

At least equally important, is the awareness that a combination of psychoanalytic insights applied in a group treatment milieu offers a powerful and vital means of addressing alienation and detachment which has become an increasingly pathological tendency in our society.

Certainly, our field offers no panacea; but we have reason to feel encouraged and to have conviction that our methods and theories offer meaningful techniques which provide a deeper and more promising kind of support. This support comes from *belonging* to a group of individuals who struggle together, in a climate of evolving mutual regard and cohesiveness to help themselves and one another to overcome constriction and despair.

Saul Scheidlinger has stimulated, encouraged and inspired us. Many years ago one of my teachers, Theodor Reik (1949), advised young analysts to develop "the courage not to understand." Perhaps Saul Scheidlinger has helped us to go as far as possible today to understand and to recognize the limits of understanding which we must endure! At the same time, his example inspires us onward, perhaps to surpass our expectations and to yet achieve more. We need the courage to recognize our limitations while continuing to seek richer and more encompassing hypotheses.

REFERENCES

Balint, M. (1968), *The Basic Fault.* London: Tavistock Publications.

Freud, S. (1930 [1929]), *Standard Edition,* 21:59–145. Civilization and Its Discontents. London: Hogarth Press, 1961.

Greenacre, P. (1971), *Emotional Growth I.* New York: International Universities Press.

Jacobson, E. (1964), *The Self and the Object World.* New York: International Universities Press.

Liberman, R. P., DeRisis, W. J., & Meuser, K. T. (1989), *Social Skills Training for Psychiatric Patients.* Champaign, IL: Research Press.

Luborsky, L. (1984), *Principles of Psychoanalytic Psychotherapy: A Manual for Supportive-Expressive Treatment.* New York: Basic Books.

Mahler, M., Pine, F., & Bergman, A. (1975), *The Psychological Birth of the Human Infant.* New York: Basic Books.

Parloff, M. B. (1979), Can psychology research guide the policy maker? *Amer. Psychol.,* 34:296–306.

Pratt, J. H. (1917), The tuberculosis class: An experiment in home treatment. *Proceedings, New York Conference on Hospital Social Service.* 4:49–68.

Reik, T. (1949), *Listening with the Third Ear.* New York: Farrar, Straus.

Scheidlinger, S. (1974), On the concept of the mother group. *Internat. J. Group Psychother.,* 24:417–428.

——— (1980), *Psychoanalytic Group Dynamics: Basic Readings.* New York: International Universities Press.

——— (1982), *Focus on Group Psychotherapy: Clinical Essays.* New York: International Universities Press.

Tuttman, S. (1980), The question of group therapy—from a psychoanalytic viewpoint. *J. Amer. Acad. of Psychoanalysis,* 8:217–234.

——— (1986), Theoretical and technical elements which characterize the American approaches to psychoanalytic group psychotherapy. *Internat. J. Group Psychother.,*36:499–515.

Publications by Saul Scheidlinger, Ph.D.

1945

Activity group therapy with a delinquent dull boy of eleven. Coauthored with S. R. Slavson & H. Weiner. *The Nervous Child*, April.

1947

Activity group therapy with primary behavior disorders in children. In: *The Practice of Group Therapy*, ed. S. R. Slavson. New York: International Universities Press.

The treatment potentialities of the summer camp for children with personality disturbances. Coauthored with L. P. Scheidlinger. *The Nervous Child*, April.

Use of casework services in group work agencies, *Social Service Review*, June.

Group psychotherapy. Coauthored with S. R. Slavson. In: *Progress in Neurology and Psychiatry*, ed. E. Spiegel. New York: Grune & Stratton.

1948

Group therapy—Its place in psychotherapy. *Journal of Social Casework*, October.

A comparative study of the Boy Scout Movement in various national and social groups. *American Sociological Review*, December.

1949

Understanding the adolescent in a group setting. *Journal of Educational Sociology*, September.

1952

Psychoanalysis and Group Behavior. New York: W. W. Norton.

Group psychotherapy. In: *Progress in Clinical Psychology*, ed. D. Brewer & L. Abt. New York: Grune & Stratton.

Group factors in promoting school children's mental health. *American Journal of Orthopsychiatry*, April.

Freudian group psychology and group psychotherapy. *American Journal of Orthopsychiatry*, October.

1953

Author's comments on a review of "Psychoanalysis and group behavior." *Journal of Abnormal and Social Psychology*, 48.

The concepts of social group work and of group psychotherapy. *Social Casework*, July.

Group therapy in a family service program. Coauthored with A. D. Taggart. *Social Casework*, November.

1954

Group psychotherapy. In: *Social Work Yearbook*. New York: American Association of Social Workers.

419

Group psychotherapy. Round Table on "The group in education, group work and psychotherapy." *American Journal of Orthopsychiatry*, January.

1955

Should teachers be group therapists? *Progressive Education*, May.

The relationship of group therapy to other group influence attempts. *Mental Hygiene*, July.

The concept of identification in group psychotherapy. *American Journal of Psychotherapy*, October.

1956

Group psychotherapy in family services. Coauthored with H. Freeman. In: *The Fields of Group Psychotherapy*. ed. S. R. Slavson. New York: International Universities Press.

Social group work and group psychotherapy. *Social Work*, July.

Chairman, Panel on "Social group work in psychiatric residential settings." *American Journal of Orthopsychiatry*, October.

1959

Activity group therapy with children in a family agency. Coauthored with M. Douville, C. Harrahill, & J. D. Minor, *Social Casework*, April.

1960

Group process in group psychotherapy. *American Journal of Psychotherapy*, January and April.

Experiential group treatment of severely deprived latency-age children, *American Journal of Orthopsychiatry*, April.

Group therapy with "hard-to-reach" clients in a family service agency. *International Mental Health Research Newsletter*, December.

1961

Group therapy of women with severe dependency problems. Coauthored with M. Pyrke. *American Journal of Orthopsychiatry*, October.

1962

Activity group therapy of a dull boy with severe body ego problems. Coauthored with M. Eisenberg, C. H. King, & R. Ostrower. *International Journal of Group Psychotherapy*, January.

1963

Discussion of symposium on "The relationship of group psychotherapy to group dynamics." *International Journal of Group Psychotherapy*, October.

1964

Group Treatment in Family Service Agencies. Coauthored with FSAA Committee, New York.

What do a man's children need most from him? In: *The Why Report*. New York: Arthur Bernhard.

Identification, the sense of belonging and of identity in small groups. *International Journal of Group Psychotherapy*, July.

1965

Three group approaches with socially deprived latency-age children. *International Journal of Group Psychotherapy*, October.

1966

Group therapy of women with severe character disorders: The middle and final phase. Coauthored with M. Holden. *International Journal of Group Psychotherapy*, April.

The concept of latency: Implications for group treatment. *Social Casework*, June.

The concept of empathy in group psychotherapy. *International Journal of Group Psychotherapy*, October.

1967

Chairman's introduction: Panel on "Current conceptual and methodological issues in group psychotherapy research." *International Journal of Group Psychotherapy*, January.

1968

Group therapy with the socially disadvantaged. Coauthored with H. B. Peck. In: *Current Psychiatric Therapies*, Vol. 8, ed. J. Masserman. New York: Grune & Stratton.

The concept of regression in group psychotherapy. *International Journal of Group Psychotherapy*, January.

Therapeutic group approaches in community mental health. *Social Work*, April.

Group psychotherapy in the sixties. *American Journal of Psychotherapy*, April.

Introduction to symposium "Current trends in group therapy with children and adolescents." *International Journal of Group Psychotherapy*, October.

1969

Innovative group approaches. In: *Progress in Community Mental Health*, ed. L. Bellak & H. Barton. New York: Grune & Stratton.

A mental health consultation–education program with group service agencies in a disadvantaged area. Coauthored with A. Sarcka. *Community Mental Health Journal*, 5.

1970

Evaluation of a mental health consultation service in a ghetto area. Coauthored with E. C. Struening & J. G. Rabkin. *American Journal of Psychotherapy*, 24.

1971

A mental health consultation service to neighborhood organizations in an inner city area. Coauthored with A. Sarcka & H. A. Mendes. *Community Mental Health Journal*, December.

1972

Psychoanalytic group psychoanalysis: Children and adolescents. Coauthored with E. Rauch. In: *Handbook of Child Psychoanalysis*, ed. B. B. Wolman. New York: Van Nostrand Reinhold.

1974

On the concept of the mother group. *International Journal of Group Psychotherapy*, October.

1977

Group therapy for latency-age children: A bird's eye view. *Journal of Clinical Child Psychology*, Spring.

1979

Individual and group psychology—Are they opposed? In: *Evolution of Group Analysis*, ed. M. Pines. London: Routledge & Kegan Paul.

Group therapy combined with individual psychotherapy. Coauthored with K. Porter.

In: *Specialized Techniques in Psychotherapy*, ed. T. B. Karasu & L. Bellak. New York: Brunner/Mazel.

1980

Psychoanalytic Group Dynamics: Basic Readings, ed. New York: International Universities Press.

1982

Focus on Group Psychotherapy: Clinical Essays. New York: International Universities Press.

On scapegoating in group psychotherapy. *International Journal of Group Psychotherapy*, April.

1984

The adolescent peer group revisited. Turbulence or adaptation. *Small Group Behavior*, August.

Psychoanalytic group psychotherapy today—An overview. *Journal of the American Academy of Psychoanalysis*, October.

Group psychotherapy in the 1980's. Problems and prospects. *American Journal of Psychotherapy*, October.

Short-term group psychotherapy for children—An overview. *International Journal of Group Psychotherapy*, October.

1985

Group treatment of adolescents—An overview. *American Journal of Orthopsychiatry*, January.

1987

Trigant Burrow. A pioneer revisted. *Group Analysis*, March.

Interpretation in group psychotherapy. *International Journal of Group Psychotherapy*, July.

1990

Group psychotherapy of adolescents. Coauthored with S. Aronson. In: *Adolescent Psychotherapy*, ed. M. Slomowitz. Washington, DC: A.P.A. Press.

Internalization in group psychotherapy: The group within. *Journal of the American Academy of Psychoanalysis*, 18:494–504.

Psychodynamic group psychotherapy. In: *What is Psychotherapy? Contemporary Perspectives*, ed. J. K. Zeig and W. M. Munion. San Francisco: Jossey-Bass, pp. 331–335.

EDUCATIONAL FILMS AND TAPES

1970

A Three-Letter Word for Love. Educational Consultants, Melvin Roman and Saul Scheidlinger. Hobel Leiterman Productions.

1972

All About Sex. Educational Directors, Saul Scheidlinger and Sol Gordon. Texture Films.

1975

Sex and the Professional. Educational Directors, Saul Scheidlinger and Pedro Ruiz. Texture Films.

1986

An Early Adolescent Boy's Therapy Group. Albert Einstein College of Medicine. Saul Scheidlinger, Producer, 1986.

1989

An Adolescent Girls' Therapy Group. Albert Einstein College of Medicine, Saul Scheidlinger, Producer.

Name Index

423

Subject Index

431